# Essentials of Higher Physics

# Essentials of Higher Physics

**Mary Webster**, *B.Sc.*

*Lecturer, Clydebank Technical College*

 Heinemann Educational Books

**Heinemann Educational Books**

LONDON  EDINBURGH  MELBOURNE  AUCKLAND  TORONTO
HONG KONG  SINGAPORE  KUALA LUMPUR  NEW DELHI
IBADAN  NAIROBI  JOHANNESBURG  LUSAKA
KINGSTON


ISBN 0 435 68836 7
© Mary Webster 1978
First published 1978

Published by Heinemann Educational Books Ltd,
48 Charles Street, London W1X 8AH

Filmset in 'Monophoto' Times 10 on 11 pt and
printed in Great Britain by
Richard Clay (The Chaucer Press), Ltd,
Bungay, Suffolk

# Preface

This book contains a succinct and cogent coverage of the material required for the Scottish Higher Physics examination.

The uses of this book are twofold: firstly, it can be used throughout the year as a précis of the material required for each topic. The text could be employed directly by teachers in order to alleviate the problem of providing each student with satisfactory notes. Accordingly more time could then be devoted to experiments, discussions, and problems. Secondly, it provides the basis for constructive revision prior to an examination. An adequate summary of principles, equations, and formulae is given in the framed sections. A useful reminder of important details may be obtained by reading all sentences commencing 'Note:'.

Problems are given at the end of each lettered section in order that skill may be achieved in modes of solution and to highlight further certain aspects of the section. Detailed solutions are provided at the end of the book. Naturally these problems are in no way to be regarded as a substitute for questions from past examination papers. To accentuate the need for continual practice in problem solving an exercise section with brief answers is included.

SI units are employed throughout.

I should like to thank all those who have helped in the preparation of this book; especially certain students for their pertinent questions, my colleague Mr. George Maxwell, and the publishers for their assistance. I am particularly grateful to Mr. J. L. Patterson for so carefully reading and editing the manuscript and providing many excellent suggestions and improvements. Finally, a special note of gratitude is due to my husband, Brian Webster, for his continual encouragement.

1978                                                                          M.W.

# Contents

# 1 Mechanics

## A: Units, Dimensions, Scalars, and Vectors, and Measurement

### 1:A.1 *SI System of Units*

When any quantity is measured its **unit** must be stated. A length of 17 has no meaning. For a unit, such as the metre, to be accepted and understood by scientists throughout the world a standard 'metre' had to be agreed upon. In Paris, in 1960, an International Committee proposed the SI system of units (Système International D'Unites), which has seven **basic units** corresponding to seven **independent** physical quantities.

| Quantity | length | mass | time | electric current | thermodynamic temperature | amount of substance |
|----------|--------|------|------|------------------|---------------------------|---------------------|
| Unit | metre | kilogram | second | ampere | kelvin | mole |

(The seventh basic unit, the **candela**, is the unit of luminous intensity and does not require discussion in this book.)

These basic units are defined in terms of a particular property of a given substance. As examples, the definitions of the units of length, mass, and time are given below.

**Length:** metre
This used to be based on a platinum–iridium rod kept in Paris. It is now defined in terms of the wavelength of a particular spectral line of krypton, $^{86}$Kr.

$$1 \text{ metre} = 1\ 650\ 763.73 \text{ wavelengths of this radiation}$$

**Mass:** kilogram
Defined as the mass of a piece of platinum–iridium kept under standard conditions at Sèvres, near Paris, France.

**Time:** second
This used to be based on the mean solar day. It is now defined in terms of the period of a particular radiation emitted by caesium, $^{133}$Cs.

$$1 \text{ second} = 9\ 192\ 631\ 770 \text{ periods}$$

The **ampere** is defined in terms of the current required by two specified conductors to produce a certain force (see Section 3:B.1).

For interest it may be noted that the **kelvin** is defined in terms of the temperature at which steam, water, and ice may co-exist, this point being termed the triple point of water. Then a temperature scale based on the two fixed points for melting ice and boiling water may be established.

The **mole** is discussed later (see Section 2:A.2).*

**Basic units** used in this text, with their abbreviations:

| | | |
|---|---|---|
| metre (m) | kilogram (kg) | second (s) |
| ampere (A) | kelvin (K) | mole (mol) |

Units for other quantities are termed **derived units**, as they may be obtained by a simple combination of the above units, *without numerical* factors.

**Examples:**   A velocity of one metre per second is that velocity possessed by an object when its displacement increases by one metre in every second. Hence the unit for velocity is $m\ s^{-1}$.

A unit of energy would be $kg\ m^2\ s^{-2}$ but for convenience this is abbreviated to the joule, J.

The specific heat capacity of a substance has a unit of $J\ kg^{-1}\ K^{-1}$.

In terms of basic units, potential difference would have a unit of $kg\ m^2\ s^{-3}\ A^{-1}$ which is called the volt, V.

## Common prefixes

| | | |
|---|---|---|
| $m - 10^{-3}$ (milli) | $\mu - 10^{-6}$ (micro) | $n - 10^{-9}$ (nano) |
| $p - 10^{-12}$ (pico) | $k - 10^{3}$ (kilo) | $M - 10^{6}$ (mega) |

## 1:A.2   Dimensions

The dimension of a quantity is an algebraic symbol assigned to a quantity independent of its units.

**Example:**   The distance between stars in light years; the wavelength of light in nm; the height of a man in metres; these are all length quantities with dimensions [L].

For mechanics and electricity there are four essential dimensions:

Length [L],   Mass [M],   Time [T],   Current [I].

All other mechanical and electrical quantities may be expressed in terms of these four dimensions.

**Examples:**   Momentum – $[M][L][T]^{-1}$   Charge – $[I][T]$
sin $\theta$ – no dimensions, as it is a ratio of the lengths of two sides of a right-angled triangle.

## 1:A.3   Scalars and Vectors

A quantity is a **scalar** if it has magnitude only.

**Example:**   The length of a piece of paper; the energy used by a light bulb.

---

* Memorization of the details of the SI system of units is not necessary.

A quantity is a **vector** if it has magnitude and direction.

**Example:** The force of gravity on a book lying on a table is downwards; the momentum of a moving car is forwards (unless in reverse gear!); an electric field will send electrons in a certain direction only.

## Addition of scalars

Two scalar quantities may be added or subtracted arithmetically providing the units are the same.

**Example:**    3 cm + 10 cm = 13 cm
but      2 inches + 7 cm = (2 × 2.54) + 7 cm

## Addition of vectors

With vector quantities account must be taken of their *directions*.

**Example:** Two forces of 4 N and 2 N are pushing an object. The angle between the two forces is 60°, see Figure 1.1(a). Determine the total force.

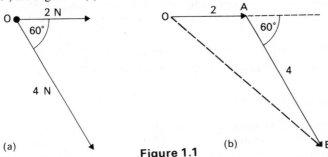

(a)           **Figure 1.1**   (b)

The direction of the forces are shown by the arrows. The vector sum of these forces may be obtained by construction, as in Figure 1.1(b). OA is 2 units long and AB is 4 units long. Notice the position of the 60° angle.

The resultant total force, or vector sum, is OB which may be measured. The angle AÔB will give its direction.

$$\text{OB} = 5.3 \text{ units} \qquad \text{A}\hat{\text{O}}\text{B} = 41°$$

Thus the resultant force has a magnitude of 5.3 N and acts in a direction of 41° to the 2 N force.

*Note:* The arrow on AB follows on from the arrow on OA. They must *not* be in opposing directions. (The head to tail rule.)

The same process may be applied for a number of vectors.

**Example:** Three forces **a**, **b**, and **c** act on a body at a point O (Figure 1.2(a)).

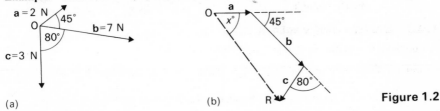

(a)           (b)         **Figure 1.2**

The resultant force, or vector sum, is obtained by construction (Figure 1.2(b)). The magnitude is given by OR and acts in a direction $x°$ from **a**.

Resultant force = 9 N at an angle of 55° from **a**.

In some simple cases it is easy to calculate the vector sum, particularly when right angles are involved. (For the more mathematically inclined the cosine and

sine rules can be used for any triangle namely;

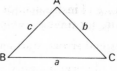

$$c^2 = a^2 + b^2 - 2ab \cos C \text{ and } \frac{a}{\sin A} = \frac{b}{\sin B} = \frac{c}{\sin C} .)$$

## Components of a vector

Two vectors may be added together to give a single resultant vector. *Conversely*, a single vector may be split into two vectors which equal that single vector. These two vectors are usually chosen to be at right angles to each other.

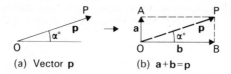

(a)  Vector **p**     (b)  **a**+**b**=**p**

**Figure 1.3**   Components of a vector

The vector sum of **a** + **b** is equal to the vector **p**, see Figure 1.3(b).

$$\overrightarrow{OB} + \overrightarrow{BP} = \overrightarrow{OP} \qquad BP = a$$
$$b \quad + a \quad = p$$

**a** and **b** are the right angled **components** of vector **p**.
**p** is said to have been **resolved** into the two components **a** and **b**.

Magnitude of **b** = OP cos $\alpha$
Magnitude of **a** = OP sin $\alpha$     $A\hat{P}O = \alpha$

**Example:**   What are the horizontal and vertical components of a 20 N force acting at 30° to the horizontal (Figure 1.4)?

Magnitude of the horizontal component, **b** = 20 cos 30° = 10 $\sqrt{3}$ N
Magnitude of the vertical component, **a**   = 20 sin 30° = 10 N

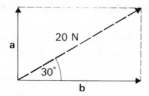

**Figure 1.4**

## 1:A.4 *Measurement*

In any experimental determination or demonstration the factors affecting the accuracy of the measurement should be considered. These include:

(1) Limitations of the instrument in use: an ammeter of 0–10 A range with 1 A graduations can only give readings to about the nearest 0.2 A.

(2) Choice of instrument or design of the experiment: a stop watch is a poor device for timing a weight dropped from a table to the floor!

(3) Personal errors: starting and stopping a stop watch.

For every physical quantity encountered the following should be known:

---

(1) Its common unit.
(2) If it is a scalar or a vector.
(3) Its mode of measurement.

---

**Problem**
**1.1** Determine the dimensions of: force, power, potential difference, frequency, focal length of a lens, linear magnification of an object by a lens, half life of a radioactive isotope.

# B: Time, Velocity, and Acceleration

## 1:B.1 *Time*

Unit: second (s), scalar.

Measured by a stop watch, electronic clock, or scalar, ticker timer, or by 'stopping' a periodic motion with a stroboscope.

### *Stroboscopes*

Mechanical: motor- or hand-driven disc with one or more equally-spaced slits.
Light: a regularly flashing light.

The rate of revolution, or flashing, is adjusted until the periodic motion viewed, for example of water waves or a rotating handle, is stationary. The number of flashes per second, or the rate of revolution $R$ for a single slit disc, will equal the frequency of the motion viewed. For a stroboscope with $N$ slits, the frequency is $N$ times $R$, as the motion or object will be seen as each slit takes the place of the previous one.

If the rate of revolution or flashing is doubled (or tripled) then the motion or object will be seen twice (or three times). This is called double (or triple) viewing.

If the rate is halved then single viewing is still obtained but the motion or object is only viewed every other cycle. Thus the correct frequency for the motion is the *highest single-viewing frequency*.

## 1:B.2 *Distance, Displacement, Speed, and Velocity*

### *Distance*

Unit: metre (m), scalar.

> Distance is the total length along a specified path.

**Example:** A bird flies 6 km east then 3 km north. Its total flight distance is 9 km.

### *Displacement*

Unit: metre (m), vector.

> The displacement of an object is the length and direction of a line drawn from a starting point to the final position of that object.

**Example:** A man walks from A to B by the path shown in Figure 1.5. If the length of AB is 3.5 km then the displacement from A is 3.5 km, 78 E of N.

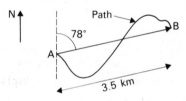

**Figure 1.5**

**Example:** A man travels 20 km north, 6 km east, and 12 km north-east. What is his distance and displacement from his starting point?

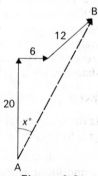

**Figure 1.6**

His displacement is the length AB at an angle $x°$ E of N (Figure 1.6). By construction these may be measured, giving his displacement as 32 km, 27° E of N.

His distance is $20 + 6 + 12 = 38$ km.

## Speed

Unit: m s$^{-1}$, scalar.
Speed is the rate at which an object moves.

$$\text{Speed} = \frac{\text{distance covered}}{\text{time taken}}$$

$$\text{Average speed} = \frac{\text{total distance}}{\text{total time}}$$

## Velocity

Unit: m s$^{-1}$, vector.
Velocity is the rate at which an object moves in a certain direction.

For a *constant velocity*:

$$\text{Velocity} = \frac{\text{displacement}}{\text{time taken}}$$

When the *velocity is changing*:

$$\text{Velocity} = \frac{\text{small displacement}}{\text{time taken for that small displacement}}$$

Ideally the time interval should approach zero.

Both speed and velocity may be measured by determining the time taken for a given distance or displacement to be covered. If the velocity is changing the time interval should be small so a ticker timer or light beam/photocell and scalar arrangement must be used. With the latter arrangement the object whose velocity is to be determined interrupts a narrow light beam directed on to a photocell. The electric clock or scalar connected to the photocell only records the time when the light does *not* reach the photocell. Thus, if a clock records a time of 0.36 s when an object of diameter (or length) 2.7 cm passes through the light beam, the velocity of the object is $\frac{2.7}{0.36} = 0.75$ cm s$^{-1}$. The drag or friction on the tape of a ticker timer limits the accuracy of its use for determining speed or velocity. Multiple-flash photography may be used for more accurate velocity determinations.

For a *uniformly changing* velocity and *linear* motion.

$$\text{average velocity} = \tfrac{1}{2}(\text{initial velocity} + \text{final velocity})$$

*Note:* The difference between speed and velocity: speed is a scalar quantity with magnitude only; a negative velocity implies a reverse direction.

### Relative velocity

To determine the relative velocity of a moving object A with respect to another moving object B, the velocity of B must be subtracted from that of A. (This is equivalent to bringing B to rest by subtracting the velocity of B from both A and B.)

**Example:**   An object A travels due north at 10 m s$^{-1}$ and passes another object B also moving north at 6 m s$^{-1}$. The velocity of A relative to B is $(10 - 6) = 4$ m s$^{-1}$ due north. Notice that the velocity of B relative to A is 4 m s$^{-1}$ due south, i.e. $-4$ m s$^{-1}$ north, see Figure 1.7.

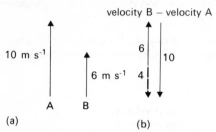

(a)                                 (b)                        **Figure 1.7**

Sometimes the objects are travelling in different directions.

**Example:**   What is the relative velocity of a wind blowing due west at 30 m s$^{-1}$ to a person standing on a ship moving north at 40 m s$^{-1}$?
    The velocity of the ship must be subtracted (vectorially) from the velocity of the wind.
    Subtraction of a vector 40 m s$^{-1}$ north is equivalent to adding a vector of 40 m s$^{-1}$ south, see Figure 1.8(b).

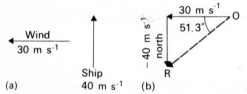

(a)            (b)                          **Figure 1.8**

    To a person on the ship the wind appears to have a velocity of magnitude OR = 50 m s$^{-1}$ in a direction 53.1° S of W.

A common problem in physics examinations is when two objects are moving relative to a third.

**Example:**   A man walks across the deck of a ship at 5 m s$^{-1}$ due west with respect to the ship. The ship is moving at 12 m s$^{-1}$ north with respect to the sea. Determine the man's velocity relative to the *sea*.

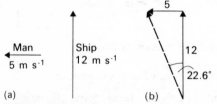

(a)                          (b)                      **Figure 1.9**

    Here the *sum* of these two velocities is required, namely 13 m s$^{-1}$ in a direction 22.6 W of N, see Figure 1.9.

## 1:B.3 *Acceleration*

Unit: m s$^{-2}$, vector.
Acceleration is the rate at which the velocity is changing.

For a *uniform acceleration*:

$$\text{Acceleration} = \frac{\text{change in velocity}}{\text{time taken for that change}}$$

For a *non-uniform acceleration* the time interval should be as small as possible, tending to zero.

*Note:* The acceleration should be stressed as being the change in velocity with *time* and not with distance. It is the change in velocity which takes place in one second.

For a *uniform acceleration* and *linear motion*:

$u$ – initial velocity     $v$ – final velocity
$a$ – acceleration     $t$ – time taken
$s$ – displacement

$$a = \frac{v - u}{t}$$

which is

$$v = u + at \tag{1}$$

For a uniform acceleration:

$$\text{Average velocity} = \tfrac{1}{2}(u + v) \quad \text{and also} = \frac{s}{t}$$

which together give

$$s = \tfrac{1}{2}t(u + v)$$

Using $v = u + at$ and substituting for $v$,

$s = \tfrac{1}{2}t(u + u + at)$      $$s = ut + \tfrac{1}{2}at^2 \tag{2}$$

Eliminating $t$ from (1) and (2) gives

$$v^2 = u^2 + 2as \tag{3}$$

These three equations are called the **equations of motion.**

$$v = u + at \qquad s = ut + \tfrac{1}{2}at^2 \qquad v^2 = u^2 + 2as$$

and providing

(1) the acceleration is uniform and the motion is linear,
(2) the units are correct, and
(3) the acceleration is given a negative sign for a deceleration,

any unknown quantity may be calculated from these three equations.

**Example:**   List the quantities given in the question below with their units and add to the list the quantity to be calculated. Then choose that equation containing those four quantities.

A ball accelerates at 5 m s$^{-2}$ from rest for 4 s. What distance has it travelled?

$a = +5 \text{ m s}^{-2}$     (There is no information about the final velocity nor is its
$u = 0$                 calculation required so it is not included in the list.)
$t = 4 \text{ s}$
$s = ?$

Check that the units are consistent and $a$ has the correct sign.

The equation required is $s = ut + \frac{1}{2}at^2$.
$$s = 0 + \tfrac{1}{2} \times 5 \times 16$$
Distance, $s = 40$ m

## 1:B.4   Graphs of Acceleration a, Velocity v, Displacement s, with Time t

### Interpretation of graphs

When two quantities are plotted against each other the **gradient** (or slope) of the graph obtained is the rate at which one quantity (usually the ordinate $y$) varies with respect to the other (usually the abscissa $x$).

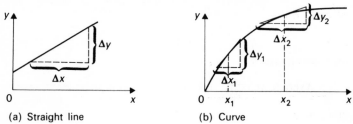

(a) Straight line                     (b) Curve

**Figure 1.10**   Gradients

The gradient is the ratio $\dfrac{\Delta y}{\Delta x}$.

*Note:* If the graph is a straight line the gradient $\dfrac{\Delta y}{\Delta x}$ is constant. If the graph is a curve the tangent to the curve at the point of interest is drawn and the gradient $\dfrac{\Delta y}{\Delta x}$ determined for that point. In Figure 1.10(b), the gradient at $x_2$ is *less* than that at $x_1$, showing that the gradient is decreasing.

### Graphs for linear motion
(1) **No acceleration:** constant velocity

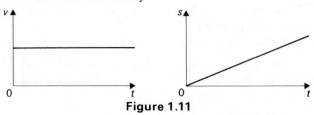

**Figure 1.11**

## (2) **Constant acceleration**

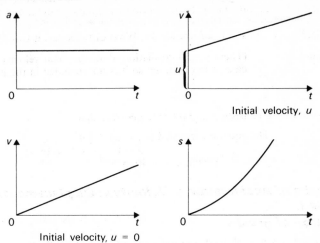

**Figure 1.12**

## (3) **Constant deceleration**

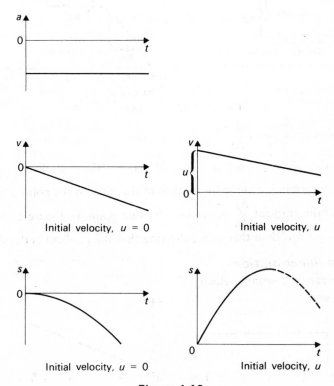

**Figure 1.13**

## (4) Changing acceleration and deceleration

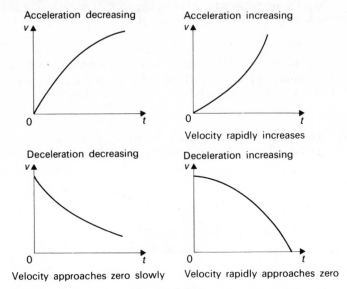

**Figure 1.14**

## Interpretation of the graphs in Figures 1.11–1.14

(1)   The gradient of a displacement/time graph gives the velocity at that time. Thus a straight-line displacement/time graph implies a constant velocity, but a *curve* implies a *changing* velocity because the gradient is changing.

(2)   The gradient of a velocity/time graph gives the acceleration at that time. Again observe the straight-line velocity/time graphs where the acceleration is constant.

(3)   The area under a velocity/time graph gives the displacement covered in that time interval. For example, an object increases its velocity from rest to $v_1$ in time $t_1$ with uniform acceleration.

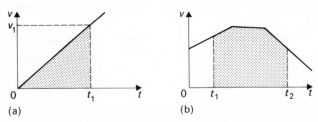

**Figure 1.15**   Area under a graph

The velocity/time graph will be a straight line (Figure 1.15(a)).

$$\text{Displacement} = \text{average velocity} \times \text{time} = \tfrac{1}{2}v_1t_1$$
$$= \text{area under the graph.}$$

This can be extended to any velocity/time graph irrespective of its shape. In Figure 1.15(b), the displacement between $t_1$ and $t_2$ is equal to the shaded area. The important points are summarized below:

> The gradient of a displacement/time graph gives the velocity.
> The gradient of a velocity/time graph gives the acceleration.
> The area under a velocity/time graph gives the displacement.

**Example:** Show, on a velocity/time graph, the areas represented by the terms $ut$ and $\frac{1}{2}at^2$ in the equation $s = ut + \frac{1}{2}at^2$, and interpret the meanings of these terms.

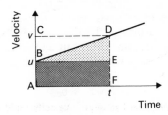

**Figure 1.16**

The darker shaded area ABEF in Figure 1.16 $= ut$. This is the displacement which would occur if the object *only* had a steady velocity $u$.

The lighter shaded area BED $= \frac{1}{2}$ BE $\times$ ED          ED = change in velocity
$\qquad\qquad\qquad\qquad = \frac{1}{2} t \times at \qquad\qquad\qquad = a \times t$
$\qquad\qquad\qquad\qquad = \frac{1}{2} at^2 \qquad\qquad\qquad\qquad u \times t$

This area represents the displacement due to the *change* in velocity.

**Example:** A ball is thrown vertically upwards with a velocity of 30 m s$^{-1}$. Draw velocity/time and speed/time graphs to illustrate the motion of the ball in the first six seconds.

The ball will decelerate due to gravity, (see next section). It will come to rest after 3 s

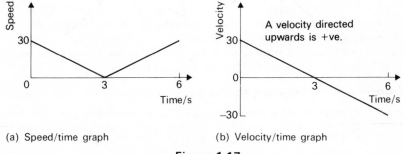

(a) Speed/time graph                    (b) Velocity/time graph

**Figure 1.17**

at the top of its flight, then fall, accelerating under the influence of gravity, until it reaches the ground after 6 s.

*Note:* Velocity has magnitude and direction but speed has magnitude only. However, a single velocity/time graph can only show direction for linear motion, in this case up and down vertically. Similarly a displacement/time graph may only be used for linear motion, where a negative displacement implies a reverse direction. Unless otherwise stated it is usually assumed that a motion is rectilinear.

### 1:B.5 *Gravity and Projectiles*

#### *Acceleration due to gravity*

The acceleration due to gravity, *g*, is the acceleration that any *freely falling* body will have, regardless of its mass, due to the attraction of the Earth. The value of *g varies* over the surface of the Earth. In Britain, *g* is usually taken as 9.8 m s$^{-2}$ or N kg$^{-1}$ (see Section 1:C.1) but as the value given in most examination papers is 10 m s$^{-2}$, this value will be used in all examples.

#### *A bouncing ball*

Figure 1.18 shows downward velocity as negative. The ball, released from rest at time 0, fell downwards due to gravity and its velocity increased between time

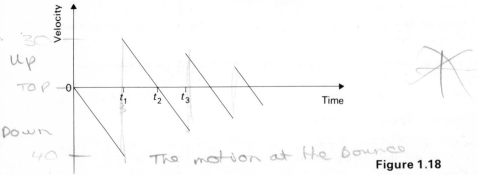

*The motion at the bounce*

**Figure 1.18**

0 and time $t_1$. At $t_1$ the ball struck the ground and the velocity became directed upwards. The ball's upward velocity slowed between $t_1$ and $t_2$ and then increased in a downward direction between $t_2$ to $t_3$.

*Note:* The ball is stationary, with its velocity zero at time $t_2$, at the top of the bounce. Also observe the loss of maximum velocity at each bounce due to a loss of energy at impact (see Section 1:C.4).

Care must be taken when using the equations of motion to use *a*, the acceleration, as −10 m s$^{-2}$ when an object is thrown upwards.

#### *Horizontal and vertical velocities*

Sometimes an object already has a steady horizontal velocity and falls under gravity where it acquires a changing vertical velocity. For example, an object released from an aircraft falls to the ground. The horizontal velocity will continue almost unchanged, but the vertical velocity will increase by 10 m s$^{-1}$ in every second. The magnitude of the vertical velocity must be calculated separately. The resultant velocity at any time may be obtained by the vector addition of the two velocities.

*Note:*  The independence of horizontal and vertical velocities.

**Example:**  A ball is thrown at 30° to the horizontal with a velocity of 80 m s⁻¹. (*a*) What are the initial horizontal and vertical components of the velocity of the ball? (*b*) What is the resultant velocity of the ball after 3 s?

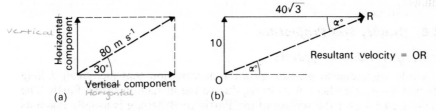

**Figure 1.19**  Horizontal and vertical velocities

From Figure 1.19,

(*a*) the horizontal component of the velocity $= 80 \cos 30° = 40 \sqrt{3}$ m s⁻¹ and
the vertical component of the velocity $= 80 \sin 30° = 40$ m s⁻¹

(*b*) The horizontal and vertical velocities may be treated independently.
The horizontal component of the velocity remains *unchanged* $= 40 \sqrt{3}$ m s⁻¹. In the vertical direction there is a retardation of 10 m s⁻² due to gravity.

Using $v = u + at$ where $v = ?$, $u = 40$ m s⁻¹, $a = -10$ m s⁻², $t = 3$ s,
$v = 10$ m s⁻¹.

Hence the velocity after 3 s is the vector addition of these two velocities. This may be determined by construction or calculation, as in Figure 1.19(b).

Resultant velocity $= 70$ m s⁻¹, at an angle $\alpha$ of 8.2° to the horizontal.

## Uniform motion in a circle

Consider an object with uniform speed travelling in a circle. For example: a conker whirled in a horizontal circle on the end of a piece of string; a satellite moving in a circular orbit around the Earth.

Because the *direction* of motion changes with time the velocity is *not* constant and the object has an acceleration. In both of the above examples there is a force towards the centre of the circle; namely the tension in the string or the gravitational attraction of the earth.

The direction of the velocity at any instant is tangential to the circle. The magnitude of the velocity at P equals the magnitude of the velocity at Q but

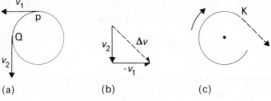

**Figure 1.20**  Circular motion

since velocity is a vector quantity the *change in velocity*, Δv, must be determined by vector subtraction, as in Figure 1.20(b). This change in velocity is finite, therefore the object must have an acceleration. Remember only the change in *speed* is zero!

If in the above example the string holding the conker is cut at K, the force on the conker becomes zero and the velocity will no longer change (see Section 1:C.2). The conker will fly off at a *tangent* to the circle at the point K, in Figure 1.20(c).

(Apart from this example, which emphasizes the vector nature of velocity, motion in a curved path will not be considered further.)

**Problems**

**1.2** (*a*) The knob of a ticker timer, run off the 50 Hz mains, is illuminated by a 5-slit strobe. How many revolutions per second are required for single viewing?

(*b*) A water wave is viewed through a 6-slit strobe and is 'stopped' when the frequency of the strobe is 20, 30, and 60 revolutions per second, but double viewing is obtained at 120 revolutions per second. What is the frequency of the waves?

**1.3** A car increases its velocity from rest to 30 m s$^{-1}$ in 2 seconds. What is its acceleration and how far has it travelled?

**1.4** Describe the motion of the object whose velocity $v$ is shown by the graph in Figure 1.21.

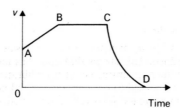

**Figure 1.21**

**1.5** Draw displacement/time, velocity/time, and acceleration/time graphs for the following motions:

(*a*) an object falling from rest under the influence of gravity.

(*b*) a parachutist.

(*c*) a box dropped from a balloon travelling vertically upwards at 30 m s$^{-1}$.

(*d*) a motor car starting from rest, accelerating at 12 m s$^{-2}$ for 5 s, travelling at constant velocity for 8 s, then skidding to a halt in 4 s.

Numerical values are required on the axes for (*c*) and (*d*).

**1.6** A train 50 m long standing at rest in a station is given the all clear by a signal 150 m in front of the engine. The train accelerates uniformly at 1 m s$^{-2}$ out of the station. Calculate: (*a*) the velocity with which the front and back of the train each pass the signal. (*b*) The time taken for the whole train to pass the signal.

**1.7** A ball is projected at an angle of 30° to the horizontal with a velocity of 40 m s$^{-1}$ near to the edge of a cliff. The ball strikes a rock at the foot of the cliff 10 seconds later.

(*a*) Draw graphs of the horizontal and vertical components of the velocity for the total flight of the ball. Numerical values are required on the axes.

(*b*) How far away from the foot of the cliff is the rock on which the ball landed?

(*c*) Determine the velocity of the ball just before it landed on the rock (magnitude and direction).

**1.8**   An object is released from an aircraft travelling horizontally at 1000 m s$^{-1}$ and takes 40 s to reach the ground.

(*a*) What is the horizontal distance travelled?

(*b*) What is the height of the aircraft when the object was released?

(*c*) What is the vertical velocity before impact?

(*d*) Show by graphical means or otherwise, the magnitude of the resultant velocity just before hitting the ground.

# C:  Mass, Force, Work, Energy, Power, and Momentum

## 1:C.1   *Mass, Weight, and Gravitational Field Strength*

### Mass

Unit: kilogram (kg), scalar.

The mass of an object will remain unchanged unless it undergoes some chemical reaction or radioactive decay.

Mass has **inertia**, that is a resistance to motion. A mass also has gravitational attraction to other masses.

**Experiment 1.1**   *To show inertia*

The rate of vibration of a wig-wag machine and a hacksaw blade are observed to decrease when masses are added. This shows that mass has inertia, that is a desire to remain at rest. In principle such apparatus could be calibrated with standard masses and a measurement of frequency used to obtain values of unknown masses. In practice many balances, for determining mass, involve a lever, often with movable standard masses to restore equilibrium.

### Weight

Unit: newton (N), vector.

The weight of an object is the **force** of gravitational attraction exerted by a large body, such as the Earth, on that object. The direction of the force will be towards the centre of gravity of the large body. Thus the weight of an object is a variable quantity depending on the position of the object. The force of attraction will be greater for an object on the Earth than on the Moon.

For an object of mass *m* the weight *W* is given by

$$W = mg$$

(using $F = ma$, see page 19)

where *g* is the acceleration due to gravity at that place.

Notice that as *g* varies over the Earth's surface, and is considerably less on the Moon, *W* also *varies*.

As $m = \dfrac{W}{g}$, if $g$ is known at a given position the mass of an object may be obtained indirectly from a measurement of the weight.

*Note:* The difference between mass and weight: mass is a scalar and remains constant with position but weight is a vector and varies depending on the distribution of other masses in that region.

A **field** is a concept used to describe some interaction between two objects or particles. One particle may produce a 'field' around it and the 'field' causes the second particle to experience some interaction, a force for example. A mass such as the Earth produces a **gravitational field** and another mass, the Moon, will experience a *force* of attraction due to this field. (See also electric fields, Section 3:A.2.)

### Gravitational field strength

Unit: N kg$^{-1}$, vector.
The gravitational field strength at a point may be defined as the force on a unit mass placed at that point.

$$\text{Gravitational field strength} = \frac{F\!\!-\!\!-\!\!\text{N}}{m\!\!-\!\!-\!\!\text{kg}}$$

where $m$ is the gravitational mass.
(In the equation $F = ma$, $m$ is the inertial mass. The equivalence of inertial mass and gravitational mass has been demonstrated experimentally to 1 part in $10^{11}$ so the symbol $m$ will be used for *both* masses.)

*Note:* An object of mass $m$ will have a weight $W = mg$ due to the Earth's gravitational field. The gravitational field strength on this object $= \dfrac{W}{m}$, which is equal to $g$. Hence the gravitational field strength is equivalent to the acceleration due to gravity. This gives *two* units for g:

$$g = 10 \text{ m s}^{-2} \quad \text{or} \quad g = 10 \text{ N kg}^{-1}$$

### 1:C.2  Force, Newton's Laws of Motion, and Impulse

### Force

Unit: newton (N), vector.
If a force acts on a body it will change or tend to change the state of rest or uniform velocity of the body.

**Examples:** When a ball is hit with a bat it acquires a velocity. A book on a table is being pulled towards the centre of the Earth but the table prevents it attaining any velocity by exerting an equal force upwards.

An object will only move when it experiences an *unbalanced or resultant force*. If an unbalanced force acts on a body it will either be accelerated or decelerated as its velocity changes.

### Newton's First Law of Motion

A body will continue in its state of rest or uniform velocity unless acted upon by an unbalanced force.

### Newton's Second Law of Motion

The rate of change of momentum of a body is directly proportional to the force causing the change and takes place in the same direction as the force.

### Momentum

Unit: kg m s$^{-1}$, vector.
The momentum of a body at any instant is the product of the mass and the velocity at that instant. It acts in the same direction as the velocity.

$$\text{Momentum} = \text{mass} \times \text{velocity}$$
$$\text{kg m s}^{-1} \qquad \text{kg} \qquad \text{m s}^{-1}$$

### From Newton's Second Law

$F \propto$ rate of change of momentum

$$\propto \frac{\text{change of momentum}}{\text{time taken for this change}}$$

$$\propto \frac{mv - mu}{t}$$

$$\propto m\left(\frac{v - u}{t}\right)$$

$u$ – initial velocity
$v$ – final velocity
$m$ – mass
$a$ – acceleration

$F \propto ma$

If the unit of force is chosen as the newton, and is *defined* as that force which gives a mass of 1 kg an acceleration of 1 m s$^{-2}$, then the constant of proportionality is unity.

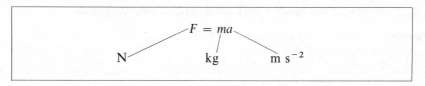

$$F = ma$$
$$\text{N} \qquad \text{kg} \qquad \text{m s}^{-2}$$

*Note:* An *unbalanced*, or *resultant*, force $F$ produces an acceleration $a$.

**Example:** What force will give a mass of 4 kg an acceleration of 3 m s$^{-2}$ if there is a constant frictional resistance of 2 N.

Force required to produce the acceleration = 12 N
Total force required = 14 N

The equation $F = ma$ is often used with the equations of motion to calculate unknown quantities.

**Example:**   A 0.5 kg ball travelling at 40 m s$^{-1}$ hits a sand bag and comes to rest in a distance of 20 cm. What is the average resistive force acting on the ball?

$a = ?$   $u = 40$ m s$^{-1}$   $v = 0$   $s = 20$ cm $= 0.2$ m
using $v^2 = u^2 + 2as$,                $a = -4000$ m s$^{-2}$

Resistive force $= 0.5 \times 4000 = 2000$ N

## Impulse

Unit: N s, vector.
The impulse of a force is equal to the force multiplied by the time interval over which the force acts.
From Newton's Second Law,

$$F = m \frac{\Delta v}{\Delta t}$$     $\Delta v$ – change in velocity
                                        $\Delta t$ – time taken

then

$$\text{Impulse} = F \, \Delta t = m \, \Delta v$$

The impulse is $F \, \Delta t$ which may be seen to also equal the change in momentum caused by the force.

**Example:**   An object of mass 50 g travelling at 20 m s$^{-1}$ hits a wall and rebounds back at 10 m s$^{-1}$. Calculate the impulse and average force on the wall if the impact lasts 0.02 s.

$$\text{Impulse} = F \, \Delta t = \text{change in momentum}$$
$$= 0.05 \, [20 - (-10)]$$
$$= 1.5 \text{ N s}$$

Since $F \, \Delta t = 1.5$, $F = 75$ N

## Newton's Third Law of Motion

If a body A exerts a force $F$ on a body B, then B exerts a force of $-F$ on A. That is, action and reaction are equal and opposite. This pair of forces, on two bodies, both have the same magnitude but opposite directions.

**Examples:**   The engine of a jet expels gas backwards and the jet moves forwards. The force on the jet in one direction equals the force on the gas in the opposite direction. A mass is attracted downwards by the Earth but the Earth is also attracted towards the mass by an equal force. However, as the Earth is large any infinitesimal movement caused will not be observed!

**Example:**   A 2 kg mass is suspended from a spring balance. If the reading on the balance is 30 N, what is the size and direction of the acceleration of the mass.
Consider the forces *on* the 2 kg mass. By Newton's Third Law, the downward pull on

the spring balance of 30 N must equal the upward tension in the suspension cord of the 2 kg mass.

$$\text{Resultant force} = 10 \text{ N upwards}$$
$$\text{Acceleration} = 5 \text{ m s}^{-2} \text{ upwards}$$

**Figure 1.22**

## Experiment 1.2

By using a friction compensated plane the equation $F = ma$ may be verified by measuring the change in velocity of a trolley, with a ticker timer and tape, for given forces $F$ on a single trolley, to show $F \propto a$, where $a$ is the acceleration. The experiment is then repeated with one force applied to different masses $m$ to show $a \propto \dfrac{1}{m}$.

*Note:* The ability to calculate accelerations from a ticker timer tape should be clearly understood. See Problem 1.9 on page 30.

## Experiment 1.3

The kicking of a football is often used to study impulse. A pupil has a strip of metal foil attached to the toe of his shoe and the ball has a similar strip at the position where it is to be kicked. Flexible wires connect the two strips to the terminals of an electric clock or scalar so that the time of contact $\Delta t$ of the strips is recorded.

After impact the ball passes through a light beam operating another electric clock so that the time $t$ for the ball's diameter $D$ to pass through the beam may be measured. The velocity $v$ of the ball is then calculated from $v = \dfrac{D}{t}$. The mass $m$ of the ball is measured on a balance. The force of impact $F$ may then be calculated from

$$F = \frac{m \, \Delta v}{\Delta t}$$

where $\Delta v = v - 0$, the ball being initially at rest.

## Force as a vector

Often only part of a force is effective in causing an accelerating or a deceleration.

**Example:** A toy train, mass 0.2 kg, is given a push of 10 N at an angle of 30° to the rails. Find the effective forward force on the train. Hence calculate the acceleration of the train.

The 10 N force may be taken as composed of two forces at right angles, OA in a forward direction parallel to the rails and OB, at 90° to OA, tending to push the train over.

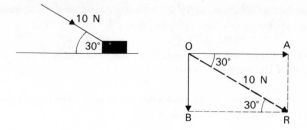

**Figure 1.23**

From the diagram the effective force is OA = 10 cos 30°, or it may be measured from the length of OA by accurate construction.

$$F = 10 \cos 30° = 10 \frac{\sqrt{3}}{2} = 5\sqrt{3} = 8.66 \text{ N.}$$

$$\text{Acceleration} \quad = \frac{F}{m}$$

$$= \frac{5\sqrt{3}}{0.2}$$

$$= 43.3 \text{ m s}^{-2}$$

**Example:** A small trolley, mass 100 g, is pulled up a plane inclined at 30° to the horizontal by a string parallel to the plane. What force is required just to prevent the trolley rolling backwards?

$P$ — force up plane
$W$ — weight of trolley due to gravity
Weight downwards $W = mg = 0.1 \times 10 = 1$ N.

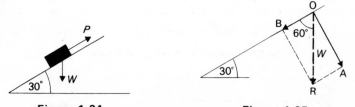

**Figure 1.24**                    **Figure 1.25**

But the effective force, due to the weight, down the plane is required. Again the force OR can be split up into two forces at right angles (Figure 1.25). OA, which is perpendicular to the plane, will have no effect along the plane. So OB is therefore the effective force down the plane.

$$\text{OB} = \text{OR} \cos 60°$$

Force down the plane = OB = $1 \times \frac{1}{2} = \frac{1}{2}$ N
A force of $\frac{1}{2}$ N is required up the plane at P to prevent the trolley slipping backwards.

*Note:* In both the above examples, the vector addition of OA and OB is OR.

When a number of different forces are acting on an object the resultant force or vector sum of the forces can be determined by vector addition (see Section 1:A.3).

If an object is in equilibrium it will have no *unbalanced* force and therefore the vector sum of the forces must be *zero*.

**Example:**   A picture of mass 2 kg hangs by two equal cords which make an angle of 60° as shown. What is the tension in each cord?

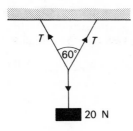

**Figure 1.26**

Since the picture is stationary the vector sum of the three forces must be zero. In a vertical direction the effective upward forces are $T \cos 30°$ for each cord.

Hence
$$2T \cos 30° = 20$$
$$T = 11.5 \text{ N}$$

## 1:C.3   *Work*

Unit: joule (J), scalar.
The work done is the effective force multiplied by the distance over which the force acts.

$$\text{Work} = \text{effective force} \times \text{distance}$$
$$\begin{array}{ccc} | & | & | \\ \text{J} & \text{N} & \text{m} \end{array}$$

If an object moves in a certain direction and an oblique force is applied then only part of that force is effective in moving the object.

**Example:**   The same toy train as in the example on page 21 is moved 2 m along its rails by a force of 10 N at 30° to the rails. Assuming no friction what is the work done?

$$\text{Effective force} = 10 \cos 30°$$
$$= 8.66 \text{ N}$$
$$\text{Work done} = \text{force} \times \text{distance}$$
$$= 8.66 \times 2$$
$$= 17.3 \text{ J}$$

## 1:C.4   *Energy*

Unit: joule (J), scalar.
There are various forms of energy including: kinetic energy, potential energy, heat, sound, light, chemical, electrical, magnetic, and nuclear energy.

### Kinetic energy, $E_k$

The kinetic energy is the energy an object has by virtue of its motion.

*Derivation of $E_k = \frac{1}{2}mv^2$*

An object in motion could do work in being brought to rest. Alternatively work must be done to bring it to rest. For an object of mass $m$ and velocity $v$, the work done to bring it to rest may be calculated.

$$E_k = \text{work done to change its velocity from } v \text{ to zero}$$

$$= \text{force} \times \text{distance} \qquad\qquad v^2 = u^2 + 2as$$

$$= m\,a \times s \qquad\qquad\qquad 0 = v^2 - 2as$$

$$= m\,\frac{v^2}{2} \qquad\qquad\qquad as = \frac{v^2}{2}$$

$$E_k = \tfrac{1}{2}\, m\, v^2$$

$$J \qquad kg \qquad m\,s^{-1}$$

### Potential energy, $E_p$

This is the energy possessed by a body by virtue of its position or state of strain.

*Derivation of $E_p = mgh$*

An object requires work to be done to raise it to a higher position against the force of gravity.

$$E_p = \text{force} \times \text{distance}$$

$$= mg \times h \quad \text{(object is raised a vertical distance } h\text{)}$$

$$E_p = mgh$$

$$J \qquad kg \; m\,s^{-2} \qquad m$$

Potential energy is gained (or lost) when an object is raised (or falls) a *vertical* distance $h$, where the acceleration due to gravity is $g$. Thus the potential energy gained by an object raised a distance $h$ on the Moon will be different to that gained on the Earth, as $g$ does not have the same value on both.

*Potential energy due to strain*

Elastic objects, such as coils, may store potential energy. A spring may be extended or compressed and in these positions it has potential energy. When it is released this energy may be imparted to another object as kinetic energy, for example, the propulsion of vehicles by stretched cords on a linear air track.

Experiment can show that the force $F$ extending a spring, an elastic cord or a wire is directly proportional to the extension (ext) produced, providing the 'elastic limit' is not exceeded.

$$F \propto \text{ext}$$

The **elastic limit** is that point beyond which an object does *not* return to its original shape and size when the deforming force is removed.

The potential energy stored in a spring, extended a distance $x$, by a force $F$, is equal to the work done in producing that extension.

$$E_p = \text{work done}$$
$$= \text{average force} \times \text{distance}$$
$$E_p = \tfrac{1}{2} F x$$

*Note:* The force is zero at the beginning and increases uniformly up to the value $F$.

## Heat

(1) The heat $E_h$ transferred to a body of mass $m$ when its temperature is raised by $\Delta T$ is given by:

$$E_h = m c \Delta T$$

where $c$ is the specific heat capacity whose units are J kg$^{-1}$ K$^1$.

(2) The heat $E_h$ required to change the state of a body of mass $m$ and specific latent heat $l$ (whose units are J kg$^{-1}$) at the normal melting or boiling point is given as:

$$E_h = m l$$

*Note:* For definitions and discussions of specific heat capacity and specific latent heat (see Section 2:D).

## Electrical energy

(See Section 3:B.4.)

## Conservation of energy

> The total energy of a closed system must be *conserved*
> although the energy may change its form.

An object held above the ground has potential energy but in falling it loses potential energy and gains kinetic energy until impact with the ground when it rebounds with a smaller kinetic energy (unless it is a perfectly elastic bounce). The energy lost is converted into heat, light, and sound.

**Example:**   A ball of mass 0.2 kg is dropped from a height of 2 m above the ground and rebounds to a height of 1.8 m. What is the kinetic energy lost on impact?

$$E_k \text{ just before impact} = E_p \text{ at the start}$$
$$= 0.2 \times 10 \times 2$$
$$= 4 \text{ J}$$
$$E_k \text{ after impact} = E_p \text{ at top of first rebound}$$
$$= 0.2 \times 10 \times 1.8$$
$$= 3.6 \text{ J}$$
$$\text{Kinetic energy } E_k \text{ lost at impact} = 0.4 \text{ J}$$

**Example:**   What velocity must a metal bullet have if it just melts when striking a target? (Assume that all the kinetic energy is turned into heat supplied to the bullet.)

Initial temperature of the bullet = 20 °C
Melting point of metal = 320 °C
Specific latent heat of fusion of the metal = $2 \times 10^4$ J kg$^{-1}$
Specific heat capacity of metal = 120 J kg$^{-1}$ K$^{-1}$

$$E_k \text{ of bullet} = \tfrac{1}{2} m v^2 \qquad v - \text{velocity of bullet}$$

$$\begin{aligned}
\text{Heat } E_h \text{ gained} &= mc\Delta T + m\,l \\
&= m \times 120 \times 300 + m \times 2 \times 10^4 \\
&= m(3.6 \times 10^4 + 2 \times 10^4) \\
&= 5.6 \times 10^4 \; m \text{ J}
\end{aligned}$$

But all $E_k \longrightarrow E_h$

$$\tfrac{1}{2} m v^2 = 5.6 \times 10^4 \; m$$
$$v^2 = 11.2 \times 10^4$$

$$\text{Velocity of bullet} = 3.35 \times 10^2 \text{ m s}^{-1}$$

Simple problems involving the conversion of mechanical and heat energy are important and should be understood. Notice that the actual value of the mass is not always required.

## 1:C.5   *Power and Efficiency*

### Power

Unit: watt (W), scalar.
Power is the rate of doing work, or the rate of expending energy.

$$\text{Power} = \frac{\overset{\displaystyle J}{\overset{|}{\text{work done}}}}{\underset{\underset{s}{|}}{\text{time taken}}} \quad \text{or} \quad \frac{\overset{\displaystyle J}{\overset{|}{\text{energy expended}}}}{\underset{\underset{s}{|}}{\text{time}}}$$

$$\underset{\underset{W}{|}}{\text{Power}}$$

$$\text{Power} = \frac{\text{force} \times \text{distance}}{\text{time}}$$

$$\text{Power} = \text{force} \times \text{velocity}$$

Attention must still be given to the direction of the force. Only the effective force in the direction of the velocity must be used in calculating the power.

### Efficiency of a machine

$$\text{Efficiency} = \frac{\text{energy out}}{\text{energy in}} \times 100\%$$

This is a percentage and has no units.

**Example:** A 0.6 kW motor is used to raise a 50 kg block up a vertical height of 8 m. How long does it take? State any assumptions made.

$$\text{Power} = \frac{50 \times 10 \times 8}{\text{time}}$$

$$0.6 \times 10^3 = \frac{4 \times 10^3}{t}$$

$$\text{Time} = 6.7 \text{ s}$$

100% efficiency has been assumed.

**Example:** A train of mass $10^5$ kg accelerates from rest to 40 m s$^{-1}$ in 20 s. The total frictional resistance is $0.5 \times 10^5$ N. Calculate (a) the total force provided by the motor and (b) the power developed at the end of the sixteenth second.

(a) Acceleration $= \dfrac{40}{20} = 2$ m s$^{-2}$

Force required to produce acceleration $= 10^5 \times 2 = 2 \times 10^5$ N

Total force provided by the motor $= 2 \times 10^5 + 0.5 \times 10^5 = 2.5 \times 10^5$ N

(b) Power = force × velocity
$$= 2.5 \times 10^5 \times 32$$
$$= 8 \text{ MW}$$

(Velocity at the end of the sixteenth second = 32 m s$^{-1}$.)

### 1:C.6 Momentum, Conservation of Momentum, and Collisions

In a collision the time interval during which the objects are in contact is small.

## Conservation of momentum

(For a definition of momentum see Section 1:C.2 page 19.)

> Providing that no external force acts the total momentum
> in *any* collision is conserved.

This law is consistent with Newton's Third Law. For an object A colliding with an object B producing changes in velocity $\Delta v_A$ and $\Delta v_B$ respectively,

$$F_A = -F_B$$
$$\frac{m_A \, \Delta v_A}{\Delta t} = -\frac{m_B \, \Delta v_B}{\Delta t}$$

$\Delta t$ – time interval over which the force acts during the collision

Thus $m_A \, \Delta v_A + m_B \, \Delta v_B = 0$

Therefore the *change* of momentum of A + the *change* of momentum of B is zero. Hence there is *no* gain or loss of momentum in the collision.

## Types of collision

(1) **Elastic collision:** Momentum *and* kinetic energy are conserved. For example, a ball bouncing off the ground back up to its original height; a moving nucleus deflected by another nucleus.

(2) **Inelastic collision:** Momentum is conserved but the kinetic energy usually *decreases*, being converted into heat or elastic potential energy, causing deformation. For example, a ball dropped on to sand or mud. In a *completely* inelastic collision, the two objects join together after impact. For example, a vehicle colliding with and joining on to another vehicle on a linear air track.

(3) **Explosions:** Momentum is conserved but the kinetic energy *increases*. For example, when two trolleys are made to fly apart the potential energy stored in the spring is converted into the kinetic energy of the trolleys. (Remember that momentum is a vector quantity. It will be zero before and after the explosion only when account is taken of the direction of the velocities.)

*Note:* Momentum is conserved in all types of collisions but kinetic energy is only conserved in elastic collisions.

**Example:** A red ball, mass 30 g, travelling at 4 m s$^{-1}$, collides with a stationary green ball, mass 50 g, which moves off with a velocity of 2 m s$^{-1}$ in the same direction as the red ball. What is the final velocity of the red ball? Is the collision elastic?

Momentum is conserved.

$$\text{Momentum before collision} = \text{momentum after collision}$$
$$30 \times 4 + 50 \times 0 = 30 \times v + 50 \times 2$$
$$v = \tfrac{2}{3}$$
$$= 0.67 \text{ m s}^{-1}$$

Notice that the masses have *all* been left in grams.

Using $E_k = \frac{1}{2} mv^2$, but with the masses now in kg,

$$E_k \text{ before collision} = \frac{1}{2} \times 0.03 \times 4^2$$
$$= 0.240 \text{ J}$$
$$E_k \text{ after collision} = \frac{1}{2} \times 0.03 \times (\tfrac{2}{3})^2 + \frac{1}{2} \times 0.05 \times 2^2$$
$$= 0.107 \text{ J}$$

The collision is *not* elastic because there has been a change in kinetic energy.

### Experiment 1.4

Using vehicles on a linear air track (to avoid friction) the velocities before and after elastic and inelastic collisions may be determined experimentally using a scalar connected to suitably placed photodiodes. The conservation of momentum can then be verified for elastic and inelastic collisions. The kinetic energy may be calculated for each collision and its conservation in elastic collisions only may be verified.

### Experiment 1.5

To study an explosion, two trolleys with ticker tapes attached may be made to fly apart. Their velocities after the explosion may then be determined and the vector sum of the final momenta may be shown to equal zero.

## *Momentum as a vector*

Since momentum is a vector quantity it follows that if the colliding objects are not in the same straight line the total momentum before and after a collision must be found from the *vector* addition of the separate momenta.

**Example:** An object A collides with a stationary object B at O. Initial momentum $= m_a u_a$. The final momentum is obtained by the vector addition of $m_a v_a$ and $m_b v_b$, as shown in Figure 1.27. Hence the length of PR will correspond to the total final momentum. As momentum is conserved the final momentum must equal the initial momentum in magnitude and direction and so the direction of PR will be the same as that of $m_a u_a$, the initial momentum of A.

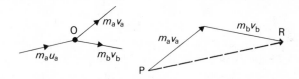

**Figure 1.27**

### Experiment 1.6

The example above may be verified experimentally using $CO_2$ or magnetic pucks, and stroboscopic photographs, to determine the magnitude and direction of the velocities.

The same principles are applied in nuclear collisions, for example, when an α particle collides with a helium nucleus. The velocities of the particles may be determined from cloud chamber photographs. These collisions may usually be considered as elastic, if no change in internal structure occurs, and if the particles are not captured, see Figure 1.28.

**Figure 1.28** A cloud chamber photograph showing the paths of χ particles in a chamber containing helium. Notice the angle between the directions of motion after the collision. (*P.M.S. Blackett, F.R.S., Proc. Roy. Soc.,* 107A, **349**, 1925)

*Note:* If an object A collides obliquely with a stationary object B of *equal mass* and the collision is *elastic*, the angle between the directions of motion of A and B after the collision will be 90°. If *either* the masses are not equal *or* the collision is inelastic the angle may *not* be 90° (see Problem 1.11).

**Problems**

**1.9** Figure 1.29 shows the distance between successive dots on a piece of ticker tape whose dots are made at the rate of 50 per second.
(*a*) What is the velocity at the point X?
(*b*) What can be stated concerning the acceleration?

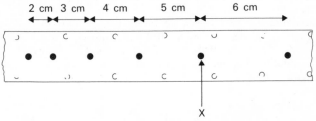

**Figure 1.29**

**1.10** A 2 kg mass is suspended by a balance from the roof of a lift. The scale of the balance is from 0 to 40 N. What will the balance read:
(*a*) when the lift is at rest,
(*b*) when the lift is moving upwards at a constant velocity of 3 m s$^{-1}$,
(*c*) when the lift is accelerating upwards at 2.5 m s$^{-2}$?

**1.11** A magnetic puck A of mass 0.5 kg and velocity 10 m s$^{-1}$ collides with a stationary identical puck B and they move off at right angles to each other.
(*a*) Calculate (i) the initial momentum of A, (ii) the velocity of B after collision if the velocity of A is 8 m s$^{-1}$ after the collision.
(*b*) Consider the kinetic energy and state if the collision was elastic or inelastic.

**1.12** Assuming no change in internal structure, how would the conservation of momentum and kinetic energy, and the angle between the direction of motion of the particles after collision compare with those in Problem 1.11, for collisions between
(*a*) an α particle and a stationary helium nucleus,
(*b*) an α particle and a stationary nitrogen atom?

**1.13** A catapult has a horizontal force of 320 N on a steel ball of mass 0.02 kg when extended back a horizontal distance of 10 cm.
(a) What is the initial acceleration of the ball?
(b) Calculate its average acceleration when in contact with the catapult.
(c) Calculate the velocity of the ball when leaving the catapult.
(d) What is the effect on this velocity if two identical cords were used, in the same arrangement, doubling the force? State any assumptions made.

**1.14** A ball of mass 2 kg moves in a straight line with a velocity of 20 m s$^{-1}$. A constant force acts for 3 s changing the velocity to 4 m s$^{-1}$ in the opposite direction. Calculate:
(a) the initial momentum of the ball,
(b) the impulse acting on the ball,
(c) the magnitude and direction of the force, and
(d) the displacement of the ball.

**1.15** A trolley of mass 2 kg is released from rest 6 m from the bottom of a slope which makes an angle of 30° to the horizontal. The constant frictional force opposing the trolley is 4 N.
(a) What is the resultant force on the trolley down the plane?
(b) Calculate the speed of the trolley at the bottom of the plane.
(c) If the trolley then moves along a horizontal table, at the bottom of the plane, which has the same frictional force, how far along the table will the trolley travel before coming to rest?
(d) Draw a graph of speed against time for the trolley's journey from the top of the plane until it comes to rest. Numerical values are required on the axes.

**1.16** Forces A, B, and C of magnitude 6 N, 9 N, and 12 N respectively act from a point O and are in equilibrium. Find the size of angle AÔB.

**1.17** $g$ is the acceleration due to gravity on Earth. A 3 kg block is released from rest on a planet where the gravitational field strength is $\frac{g}{4}$ N kg$^{-1}$. What is the velocity of the block after 6 s? Calculate the decrease in potential energy of the block after these 6 s.

# 2   Properties of Matter

## A:   Density, the Mole, and Molecular Size

### 2:A.1   Density

Unit: $kg\ m^{-3}$, scalar.

The density of a substance is defined as the mass per unit volume of that substance. Accordingly, in SI units, the density is the mass in kilograms of one cubic metre of a substance.

*Examples of densities ($kg\ m^{-3}$)*

| Gases | | Liquids | | Solids | |
|---|---|---|---|---|---|
| steam | 0.58 | water | $10^3$ | ice | $0.92 \times 10^3$ |
| oxygen | 1.43 | alcohol | $0.79 \times 10^3$ | copper | $8.9\ \times 10^3$ |
| hydrogen | 0.09 | mercury | $13.6 \times 10^3$ | perspex | $1.19 \times 10^3$ |

The density depends on:

(1) the mass of the atoms or molecules, that is the relative atomic or molecular masses.
(2) the distance between the centres of the atoms or molecules. For example, water and steam have the same molecular components, $H_2O$, but different degrees of associativity, such that in the liquid the molecules are closer together and hence its density is greater.

### Comparison of molecular spacing using densities

From the density values above, the mass of 1 $m^3$ of water is $10^3$ kg.

$$\Rightarrow 1 \text{ kg of water has a volume of } \frac{1}{10^3} = 10^{-3} \text{ m}^3$$

$$1 \text{ kg of steam has a volume of } \frac{1}{0.58} = 1.72 \text{ m}^3$$

If 1 kg of water is evaporated then $10^{-3}$ $m^3$ of water will yield 1.72 $m^3$ of steam.

$$\frac{\text{volume of steam}}{\text{volume of water}} = \frac{1.72}{10^{-3}} = \frac{1720}{1}$$

Thus the volume occupied by steam molecules is 1720 greater than that for the water molecules and the mean distance between steam molecules is $\sqrt[3]{1720}$ $\simeq$ 12 times greater than that between water molecules.

If the pressure on the steam is increased, the density will increase as the distance between the molecules decreases.

---

In general, the separation of molecules or atoms in the gaseous state is of the order of *ten* times that of the liquid or solid state.

The volume of a given mass of gas is of the order of $10^3$ greater than the volume of the same mass in the liquid or solid state.

---

### 2:A.2  Definition of the Mole and Avogadro's Constant

#### Unified atomic mass unit

The mass of one atom of the isotope $^{12}_{6}C$ is exactly 12 unified atomic mass units.

#### Relative atomic mass of an atom

This is equal to

$$\frac{\text{mass of the atom}}{\text{mass of } ^{12}_{6}C} \times 12$$

and has *no* units.

#### Formula mass

The relative atomic masses of the individual atoms in the molecule are added together to give the formula mass of the molecule.

#### Mole

This is a basic SI unit (see Section 1:A1).
The mole is the amount of substance which contains as many elementary entities as there are carbon atoms in $12 \times 10^{-3}$ kg (0.012 kg) of carbon-12. The entities may be ions, atoms, or molecules.

#### Avogadro's Constant, $N_A$

Unit: $mol^{-1}$, scalar.
Avogadro's Constant is the number of entities in one mole. That is, the number of atoms in $12 \times 10^{-3}$ kg of carbon-12.

$$N_A = 6.022\ 169 \times 10^{23}\ mol^{-1}$$

*Note:*  This implies that the relative atomic mass or formula mass expressed in $10^{-3}$ kg is a mole of that substance and contains $6.022 \times 10^{23}$ particles.

**Examples:** The relative atomic mass of tin is 118.7, thus $118.7 \times 10^{-3}$ kg of tin contains $6.022 \times 10^{23}$ atoms of tin.

For water the formula mass is $(2 + 16) = 18$, and $18 \times 10^{-3}$ kg of water will contain approximately $6.022 \times 10^{23}$ molecules of water.

Conversely, as one molecule of water has a mass of approximately $30 \times 10^{-27}$ kg, the molar mass of water is $(30 \times 10^{-27} \times 6.022 \times 10^{23})$ kg.

### 2:A.3 *Determination of Molecular or Atomic Spacing using Avogadro's Constant*

#### Solids

The volume of one atom or molecule may be determined using Avogadro's Constant. If it is assumed that the particles occupy 'cubic cells', the cube root of the volume will be the length of a 'cell' and equal to the distance between centres of adjacent particles, $AB = QR$, see Figure 2.1.

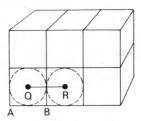

**Figure 2.1**   Cubic cells

**Example:** Find the distance between the centres of aluminium atoms in the solid state. Using: density of aluminium $= 2.7 \times 10^3$ kg m$^{-3}$, relative atomic mass of aluminium $= 27$, and $N_A = 6 \times 10^{23}$ mol$^{-1}$.

One mole of Al, that is $27 \times 10^{-3}$ kg of Al, contains $6 \times 10^{23}$ atoms
From the density,

$$2.7 \times 10^3 \text{ kg occupy } 1 \text{ m}^3$$

and
$$27 \times 10^{-3} \text{ kg occupy } \frac{27 \times 10^{-3}}{2.7 \times 10^3} \text{ m}^3 = 10^{-5} \text{ m}^3$$

Thus
$$6 \times 10^{23} \text{ atoms occupy } 10^{-5} \text{ m}^3$$

$$1 \text{ atom occupies } \frac{10^{-5}}{6 \times 10^{23}} = 1.7 \times 10^{-29} \text{ m}^3$$

$$\text{Volume of one atom} = 17 \times 10^{-30} \text{ m}^3$$

$$\text{Length of a cubic cell} = \sqrt[3]{17 \times 10^{-30}}$$
$$= 2.6 \times 10^{-10} \text{ m}$$

Thus the distance between centres $= 2.6 \times 10^{-10}$ m or 0.26 nm.

This example shows that the distance between the centres of the aluminium atom is of the order of $3 \times 10^{-10}$ m or 0.3 nm. This separation may be determined experimentally using X-ray diffraction, the results of which are found to be of the order predicted above.

## Gases

Avogadro's Law (see Section 2:C.1) states that equal volumes of ideal gases under the same conditions of temperature and pressure contain the same number of particles. Hence, one mole of any gas containing $6.022 \times 10^{23}$ particles will occupy the same volume. This volume, termed the **molar volume**, is found to be $22.4 \times 10^{-3}$ m$^3$ at s.t.p.* and varies with temperature and pressure.

$$6 \times 10^{23} \text{ particles of any gas occupy } 22.4 \times 10^{-3} \text{ m}^3$$

$$1 \text{ particle of a gas occupies } \frac{22.4 \times 10^{-3}}{6 \times 10^{23}} \text{ m}^3$$

$$= 3.7 \times 10^{-26} \text{ m}^3$$

Hence, the mean separation of the particles

$$= \sqrt[3]{3.7 \times 10^{-26}}$$
$$= 3.3 \times 10^{-9} \text{ m}$$

In this calculation the approximate value of $6 \times 10^{23}$ mol$^{-1}$ is used for Avogadro's Constant.

The mean separation of particles in the gaseous state is thus of the order of $3 \times 10^9$ m or 3 nm. That is *ten* times the separation of that in the solid state, which is in agreement with the density predictions.

## Liquids

The densities of liquids are of the same order as those of solids, which indicates that the separation of particles in the liquid state is also of the order of $3 \times 10^{-10}$ m or 0.3 nm. In the case of liquid water, $H_2O$, the distance between oxygen atoms is observed to be 0.23 nm.

## Oil-film experiment; Langmuir trough

### Experiment 2·1

The bottom of a shallow trough is covered with clean water, and lycopodium powder is sprinkled on the top. The diameter of a small drop of oil on the end of a wire loop is measured just before it is released gently on to the surface of the water. By measuring the area of spreading the thickness of the molecular layer may be determined.

$$\text{Volume of drop} = \text{area} \times \text{thickness}$$
$$\text{Diameter of drop} = d$$

$$\therefore \quad \text{Volume of one drop} = \frac{4\pi\left(\dfrac{d}{2}\right)^3}{3}$$

$$\text{Area of spreading} = A$$

$$\text{Thickness of oil} = \frac{4\pi\left(\dfrac{d}{2}\right)^3}{3 \times A}$$

* As the volume of a gas depends on its temperature and pressure, a standard temperature and pressure, s.t.p., is defined as 273.15 K and 101 325 Pa, the latter being equivalent to the pressure exerted by a 0.76 m column of mercury (see Section 2:B.2).

If it may be assumed that a unimolecular layer is obtained and that the molecules are approximately spherical, the thickness gives the diameter of one molecule or the distance between centres.

However, many organic molecules are *not* spherical but are composed of a 'chain' of atoms such that the length of a molecule may be very much greater than its width. Many of these molecules tend to orientate themselves vertically in the surface of the water. Hence the thickness of the layer in the above experiment will give the *length* of the 'chain' of the molecule. For example, oleic acid, $C_{17}H_3COOH$, which is often used in Experiment 2.1, might give values of over $10^{-9}$, that is one order greater than that expected for the liquid state of inorganic molecules.

**Problems**

**2.1** From an X-ray diffraction experiment the distance between the centres of the atoms in metallic copper is found to be $2.3 \times 10^{-10}$ m. Estimate the number of atoms in one mole of copper, given that the relative atomic mass of copper is 63 and the density of copper is $9.0 \times 10^3$ kg m$^{-3}$.

**2.2** Estimate the separation of the atoms of tin in the solid state if the density of tin is $7.28 \times 10^3$ kg m$^{-3}$, the relative atomic mass of tin is 118.7, and Avogadro's Constant is $6 \times 10^{23}$ mol$^{-1}$.

# B: Pressure and Temperature

## 2:B.1  Pressure

Unit: pascal (Pa), scalar.
Pressure is the force acting on unit area. It describes the distribution of a force over a surface and hence is a scalar quantity.

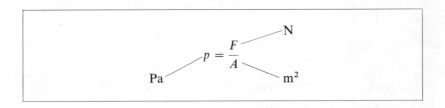

$$p = \frac{F}{A}$$

Pa — N — m$^2$

For example the pressure on the ground due to a 72 kg man standing on stilts, each of area of cross section 30 cm$^2$ will be $\dfrac{72 \times 10}{2 \times 30 \times 10^{-4}}$ which is $1.2 \times 10^5$ Pa. Compare this with his pressure when standing on shoes each of area of cross section 200 cm$^2$. Now his pressure is $\dfrac{72 \times 10}{2 \times 200 \times 10^{-4}}$ which is $1.8 \times 10^4$ Pa, almost ten times less, as the area over which the force is distributed is greater when the man is wearing shoes.

## Pressure in liquids

The pressure in a liquid depends on the density and is a function of the depth beneath the surface of the liquid. At a depth $h$ in a liquid of density $\rho$ the force on an area $A$ in the liquid is equal to the weight of liquid on $A$.

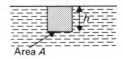

**Figure 2.2** Pressure at depth $h$

$$\text{Weight of liquid on } A = \text{volume} \times \text{density} \times \text{acceleration due to gravity}$$
$$= Ah\rho g$$
$$\text{Pressure} = \frac{\text{force}}{\text{area}} = \frac{Ah\rho g}{A}$$
$$p = h\rho g$$

---

Pressure at a depth $h$ in a liquid of density $\rho$ equals $h\rho g$.

---

*Note:* Pressures at points on the same horizontal level in a liquid will be the same.

### Experiment 2.2

The above relationship, $p = h\rho g$, may be demonstrated experimentally in two parts by floating a loaded test-tube vertically in a liquid.

Part (*a*)   Using a single liquid, the depth $h$ of the bottom of the test-tube below the surface is measured for different amounts of lead shot inside the tube. Neglecting curvature, if $A$ is the area of the base of the tube, the pressure in the liquid is $\frac{W}{A}$, where $W$ is the weight of the lead shot + tube. The results show $\frac{W}{A} \propto h$ as the density is constant.

Part (*b*)   The same test-tube is placed in liquids of different density $\rho$ and the weights $W$ required to immerse the test-tube to the same mark on the tube are recorded. Here the result shows $\frac{W}{A} \propto \rho$ as the depth $h$ has remained constant.

| | |
|---|---|
| From (a) | $p \propto h$ |
| And from (b) | $p \propto \rho$ |
| Therefore | $p \propto h\rho$ |

## 2:B.2  *Instruments for Measuring Pressure*

### *Manometer*

An open tube is partly filled with mercury and is connected to the gas under investigation. The pressure of the gas at A will be the same as the pressure at B since they are at the same level.

$$\text{Pressure of gas} = \text{pressure due to column } h \text{ of mercury}$$
$$+ \text{ atmospheric pressure, A.P.}$$
$$= h\rho g + \text{A.P.}$$

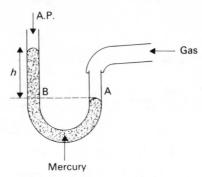

**Figure 2.3** A manometer

If the pressure of the gas is less than atmospheric then the level B will be below that of A. If this difference in levels is $h'$ then

$$\text{Pressure of the gas} = \text{A.P.} - h'\rho g$$

A water or oil-filled manometer will give larger values of $h$ as the density of water or oil is less than that of mercury, hence small pressure differences may be measured.

### Bourdon gauge

When a pressure is applied, the metal tube T will tend to straighten out turning the pointer *via* the cog wheel. This instrument thus measures pressures directly, in terms of the force on a given area, and not indirectly, as the height of a liquid column, as in the manometer or barometer.

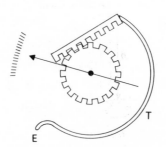

**Figure 2.4** A Bourdon gauge

*Calibration of the Bourdon gauge*

The position of the pointer on the Bourdon gauge with the exit E open to the atmosphere is noted. This will equal the atmospheric pressure which may be read from a Fortin barometer. This reading, in mm Hg, requires conversion into Pa (see the section on Barometers below). The piston of a glass syringe is attached to a spring balance graduated in newtons and the other end of the syringe is joined by a piece of rubber tubing to the Bourdon gauge at E. The spring balance is extended, its reading $F$ being the force applied to the piston of the syringe, which will move outwards reducing the pressure in the gauge.

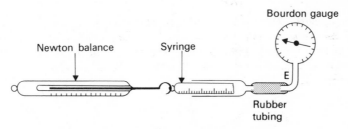

**Figure 2.5**   Calibration of a Bourdon gauge

The position of the pointer is noted for each reading $F$ in newtons on the balance. The pressure for each position being $\frac{F}{A}$, where $A$ is the area of cross section of the piston. Thus the scale may be calibrated for pressures below atmospheric.

For pressures above atmospheric the piston of the syringe must be extended before connection to the gauge, and the syringe placed vertically. It is pushed in by loading it with known masses $m$ and the position of the pointer is noted each time. Again the pressure is equal to $\frac{F}{A}$ where $F = mg$.

**Barometer** – *for measuring atmospheric pressure*

A simple barometer is made by inverting a tall tube, *full* of mercury, into a small trough of mercury. The tube must be considerably longer than 760 mm.

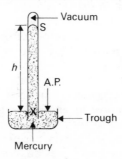

**Figure 2.6**   A simple barometer

The mercury in the tube falls to a height of about 760 mm, leaving a vacuum at the top. Atmospheric pressure on the outside surface of the mercury in the dish will equal the pressure at the same level X inside the tube due to the column of mercury.

$$\begin{aligned}
\text{A.P.} &= \text{pressure at X} \\
&= h\rho g \text{ Pa} \\
&= h \text{ mm of mercury (mm Hg)}
\end{aligned}$$

*Note:* Barometric pressure is usually stated simply as the height of the mercury column, that is in millimetres of mercury.

### Fortin barometer

In the simple barometer a scale cannot be placed at the upper mercury level S to record the pressure each day because when the mercury level rises inside the tube the level in the dish will fall, hence the reading at S will not be the total head of mercury as the lower level will not now be at the zero.

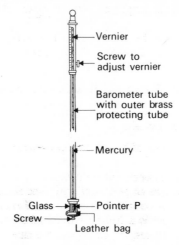

**Figure 2.7**. Fortin barometer

With the Fortin barometer the level of mercury in the leather reservoir is adjusted by means of a screw so that a pointer P just touches the lower mercury surface. The pressure each day may now be read off a permanent vernier scale at the upper mercury level, the bottom of the vernier scale being placed on the mercury meniscus by means of the adjusting screw.

### Aneroid barometer

This consists of a partially evacuated container with a flexible lid. As the pressure varies the lid will move in and out slightly, this movement being magnified by a series of levers to turn a pointer across the scale. This barometer has the advantage over the Fortin barometer or manometer of being more robust and portable, hence its use as an altimeter.

**Example:** Calculate the pressure equivalent to 0.76 m of mercury. Take $g = 9.81$ m s$^{-2}$ and the density of mercury as $13.6 \times 10^3$ kg m$^{-3}$.

$$\begin{aligned}
\text{Pressure} &= \text{depth} \times \text{density} \times g \\
&= 0.76 \times 13.6 \times 10^3 \times 9.81 \\
&= 1.01 \times 10^5 \text{ Pa}
\end{aligned}$$

## 2:B.3 *Temperature*

Unit: kelvin (K), scalar.

Temperature is a measure of the degree of hotness or coldness. Notice that temperature is not a measure of heat; but if two objects are in contact heat will flow from the object of higher temperature to that of lower temperature.

A **temperature scale** may be established by:

(1) choosing a physical property of a certain substance, called a **thermometric property**, which varies with temperature. For example, the expansion of a liquid column of mercury.

(2) selecting two fixed points and measuring the thermometric property at those points. For example, the length of the liquid column in melting ice, the ice point, and in steam from boiling water under normal pressure, the steam point.

(3) designating values to the two fixed points and dividing the interval between them into equal divisions. For example, allot the value 0 to the ice point and 100 to the steam point.

In this way a number of temperature scales can be set up depending on the thermometric property chosen.

**Thermometric properties** include:

(1) the length of a column of liquid in a glass tube, for example, mercury or alcohol.

(2) the pressure of gas at constant volume.

(3) the resistance of a coil of platinum wire (see Section 3:B.2).

(4) the e.m.f. of a thermocouple. For example, if each end of a piece of constantan wire is joined to a copper wire, and the junctions are maintained at different temperatures, an e.m.f. will be developed which depends on this difference in temperature.

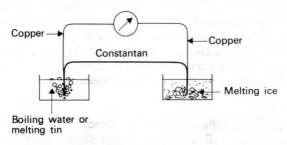

**Figure 2.8** A thermocouple

(5) the colour of light emitted by a hot source (useful at high temperatures).

(6) the speed of sound through helium (useful at low temperatures).

A **thermometer**, an instrument designed to measure temperature, utilizes a particular thermometric property of a given substance.

*Note:* Because the various thermometric properties depend in different ways on the temperature, the 'degree of hotness' of a given object will not necessarily have the same value on the different temperature scales of the various thermo-meters unless that value coincides with a fixed point.

The **constant volume gas thermometer** is chosen as a practical standard and its scale is called the **real gas scale**. The thermometric property of this thermo-meter is the pressure of a fixed mass of gas maintained at a constant volume. Other thermometers may be either calibrated against this thermometer or the temperatures recorded on them corrected to the real gas scale.

For interest only, it may be mentioned that the kelvin, a basic SI unit, can be defined in terms of the two fixed points of absolute zero, 0 K, and the triple point of water on the ideal gas scale, whose thermometric property is the pressure of a fixed mass of **ideal gas** (see Section 2:B.4) maintained at constant volume.

The two common fixed points, the ice point and the steam point, on the Celsius scale are 0 °C and 100 °C, whereas on the kelvin scale these points are 273.15 K and 373.15 K respectively. Hence, to a good approximation, 273 can be added to a temperature $\theta$ on the Celsius scale to give the corresponding temperature $T$ on the kelvin scale.

$$\theta + 273 = T$$

*Note:* An interval of one degree Celsius is the same as an interval of one kelvin, but care should be taken to use temperatures in kelvin in most calculations.

### Measurement of temperature – choice of thermometer

When measuring temperatures the choice of thermometer will depend on the range of temperatures involved, the accuracy required, and convenience of measurement. The constant volume gas thermometer may be used over a wide range of temperatures, $\sim 5$ K–1750 K, but it is an inconvenient thermometer to use. The platinum resistance thermometer, with a range of around 80 K–1400 K, and the thermocouple, with a range of $\sim 25$ K–1700 K, are more useful. Although the mercury-in-glass thermometer has a much smaller range, $-39$ °C to 357 °C, and is not so accurate, it is a useful thermometer for laboratory experiments as it gives direct readings, and is easy to use and is portable.

*Note:* A thermometer *absorbs* heat from the substance whose temperature it is measuring, thus recording a slightly lower temperature, assuming that the temperature of the substance is above that of the thermometer. It may also take *time* for the thermometer to reach thermal equilibrium with the substance be-ing measured. The thermocouple has the advantage of measuring accurately both local and varying temperatures.

### 2:B.4  Gas Laws

These are the relationships between the pressure $p$, the volume $V$, and the temperature $T$ for ideal gases.

An **ideal gas** is one in which the interactions between the gas particles are considered negligible. The following empirical laws have been discovered and constitute the behaviour of an ideal gas. Thus an ideal gas is one which *obeys* the general gas equation, namely that $\dfrac{pV}{T}$ is a constant for a fixed mass of gas.

## Boyle's Law

For a fixed mass of gas at a constant temperature, the pressure $p$ is inversely proportional to the volume $V$.

$$p \propto \frac{1}{V}$$

(constant mass and temperature)

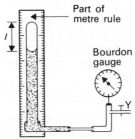

**Figure 2.9** To verify Boyle's Law

**Experiment 2.3** *Verification of Boyle's Law*

A certain mass of gas is trapped at the top of the tube and the pressure of the gas measured directly upon a Bourdon gauge (Figure 2.9). The volume of the gas may be obtained knowing the length $l$ and the area of cross section of the tube $A$, which may be assumed constant over the length.

$$V = l \times A \qquad V \propto l \quad \text{and} \quad \frac{1}{V} \propto \frac{1}{l}$$

The pressure of the gas is varied by means of a pump connected at Y. Readings of $l$ are taken for different pressure readings $p$ and a graph of $\frac{1}{l}$ against $p$ is plotted. A straight-line graph implies $p \propto \frac{1}{l}$, hence $p \propto \frac{1}{V}$, and Boyle's Law is verified if the temperature has remained constant, see Figure 2.12(a), on page 45.

## Charles' Law

For a fixed mass of gas at a constant pressure, the volume $V$ is directly proportional to the absolute temperature $T$.

$$V \propto T$$

(constant mass and pressure).

**Experiment 2.4** *Verification of Charles' Law*

The volume of the fixed mass of gas in Figure 2.10 is given by the length times the area of cross section of the tube, assuming negligible curvature. The pressure is equal to atmospheric pressure plus the pressure due to the thread of mercury. Providing the tube remains vertical the total pressure will not change.

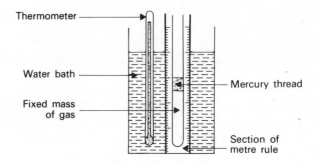

**Figure 2.10** To verify Charles' Law

The temperature of the water bath is varied and time allowed for the gas to attain this temperature before readings of volume and temperature are recorded. This is repeated for a range of temperatures. A graph of absolute temperature $T$ against volume $V$, or length of tube occupied by the gas, is plotted when a straight line through the origin implies $V \propto T$ thereby verifying Charles' Law, see Figure 2.12(b).

*Note:* The temperature $T$ is on the absolute temperature scale in units K.

## Pressure Law

For a fixed mass of gas at a constant volume, the pressure $p$ is directly proportional to the absolute temperature $T$.

$$p \propto T$$

(constant mass and volume)

**Experiment 2.5** *Verification of the Pressure Law*

The volume $V$ of the gas remains constant, being equal to the volume of the gas in the container plus the gas in the tubing leading to the Bourdon gauge (Figure 2.11).

The amount of gas in this connecting tubing must be kept to a minimum as this gas will not always be at the temperature $T$ of the water bath. The pressure $p$ of the gas for different temperatures is then recorded, ensuring that sufficient time is allowed for all the gas to attain that temperature. A graph of $p$ against $T$ should be a straight line through the origin implying $p \propto T$ so verifying the Pressure Law, see Figure 2.12(c).

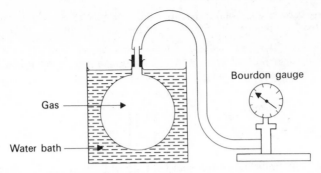

**Figure 2.11** To verify the Pressure Law

*Note:* In Experiments 2.3–2.5 it is observed that the laws are not followed at high pressures, low volumes or high temperatures, for then the intermolecular interactions come into dominance and the gas is no longer ideal.

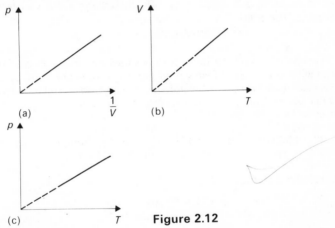

**Figure 2.12**

## General Gas Equation

On combining the three gas laws a general gas equation may be obtained. Since $p \propto \dfrac{1}{V}$, $p \propto T$, and $V \propto T$ then

For a fixed mass of gas $\dfrac{pV}{T}$ is a constant.

For an initial state $p_1 V_1 T_1$ and a final state $p_2 V_2 T_2$ clearly

$$\frac{p_1 V_1}{T_1} = \frac{p_2 V_2}{T_2}$$

This equation may be used to calculate unknown pressures, volumes or temperatures.

**Example:** A certain mass of gas has a volume of 50 cm$^3$ when the temperature is 17 °C, and the barometer reading is 74 cm of mercury. What is the volume of the gas at s.t.p.?

$$V_1 = 50 \text{ cm}^3 \qquad T_1 = 273 + 17 = 290 \text{ K} \qquad p_1 = 74 \text{ cm Hg}$$
$$V_2 = ? \qquad T_2 = 273 \text{ K} \qquad p_2 = 76 \text{ cm Hg}$$

$$\frac{74 \times 50}{290} = \frac{76 \times V_2}{273}$$

and
$$V_2 = 45.8 \text{ cm}^3$$

*Note:* The units must be *consistent*. They do not always need conversion into the standard units. All temperatures, however, *must* be in K, a factor of 273 being *added* to a temperature in degrees Celsius, °C.

## Partial pressures

If two or more gases which do not chemically react are present in the same container the total pressure is the sum of the partial pressures which each gas would exert if alone in the container.

This statement is known as Dalton's Law of Partial Pressures.

**Example:** A 7 litre container of nitrogen at $10^5$ Pa is joined by a connecting tap to a 4 litre container of oxygen at $3 \times 10^5$ Pa. Assuming no change in temperature, what is the resulting pressure of the mixture?

Using Boyle's Law $\qquad p_1 V_1 = p_2 V_2$

Partial pressure $p_N$ of the nitrogen in the total 11 litres:

$$10^5 \times 7 = p_N \times 11$$
$$p_N = \frac{7 \times 10^5}{11}$$

Partial pressure $p_O$ of the oxygen in the 11 litres:

$$3 \times 10^5 \times 4 = p_O \times 11$$
$$p_O = \frac{12 \times 10^5}{11}$$

$$\text{Total pressure} = p_N + p_O$$
$$= \frac{7 \times 10^5}{11} + \frac{12 \times 10^5}{11}$$
$$= 1.7 \times 10^5 \text{ Pa}$$

**Problems**
Use $g = 10 \text{ m s}^{-2}$
**2.3** Calculate the pressure due to (*a*) 0.8 m of mercury, (*b*) 5 m of water. (Density of mercury is $13.6 \times 10^3 \text{ kg m}^{-3}$.)
**2.4** Taking normal atmospheric pressure as $10^5$ Pa, calculate the respective heights of an 'alcohol barometer' and a 'water barometer'. (Density of alcohol is $0.79 \times 10^3$ kg m$^{-3}$.)

# C: Kinetic Theory of Gases

## 2:C.1 Derivation of the Gas Laws using the Kinetic Theory of Gases

That a gas is observed to occupy the whole volume of a vessel rather than a part of it indicates that the gaseous molecules are in a state of motion. Furthermore, as gases are readily compressible it is reasonable to consider that the distance between the individual molecules is quite large.

In the kinetic theory such observations form the basis for a number of assumptions from which equations to interpret the behaviour of gases may be derived.

### Assumptions

(1) The molecules behave as if they are hard, smooth, perfectly elastic point particles. (This implies no loss of kinetic energy in collisions.)
(2) Hence the volume of the actual molecules is negligible compared with the total volume they occupy.
(3) The forces of attraction between the molecules are negligible.
(4) The molecules are in continual random motion, colliding with the walls of a container and with each other.

It may be shown that the mean translational kinetic energy of the molecules is proportional to the absolute temperature. This is not an assumption.

### Derivation of $pV = \frac{1}{3}Nmc^2$

Consider a single molecule of gas in a container of length $l$ and area of cross section $A$.

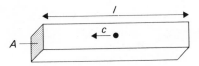

**Figure 2.13** Model for the kinetic theory

If the molecule has a mass $m$ and velocity $c$, parallel to the length $l$, its momentum as it approaches the shaded face is $mc$. If the collision with the walls is elastic, the molecule will leave this shaded face with momentum $-mc$.

Therefore the change in momentum is $mc - (-mc) = 2mc$.

The time between collisions on the shaded face is the time taken to travel the length of the box and back, a distance $2l$.

$$\text{Time taken} = \frac{\text{distance}}{\text{velocity}}$$

$$= \frac{2l}{c}$$

From Newton's Second Law,

$$\text{Force} = \text{rate of change of momentum}$$

$$= \frac{\text{change of momentum}}{\text{time}}$$

$$= \frac{2mc}{2l/c}$$

$$= \frac{mc^2}{l}$$

Pressure is force per unit area.

$$\text{Pressure} = \frac{\text{force}}{\text{area}}$$

$$= \frac{mc^2}{lA}$$

$$= \frac{mc^2}{V}$$

where $V$ is the volume of the container.

It is now assumed that the box contains $N$ molecules. On average, the same number of molecules will be moving along the box as up and down or to and fro across the box. Hence the pressure on any wall is due only to $\frac{1}{3}N$ of the molecules present.

$$\text{Pressure } p = \tfrac{1}{3}\frac{Nmc^2}{V}$$

All the molecules do not have the same velocities and the term $c^2$ is usually written as $\overline{c^2}$ to show that it is an average of all the $c^2$ terms. It is called the **mean square velocity** of the molecules.

*Note:*   The mean square velocity is the average of the squares of the velocities, and *not* the square of the average which would be written $\bar{c}^2$.

$$\text{Pressure } p = \tfrac{1}{3}\frac{Nm\overline{c^2}}{V}$$

or

$$pV = \tfrac{1}{3}Nm\overline{c^2}$$

The average translational kinetic energy is proportional to the absolute temperature.

$$\tfrac{1}{2}m\overline{c^2} \propto T$$

As $pV = \frac{2}{3} N (\frac{1}{2} \overline{mc^2})$

$pV \propto \frac{2}{3} NT$

$pV = NkT$ where $k$ is a constant known as Boltzmann's constant.

For a constant mass, that is a fixed number of molecules $N$, the above equation shows that for ideal gases:

$\dfrac{pV}{T}$ is a constant for a given mass.

This is the general gas equation, see Section 2:B.4.

The three gas laws may also be derived from the kinetic theory by way of the equation $pV = \frac{2}{3} N (\frac{1}{2} \overline{mc^2})$ or $pV = NkT.*$

(1) For a constant mass of gas, $N$ is a constant. Hence if the temperature $T$ is constant, $pV$ is a constant or $p \propto \dfrac{1}{V}$, which is Boyle's Law.

$$p \propto \frac{1}{V} \text{ (constant mass and temperature)}$$

(2) For a constant mass and a fixed pressure, $N$ and $p$ are constant so that $V \propto T$, which is Charles' Law.

(3) Again for a fixed mass of gas, $N$ is constant, therefore if the volume is constant $p \propto T$, as given in the Pressure Law.

*Note:* The temperature depends on $\frac{1}{2} \overline{mc^2}$ for *all* gases. So a molecule with a large mass will have a smaller value of $\overline{c^2}$ than one with a lighter mass at the same temperature. Hence a gas with a lighter mass will *diffuse* more rapidly than one with a high molecular mass. For example, hydrogen diffuses more rapidly than carbon dioxide at the same temperature.

### Avogadro's Law

Equal volumes of ideal gases at the same temperature and pressure contain the same number of particles.

This law may also be derived from the kinetic theory. Consider two gases at pressures $p_1$ and $p_2$ and volumes $V_1$ and $V_2$. From the equation $pV = \frac{1}{3} N\overline{mc^2}$

$$p_1 V_1 = \frac{1}{3} N_1 m_1 \overline{c_1^2}$$

and
$$p_2 V_2 = \frac{1}{3} N_2 m_2 \overline{c_2^2}$$

* The derivation of the gas laws and the formula for the mean square velocity from $pV = \frac{1}{3} N\overline{mc^2}$ should be carefully learnt.

The law is concerned with equal volumes at a given pressure so

$$p_1 = p_2 \quad \text{and} \quad V_1 = V_2$$
$$\Rightarrow \tfrac{1}{3}N_1 m_1 \overline{c_1^2} = \tfrac{1}{3}N_2 m_2 \overline{c_2^2}$$

The temperature of the two gases are equal giving

$$\tfrac{1}{2}m_1 \overline{c_1^2} = \tfrac{1}{2}m_2 \overline{c_2^2}$$
$$\Rightarrow N_1 = N_2$$

Therefore the number of molecules in equal volumes are the same.

## 2:C.2   *Mean Square Velocities*

These may be calculated using the equation $pV = \tfrac{1}{3} Nm\overline{c^2}$.*

$$p = \tfrac{1}{3}\frac{Nm}{V}\overline{c^2}$$
$$= \tfrac{1}{3}\rho\,\overline{c^2} \text{ where } \rho \text{ is the density}$$

$$\overline{c^2} = \frac{3p}{\rho}$$

To obtain an idea of the average speed of the molecules the **root mean square velocity**, $c_{\text{r.m.s.}}$, is of interest.

$$c_{\text{r.m.s.}} = \sqrt{\overline{c^2}}$$

and

$$c_{\text{r.m.s.}} = \sqrt{\frac{3p}{\rho}}$$

**Example:**   Determine the root mean square velocity of the oxygen molecule at s.t.p. The density of oxygen at s.t.p. is 1.43 kg m$^{-3}$.

$$p = 1.01 \times 10^5 \text{ Pa} \qquad \rho = 1.43 \text{ kg m}^{-3}$$
$$\overline{c^2} = \frac{3p}{\rho}$$
$$= \frac{3 \times 1.01 \times 10^5}{1.43}$$
$$= 2.1 \times 10^5$$
$$\sqrt{\overline{c^2}} = 4.5 \times 10^2 \text{ m s}^{-1} \text{ at } 0\,^\circ\text{C and normal atmospheric pressure.}$$

* The derivation of the gas laws and the formula for the mean square velocity from $pV = \tfrac{1}{3} Nm\overline{c^2}$ should be carefully learnt.

The velocity $c_{\text{r.m.s.}}$ of hydrogen is higher than that of oxygen due to its lower density (see Problem 2.5 on page 53). Because of their higher velocities the hydrogen molecules are able to escape from the Earth, hence the lack of hydrogen in our planet's atmosphere.

*Note:*
(1) At s.t.p. molecular velocities are of the order of $10^2$ to $10^3$ metres per second.
(2) The average kinetic energy of all gases are the same at any given temperature; $E_k \propto T$.
(3) For a given gas a large increase in temperature is required for a small alteration in the velocities as the temperature is proportional to the square of the velocities; $\overline{c^2} \propto T$.

**Experiment 2.6** *Determination of root mean square velocities*

A molecular beam emerging from an oven is collimated by a pair of slits such that a narrow beam reaches a rotating drum, upon which a film is fixed to the inner surface (Figure 2.14). When the slits are aligned to the small opening in the drum the molecules may enter and cross to make a mark at S, the stationary mark. If the drum is rotated the

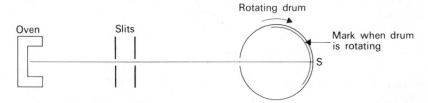

**Figure 2.14** Apparatus for measuring $c_{\text{r.m.s.}}$

molecules will hit the film at a different point. From the distance between the marks, the diameter of the drum, and its rate of revolution, the speed of the molecules may be calculated. It is observed that the second mark made by the molecules when the drum is rotating is a broad band, dark at the centre and shading on either side, showing that the molecules do not all have the same velocity. The faster ones will reach the film nearer the mark S than the slower ones (Figure 2.15).

If the temperature of the oven is increased and the experiment repeated a mark is obtained nearer to the stationary mark S showing that the velocities of the molecules have increased. Again the deposit on the film is greatest at the centre and less on either side. However, as the temperature is further increased the *spread* of the velocities decreases (Figure 2.16).

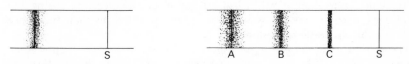

**Figure 2.15** Velocity spread    **Figure 2.16** $c_{\text{r.m.s.}}$ increase with temperature

Marks A, B, and C in Figure 2.16 are for molecules leaving the oven at temperatures $T_A$, $T_B$, and $T_C$ respectively.

Observe, that because C is nearest the stationary mark S, $T_C > T_B > T_A$.

### 2:C.3  *Differences between an Ideal and a Real Gas*

Gases which obey the general gas equation are termed ideal gases (see Section 2:B.4). However, at high temperatures and pressures departure from the ideal are observed. Better agreement may be observed if account is taken of two factors.

(1) The molecules of a gas do exert a force of attraction on each other, hence the actual pressure $p$ observed is less than that considered in the theory.
(2) The molecules themselves occupy a finite part of the overall volume of the vessel.

According to Van der Waals a more general equation to describe the properties of gases is of the form

$$\left(p + \frac{a}{V^2}\right)(V - b) = RT \qquad \text{where } R \text{ is a constant}$$

The term $\frac{a}{V^2}$ takes care of the attraction between molecules while $b$ corrects for the effective volume occupied by the molecules themselves.

Even with this equation the behaviour observed under some conditions of temperature and pressure is not accounted for.

*Note:*  The factors (1) and (2) above should be carefully learnt. Memorization of the equation is of less importance.

### 2:C.4  *Comparison of Solids, Liquids, and Gases*

The arrangement of the molecules in each state is the result of competition between thermal forces $F_T$ which tend to produce collisions or vibrations and to generate disorder among molecules, and cohesive forces $F_C$ which tend to order them. In gases, $F_T$ is larger than $F_C$ and therefore there is random motion. In liquids, $F_T$ and $F_C$ may be about the same, often giving a partly ordered structure. In solids, $F_C$ is larger than $F_T$ and an ordered structure usually prevails,·as in the structure of crystals.

To change a solid into a liquid, energy must be supplied to overcome any cohesive forces. When this energy is in the form of heat it is termed the latent heat (see Section 2:D). Similarly latent heat is evolved when the liquid returns to the solid state or a gas to the liquid state.

### *Interatomic forces*

In the solid state there is a force of attraction between certain atoms, but at close distances the two atoms will repel each other due to their incompressibility and electrostatic repulsion.

The zero of potential energy in Figure 2.17 is arbitrary and is chosen as the energy when the atoms are completely separated. Notice that at large separations the graph is asymptotic to the $r$ axis. At A the atoms are tending to repel each other so that energy is increasing as the atoms are brought closer together. There is an equilibrium position at E where the attractive·and repulsive forces are in balance and the atoms are at their *lowest energy* level. For

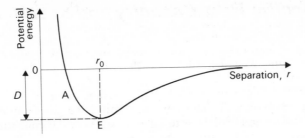

**Figure 2.17** Graph of *potential energy* against separation for two atoms

two atoms which combine to give a diatomic molecule the value D will yield the dissociation energy of the molecule.

When the energy is at a minimum position E and separation $r_0$ (Figure 2.17), the sum of the *forces* on the nuclei is *zero*. At small separations, $r < r_0$, the internuclei repulsion increases rapidly, hence the steep rise shown at A in

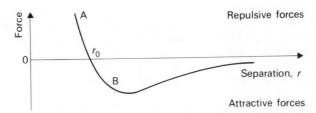

**Figure 2.18** Graph of *force* between two atoms against their separation

Figure 2.18. For small separations, $r > r_0$, the attractive forces first increase in the region labelled B and then decrease in the region labelled C. At about 1.5 nm the interaction between the atoms is negligible.

*Note:* The equilibrium interatomic separation is found when the energy is a minimum or the forces are zero.

**Problems**
Use density of hydrogen at s.t.p. $= 9 \times 10^{-2}$ kg m$^{-3}$, standard pressure $= 10^5$ Pa, and atomic mass of hydrogen $= 1.67 \times 10^{-27}$ kg.
Answers to two significant figures are quite sufficient.
2.5 (*a*) Calculate the root mean square velocity of hydrogen molecules at s.t.p.
   (*b*) Calculate the average kinetic energy of the hydrogen molecule, at s.t.p., assuming the molecular mass of hydrogen to be twice the atomic mass.
   (*c*) What is the average kinetic energy of oxygen molecules at s.t.p.?
   (*d*) Calculate the average kinetic energy of nitrogen molecules at 27 °C.
2.6 Estimate at what temperature hydrogen molecules would have a root mean square velocity of $10^5$ m s$^{-1}$ at standard pressure.

# D: Specific Heat Capacity and Specific Latent Heat

There are three distinct states of matter: solid, liquid, and vapour or gas. Some substances sublime when heated, that is they change directly from a solid to a vapour, for example, iodine.

When a solid, a liquid or a gas is heated its temperature may rise or a change of state may occur without change in temperature. If a given amount of heat is supplied to two different solids or to different states of the same substance then different changes in temperature may occur.

## Specific heat capacity

Unit: $J\ kg^{-1}\ K^{-1}$, scalar.

Specific heat capacity $c$ is the heat required in joules to raise the temperature of one kilogram of the substance by one kelvin.

Notice that a difference of one kelvin is the same as a difference of one degree Celsius.

*Note:* The specific heat capacity depends on the temperature at which it is measured. The heat required to change the temperature of one kilogram of a solid from 10 °C to 20 °C may not be the same as that required to change the temperature of the same one kilogram from 80 °C to 90 °C. However, for the accuracy required here, this variation may be neglected. For interest it may be noted that the specific heat capacity for water is $4.185\ J\ kg^{-1}\ K^{-1}$ at 288 K.

## Heat capacity

Unit: $J\ K^{-1}$, scalar.

The heat capacity of an object is the heat required to raise its temperature by one kelvin.

The heat capacity thus refers to a particular object as opposed to unit mass of a given substance.

## Specific latent heat of fusion

Unit: $J\ kg^{-1}$, scalar.

The specific latent heat of fusion $l$ is the heat required in joules to change the state from solid to liquid of one kilogram of the substance at its normal melting point.

## Specific latent heat of vaporization

Unit: $J\ kg^{-1}$, scalar.

The specific latent heat of vaporization $l$ is the heat required in joules to change the state of one kilogram of the substance from liquid to vapour at its normal boiling point.

*Note:* The specific latent heat varies with pressure and is therefore usually quoted for standard pressure.

In calculations the heat supplied, for example, by an electrical heater, will either yield a temperature rise $\Delta T$ and/or a change of state. Unknown quantities can be calculated using $H = mc\Delta t$ and $H = ml$, where $c$ is the specific heat capacity and $l$ is the specific latent heat.

### Experiment 2.7 *To study change in temperature with time*

A fixed mass of substance is heated by an electrical heater which has a constant power output, that is the energy supplied per second is constant. A graph of temperature against time is plotted (Figure 2.19).

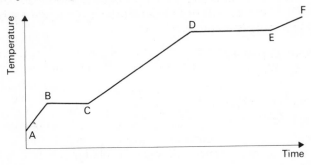

**Figure 2.19**

The time interval for a given temperature rise or change of state, or phase, is proportional to the heat required.

From the graph (Figure 2.19):

| | | |
|---|---|---|
| AB – solid state | B – melting point | BC – change of state |
| CD – liquid state | D – boiling point | DE – change of state |
| EF – vapour state | | |

As the time BC is less than DE, the mass remaining constant and the power supply uniform, the specific latent heat of fusion is less than the specific latent heat of vaporization. Also, as AB is steeper than CD the specific heat capacity for the solid is less than that for the liquid, a larger rise in temperature being obtained by the solid for less heat supplied.

**Example:** A 20 W heater is used to supply heat to 20 g of ice and a graph similar to Figure 2.19 is obtained. What are the time intervals BC, CD, and DE, given: $l_{\text{fusion of ice}} = 33 \times 10^4$ J kg$^{-1}$, $c_{\text{water}} = 4.2 \times 10^3$ J kg$^{-1}$ K$^{-1}$, $l_{\text{vaporization of water}} = 23 \times 10^5$ J kg$^{-1}$?

Heat supplied $= 20 \times t$ J where $t$ is the time required
Heat required to melt the ice $= 0.02 \times 33 \times 10^4$ J

Assuming no heat loss
$$20 \times t = 0.02 \times 33 \times 10^4$$
$$t = 5\tfrac{1}{2} \text{ minutes}$$

Heat required to change the temperature from 0 °C to 100 °C
$$= 0.02 \times 4.2 \times 10^3 \times 100 \text{ J}$$

Assuming no heat loss
$$20 \times t = 0.02 \times 4.2 \times 10^3 \times 100$$
$$t = 420 \text{ s}$$
$$= 7 \text{ minutes}$$

Heat required to evaporate the water
$$= 0.02 \times 23 \times 10^5 \text{ J}$$

Assuming no heat loss
$$20 \times t = 0.2 \times 23 \times 10^5$$
$$t = 2300 \text{ s}$$
$$= 38 \text{ min. } 20 \text{ s}$$

Hence the time intervals BC, CD, and DE are $5\frac{1}{2}$ minutes, 7 minutes, and 38 minutes 20 seconds respectively.

## Effects of heat loss

In many experiments all the heat supplied is not absorbed by the substance but some heat is lost to the container and the surroundings and therefore incorrect results will be obtained. These may be minimized either (1) by attempting to reduce heat loss or (2) by accounting for the heat loss in a control experiment. (1) Heat loss may be reduced by avoiding draughts which lead to heat loss by convection and by using a container of a material such as polystyrene (which does not readily absorb or conduct heat) or by surrounding the container, whose heat capacity is accounted for, by an insulating jacket.
(2) For experimental temperatures below room temperature the heat absorbed from the surroundings in the time the experiment is carried out may be determined in a control experiment. For temperatures above room temperature the rate of cooling of an equal mass may be determined and hence the average heat loss estimated.

*Note:*   Liquids should be stirred before temperatures are taken and attempts made to heat solids as uniformly as possible.

### Problems
Use specific heat capacity of water $= 4.2 \times 10^3 \text{ J kg}^{-1} \text{ K}^{-1}$ and specific latent heat of vaporization of water $= 23 \times 10^5 \text{ J kg}^{-1}$.
2.7   A container of heat capacity 120 J K$^{-1}$ contains 400 g of water. What is the power of a heater which raises their temperature by 10 °C in 1 minute?
2.8   A 20 W heater was placed inside a plastic vessel containing 0.3 kg of water for 2 minutes. If the initial temperature of the water was 20 °C, what was the final temperature of the water? How would your answer vary if the container were made of copper?
2.9   A heater was found to raise the temperature of 0.6 kg of water from 20 °C to 30 °C in 1 minute. Estimate, to the nearest minute, how long it would take for this heater to evaporate 0.03 kg of water initially at 80 °C.

# 3  Electricity

## A:  Electric Charge, Electric Field, Potential Difference, and their Inter-relationships

### 3:A.1  *Electric Charge*

Unit: coulomb (C), scalar.
The charge on an electron is the smallest quantity of charge observed and is equal to $1.602 \times 10^{-19}$ coulombs.

*Note:*  The ampere is the basic electrical unit, hence the coulomb is defined as that charge which passes a point in a conductor in one second when a current of one ampere is flowing.

   A neutral atom consists of a central positive nucleus and a number of electrons whose total charge is numerically equal to that of the nucleus. If some of these electrons are removed a positive ion is formed, whilst when there is an excess of electrons a negative ion is obtained. A positively charged body attracts a negatively charged one and like-charged objects repel each other.
   A charge placed in the region of other charges will experience a force of attraction or repulsion. The magnitude of this force is an indication of the **electric field** at that position. The direction of the force, that is the direction of the field, indicates the nature – positive or negative – and the distribution of charges in the region.

### 3:A.2  *Electric Field Strength*

Units: $\dfrac{\text{newton coulomb}^{-1}}{\text{volt metre}^{-1}}$ , vector.

The electric field strength $E$ at any point is the force on a unit charge placed at that point.

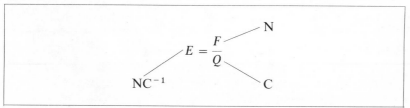

**Figure 3.1**   Lines of electric field

By convention, the *direction* of the electric field is the direction in which a free *positive* charge would move. A *line* of electric field shows the direction of the field.

A positive charge will move away from another positive charge, as in Figure 3.1(a), and towards a negative surface, as in Figure 3.1(b).

### 3:A.3   *Potential Difference*

Unit: volt, scalar.

The potential difference (p.d.) *between* two points is the work done, or energy expended, in transferring unit charge between those points.

$$\text{p.d.} = \frac{\text{energy}}{\text{charge}}$$

V · · · · · p.d. · · · · · energy — J

charge — C

In any electric field, that is in a region containing charge, some work must be done or energy be expended, if charges are moved against the field. In Figure 3.1(b) a negative charge must be pushed from plate A to B. The gravitational field provides an analogy: the top of a hill has a higher gravitational potential than the bottom and energy must be expended in taking a mass up the hill. Conversely, potential energy is lost when the mass falls down the hill. It is the *difference* in the heights which determines the amount of energy required, the actual heights above sea level or the base of the hill are unimportant. Similarly in the electrical case the potential difference is between two points in a circuit, the p.d. or voltage (see page 71) is *not* at a point or through a wire.

*Note:*   The potential difference is a scalar quantity as it has no direction.

Electrical energy = potential difference between two points
× charge moved between those points.

$$\text{Electrical energy} = VQ$$

V

Electrical energy = *VQ*

J      C

### 3:A.4 *Relationship between Potential Difference and Electric Field for a Uniform Field Only*

In a uniform field the lines of field are parallel to each other (Figure 3.2) and therefore any charge moving between the plates A and B will travel parallel to the lines of field, and 'sideways' forces need not be considered. Also the electrical force remains constant at *all* points between the plates.

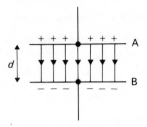

**Figure 3.2** Uniform electric field

Potential difference between plates A and B a distance *d* apart

= work done to take a unit positive charge from B to A

$$= \frac{\text{work done B} \rightarrow \text{A}}{\text{charge}}$$

$$= \frac{\text{force} \times \text{distance AB}}{\text{charge}}$$

= electric field × distance AB

$$V = E \times d$$
$$\text{V} \quad \text{V m}^{-1} \quad \text{m}$$

This equation shows how the other unit of electric field strength, volt metre$^{-1}$, is obtained.

*Note:* The electric field is a vector, therefore a vector treatment is required if the direction of the field is not parallel to the perpendicular distance *d* between the plates.

### 3:A.5 *Movement of Charges in an Electrical Field*

Since an electron has a negative charge it will freely travel from B to A in Figure 3.3. The acceleration gained by the electron will depend on the magnitude of the field.

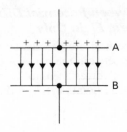

**Figure 3.3**   Electron accelerates towards A

**Example:**   An electron is at plate B, in Figure 3.3. What will be its acceleration towards A if the field is 2000 V m$^{-1}$, given that the charge on an electron is $1.6 \times 10^{-19}$ C and its mass is $9 \times 10^{-31}$ kg?

$$\text{Force on the electron} = E \times \text{charge on the electron}$$
$$= 2000 \times 1.6 \times 10^{-19}$$
$$= 3.2 \times 10^{-16} \text{ N}$$

From Newton's Second Law, $F = ma$

$$a = \frac{3.2 \times 10^{-16}}{9 \times 10^{-31}}$$
$$= 3.5 \times 10^{14} \text{ m s}^{-2}$$

Although the force is small, the acceleration is large because of the extremely small mass of the electron. The downward acceleration due to gravity may be neglected here in comparison!

In some problems it is easier to consider the energy. An electron travelling from B to A in Figure 3.3 will lose electrical energy and gain kinetic energy.

**Example:**   An electron leaves an electron gun with negligible velocity. The potential difference between the gun and the collector plate is 100 V. What is its velocity just before it touches the collector plate?

$$\text{Electrical energy} = VQ$$
$$= 100 \times 1.6 \times 10^{-19}$$
$$= 1.6 \times 10^{-17} \text{ J}$$
$$\text{Kinetic energy gained} = \tfrac{1}{2}mv^2$$
$$= \tfrac{1}{2} 9 \times 10^{-31} v^2 \text{ J}$$

Assuming all the electrical energy is converted to kinetic energy

$$\tfrac{1}{2} 9 \times 10^{-31} v^2 = 1.6 \times 10^{-17}$$
Hence $\qquad\qquad\qquad v^2 = 0.35 \times 10^{14}$
and $\qquad\qquad\qquad v \simeq 6 \times 10^6 \text{ m s}^{-1}$

In general, for calculations involving forces and accelerations, consider the electric field, when velocities, times, and distances are required, it is more useful to consider the energy and potential difference. With high electric fields and light particles the acceleration due to gravity may be negligible but with heavier, slower-moving particles it must be included in the calculation.

## Experiment 3.1 *Millikan's oil drop experiment*

Small drops of oil, released between the plates, are charged by friction as they emerge from the nozzle (Figure 3.4). One drop is singled out and viewed by the microscope. The

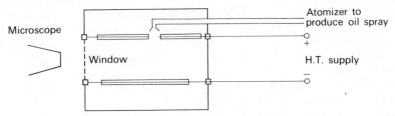

**Figure 3.4** Apparatus for Millikan's oil drop experiment

drop will fall under gravity but the air resistance will provide an upward viscous force $F_v$ and the drop will attain a steady terminal velocity, $v$.

Stoke's Law gives a relationship between the viscous force $F_v$ and the terminal velocity $v$ of a drop of radius $r$, namely

$$F_v = 6\pi\eta r v$$

where $\eta$ is the viscosity of the medium.*

Archimedean upthrust + viscous force = weight of drop

$$\tfrac{4}{3}\pi r^3 \rho' g + F_v = \tfrac{4}{3}\pi r^3 \rho g$$
$$F_v = 6\pi r \eta v = \tfrac{4}{3}\pi r^3 (\rho - \rho')g$$
$$6\pi r \eta v = m'g$$

where $r$ = radius of drop, $\rho$ = density of oil, $\rho'$ = density of air, $m'$ = effective mass, and $\eta$ = viscosity of air.

Measurement of this terminal velocity together with accepted values of $\eta$, $\rho$, and $\rho'$ enables the radius of the drop, and hence the effective mass, to be determined. A potential difference $V_1$ is now applied between the plates and adjusted so that the drop is brought to rest. The charge on this *same* drop is then altered by using a radioactive source or X-rays and the new potential difference $V_2$ required to bring the drop to rest is again recorded. This is repeated and the potential differences recorded.

Upward force due to the electric field $= \dfrac{V}{d} Q$ where $Q$ is the total charge on the drop

and $d$ the distance between the plates.

At rest, effective weight $m'g = \dfrac{V}{d} Q$ hence for each reading

$$\frac{m'gd}{V_1} = Q_1 = n_1 e$$

where $n_1$, $n_2$, ... are integers as the total charge on the drop is an integral number of electronic charges. By inspection of the $Q$ values the value of $e$ may be ascertained. As a charged drop will tend to repel the addition of further charges the *number* of electrons $n_1$, $n_2$, ... on the drop will tend to be small.

* Memorization of the formula for viscosity is not required, but it is given to show that $v$ must be measured to obtain the radius $r$.

*Note:* In some questions the upthrust is neglected, giving $mg = \dfrac{V}{d}Q$, where $m$ is the mass of the drop.

In the original experiment Millikan applied an electric field and measured the new terminal velocity of the drop, $v_1$. He then altered the charge on the drop and in each case measured the new terminal velocity $v_2, v_3, \ldots$ He did *not* alter the potential difference and bring the drop to rest as described in the laboratory experiment above.

For each velocity $v_1, v_2, \ldots$ upward forces due to electric field and viscosity equal effective weight downwards
For $v_1$,

$$6\pi r\eta v_1 + \frac{V}{d}n_1 e = m'g$$

$$= 6\pi r\eta v \qquad \text{as } m'g = 6\pi r\eta v, \text{ see above.}$$

$$\frac{V}{d}n_1 e = 6\pi r\eta(v - v_1)$$

Similarly for $v_2$,

$$\frac{V}{d}n_2 e = 6\pi r\eta(v - v_2)$$

With the $n_1, n_2, \ldots$ integers, the values of $(v - v_1)$, $(v - v_2)$ ... should be a simple multiple of a common number. However, Millikan noticed that this was not so within the limits of accuracy of his experiments and so he suspected that Stoke's Law, $F_v = 6\pi r\eta v$, was not correct for his small drops in air. Later experiments on the viscosity of small drops in gases showed Millikan's suspicions to be correct and with an amended viscosity relationship the values of $(v - v_1)$, $(v - v_2)$, ... were found to be consistent and a value for the electronic charge $e$ obtained.

### Problems

3.1  An electron, of mass $9 \times 10^{-31}$ kg and charge $1.6 \times 10^{-19}$ C, in a cathode ray tube, is accelerated by a uniform field of 3000 V m$^{-1}$ between the anode and cathode which are 5 cm apart. It continues to the screen 10 cm beyond the anode.
   (a) With what velocity does an electron reach the anode if it leaves the cathode with zero velocity and its mass remains constant?
   (b) Assuming there is negligible electric field beyond the anode, what is the velocity of the electron at the screen?
   (c) Calculate the time taken to travel from cathode to anode, and anode to screen.
   (d) How would the velocity at the anode and the transit time from cathode to anode be affected if the distance between the electrodes was kept constant but the electric field were increased?

3.2  How many electrons are there in one coulomb?

3.3  (a) State why the terminal velocity of the drop in a Millikan-type experiment to determine the electronic charge, must be measured before the electric field is applied.

(b) In such an experiment the following results for charges on the drop were obtained, in $10^{-19}$ C: 3.18, 12.80, 4.79, 6.41, 8.01. What is a likely value for the electronic charge?

# B: Current, Resistance, Electromotive Force, Electrical Energy, and Power

## 3:B.1 *Current*

In some substances, for example copper, the outer electrons of the atom are less strongly bound to the individual nuclei and may wander throughout the bulk of the material. Such a substance is termed a **conductor**, see Figure 3.5. If a potential difference is applied between two points on such a substance these conduction electrons will travel to the positive point, that is the point of highest potential giving a transient current (i.e. a current of short duration). If this potential difference is maintained then a steady current is produced.

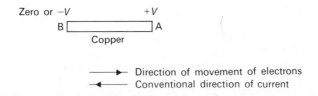

**Figure 3.5** A conductor

*Note:* By convention the direction of the current is the direction in which *positive* charge would move. Hence the current flows from a point of high potential A to a point of lower potential B, but electrons, the carriers of charge in this instance, move in the opposite direction.

If a substance does not have these conduction electrons then a moderate potential difference applied across it will not produce a current and the substance is termed non-conducting, or an **insulator**.

### *Current*

Unit: ampere (A), scalar.

The current flowing in a conductor is the total charge passing a given cross section in one second and is dependent on the *number* of charge carriers together with their speed.

The unit of current, the **ampere**, is the basic electrical unit and is defined in terms of the force produced between two current carrying conductors. It is observed that when two current-carrying wires are placed adjacent to each other there is a force of attraction between them, if their currents are in the same direction (Figure 3.6(a)). When the currents are in opposing directions the force is one of repulsion (Figure 3.6(b)).

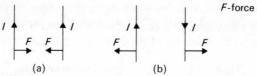

**Figure 3.6** Forces between current carrying conductors

The ampere is defined as that current flowing through two infinitely long, thin, parallel conductors one metre apart in a vacuum, which causes each to exert a force of $2 \times 10^{-7}$ N on one metre length of the other.

This force may be more easily measured by using circular current-carrying coils instead of long straight wires.

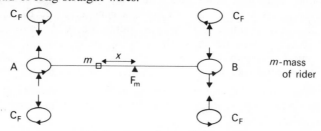

**Figure 3.7** A current balance

In the apparatus in Figure 3.7, called a **current balance**, the coils $C_F$ are fixed symmetrically above and below the movable coils A and B, and the current to the coils A and B is led in and out by the fulcrum $F_m$. With the current *off*, A and B are adjusted so that they are in equilibrium without the rider. When the same current is passed through all the coils, A and B are either attracted towards or repelled from the fixed coils as shown by the arrows between the coils, giving a clockwise torque, that is B going down and A going up. The rider is moved along a distance $x$ to re-establish equilibrium.

At balance the moment of the force $mgx \propto I^2$ where the constant of proportionality depends only on the geometry of the apparatus, hence the current is being obtained from non-electrical measurements. Ideally, the experiment should be carried out in a vacuum.

### 3:B.2 Resistance

Unit. ohm ($\Omega$), scalar.

The resistance* of a wire or piece of a substance is a measure of the opposition to the current flowing through it when a potential difference is applied.

In the gravitational case, a ball will accelerate under gravity if dropped in a vacuum, but will reach a steady velocity if dropped into a jar of viscous liquid due to the opposition to its movement of the liquid. Similarly, the electrons may be accelerated between two electrodes in a cathode ray tube but experience resistance when travelling down a wire.

---

\* Notice that as a general rule a word ending in:
-or    represents a **device**                e.g. resistor
-ance represents a **property** of the device   e.g. resistance
-ivity represents a property of the **material** e.g. resistivity

## Ohm's Law

Experiments with many common conductors show that if the potential difference between two points is increased the current increases in direct proportion.*

$$V \propto I \quad \text{or} \quad \frac{V}{I} \text{ is a constant}$$

This constant is called the resistance.

$$V = IR$$
$$\quad V \quad A \quad \Omega$$

*Note:* The potential difference $V$ is *between* two points, the current $I$ flows *through* the material, and the resistance $R$ is the total resistance of the material between those points.

## Definition of the ohm

If a potential difference of one volt applied between two points produces a current of one ampere then the resistance of the material between those two points in one ohm.

The **conductance** is the reciprocal of the resistance.

$$\text{Conductance} = \frac{1}{R} \quad \text{Unit: ohm}^{-1}$$

A **resistor** is a piece of material, usually in the form of a wire, which produces a certain opposition to the current. A long piece of wire will have more opposition than a short piece, similarly a narrow wire has a greater opposition than a thick wire. Accordingly the resistance of a resistor will depend on its shape, size, and the material from which it is made.

It can be shown that:

$$R \propto l, \; R \propto \frac{1}{A}, \text{ and } R \propto \text{resistivity of the material}$$

where $R$ is the resistance, $l$ the length, and $A$ the uniform area of cross section.

## Resistivity

Unit: ohm metre ($\Omega$ m), scalar.
The resistivity $\rho$ is defined from the equation

$$R = \frac{\rho l}{A}$$

* Materials which do not obey Ohm's Law are called *non-linear*.

Thus the resistivity of a material is the resistance of a slab of the material of length one metre and uniform area of cross section of one square metre. (Notice the area may be of any shape.)

The resistivity of copper, a good conductor, is $1.7 \times 10^{-8}$ Ω m and that of graphite, a poor conductor, is $8 \times 10^{-6}$ Ω m.

## Variation of resistance with temperature

The resistance of a good conducting resistor, e.g. a metal, *increases* when the temperature rises. This property is used in the platinum resistance thermometer (see Section 2:B.3). Remember that the variation of resistance with temperature is not linear over wide ranges of resistance.

*Note:* When a current is passed through such a resistor, the resistor is heated, its resistance increases thereby *decreasing* the current in the circuit.

Many semiconducting substances exhibit a *decrease* of resistance with temperature (see Section 5:A.1).

A **thermistor**, a **therm**ally sensitive re**sistor**, has a large variation of resistance with temperature. Thermistors are made from semiconducting substances with controlled amounts of impurities. Many thermistors encountered in teaching laboratories show a decrease of resistance with temperature but other thermistors may exhibit an increase of resistance with temperature over certain temperature ranges.

Although this decrease of resistance with temperature is non-linear the *small size* of thermistors renders them useful as *thermometers*.

## Resistors in series

$R$ is the total resistance between A and B.
$V$ is the total potential difference between A and B.
$V_1$ is the potential difference between A and M, *across* $R_1$.
$V_2$ is the potential difference between M and B, *across* $R_2$.
$I$ is the current through both $R_1$ and $R_2$.

**Figure 3.8**  Resistors in series

*Note:* The current is the same at all points in any series circuit. As no current is 'lost', the currents at A, through $R_1$, at M, through $R_2$ and at B are all equal.

Then
$$V = V_1 + V_2$$
$$IR = IR_1 + IR_2 \qquad \text{using } V = IR \text{ for each term}$$
hence
$$R = R_1 + R_2$$

> The total resistance of resistors in series is the sum of the individual resistances.

*Note:* The potential differences *across* $R_1$ and $R_2$ may be added to give the total potential difference between A and B.

## Resistors in parallel

$R$ is the total resistance between A and B.

If $V$ is the potential difference between A and B then

$$\text{p.d. across } R_1 = \text{p.d. across } R_2 = V$$

since the potential difference is between two points it is *not* affected by the *path* taken between those points. Similarly a mass which falls down the steep side of

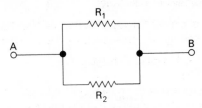

**Figure 3.9** Resistors in parallel

a hill loses as much potential energy as the same mass falling the same vertical distance down a longer moderate slope of the hill, assuming no energy loss due to friction.

The total current $I$ at A will divide, part $I_1$ passing through $R_1$ and the rest $I_2$ through $R_2$. As no current is lost

$$I = I_1 + I_2$$

$$\frac{V}{R} = \frac{V}{R_1} + \frac{V}{R_2} \qquad \text{using } V = IR$$

hence

$$\frac{1}{R} = \frac{1}{R_1} + \frac{1}{R_2}$$

> The reciprocal of the total resistance of resistors in parallel is the sum of the reciprocals of the individual resistances.

**Example:** Determine (*a*) the total resistance between A and B, and (*b*) the current through the 2 Ω resistor.

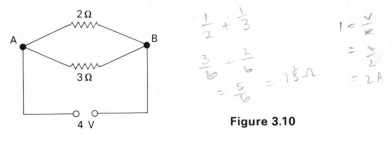

**Figure 3.10**

(a)
$$\frac{1}{R} = \frac{1}{R_1} + \frac{1}{R_2}$$
thus
$$\frac{1}{R} = \tfrac{1}{2} + \tfrac{1}{3} = \frac{3+2}{6}$$

hence
$$R = \tfrac{6}{5} = 1\tfrac{1}{5}\,\Omega$$

(b) p.d. across the 2 Ω resistor is 4 V.
   Using $V = IR$      $4 = 2I$
   and     $I = 2$ A

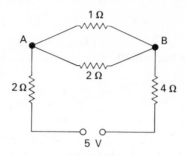

**Figure 3.11**

**Example:** Determine (a) the total resistance in the circuit, (b) the current through each resistor, (c) p.d. across the 4 Ω resistor, and (d) p.d. across the 1 Ω resistor (Figure 3.11).

(a) Total resistance $= 2 + \tfrac{2}{3} + 4$
$$= 6\tfrac{2}{3}\,\Omega$$

(b) Using $V = IR$ for the whole circuit,
$$5 = I \times 6\tfrac{2}{3}$$
hence
$$I = \tfrac{3}{4}\text{ A.}$$

This is the current through the 2 Ω and 4 Ω resistors in series with the source of 5 V. For the resistors in parallel the current will divide with twice as much taking the easier path through the 1 Ω resistor. $I$ through $1\,\Omega = \tfrac{1}{2}$ A and $I$ through $2\,\Omega = \tfrac{1}{4}$ A.

(c) $V = IR$, p.d. across $4\,\Omega = \tfrac{3}{4} \times 4$
$$= 3\text{ V}$$

(d) $V = IR$, either: p.d. $=$ current through 1 Ω resistor $\times$ resistance
$$= \tfrac{1}{2} \times 1$$
$$= \tfrac{1}{2}\text{ V}$$
   or: p.d. $=$ current into A $\times$ total resistance A to B
$$= \tfrac{3}{4} \times \tfrac{2}{3}$$
$$= \tfrac{1}{2}\text{ V}$$

*Note:* The p.d. *across* the 1 Ω resistor is the same as the p.d. *between* A and B.

### 3:B.3 *Electromotive Force*

A **cell** is a chemical device which imparts energy to the electrons passing through it so maintaining a potential difference between its terminals.

Symbol

The long line indicates the positive terminal hence the conventional direction of the current is in the direction shown above. The actual electron flow is in the *opposite* direction.

If two cells are placed in series the total potential difference is the sum of the individual ones, as each electron acquires more energy as it passes through successive cells.

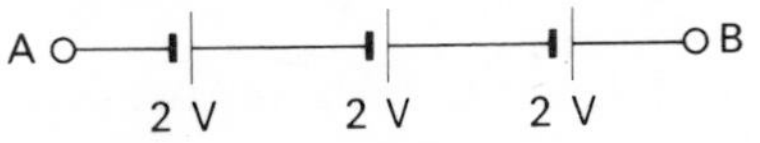

A o—┤├——┤├——┤├——o B
   2 V    2 V    2 V           Total p.d. AB = 6 V

**Figure 3.12**   Cells in series

But if the cells are in opposition:

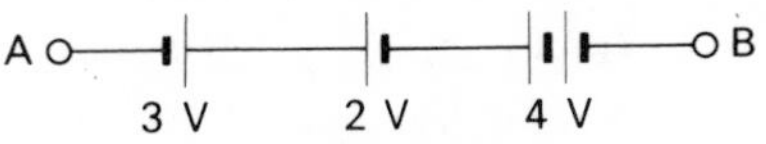

A o—┤├——┤├——┤│├—o B
   3 V    2 V    4 V           Total p.d. AB = 3 V

**Figure 3.13**

For *similar* cells in parallel, each electron will only pass through one cell and therefore the p.d. AB is only 2 V, that is the p.d. of one cell.

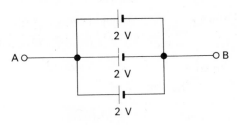

**Figure 3.14**   Cells in parallel

## Internal resistance of a cell or source

When a cell is supplying a current to an external circuit the electrons are continually passing through the cell. There is a certain opposition to this current inside the cell, which is termed the **internal resistance** of the cell.

## Electromotive force, e.m.f.

Unit: volt, scalar.

> The e.m.f. is the energy a cell or source imparts to each unit of charge passing through it.

An e.m.f. of one volt implies that each coulomb of charge acquires an energy of one joule.

When a cell is supplying current to an external circuit, some energy is lost due to the internal resistance of the cell. Hence the potential difference between the terminals of the cell, the **terminal potential difference**, **t.p.d.**, will be less than the e.m.f.

e.m.f., $E$, is equivalent to the p.d. between the terminals when the cell or source is *not* supplying an external current.

t.p.d., $V$, is the p.d. between the terminals when the cell or source *is* supplying a current $I$.

The difference between $E$ and $V$, due to the energy lost inside the cell because of its internal resistance, is termed the **lost volts**.

$$\text{Lost volts} = E - V$$

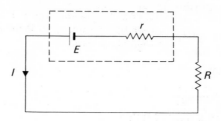

**Figure 3.15**   Cell with internal resistance $r$

$r$ represents the internal resistance and $R$ is the total external resistance

Ohm's Law may be applied to the complete circuit.

$$E = I(R + r)$$
$$E = IR + Ir$$
$$\text{e.m.f.} = \text{t.p.d.} + \text{lost volts}$$

*Note:*   The lost volts depend on the current in the external circuit as well as the actual internal resistance of the cell.

**Example:**   A cell of e.m.f. 3 V and internal resistance 1 Ω is connected to an external resistor of 4 Ω. Would it be better to place a 2 Ω resistor in series or parallel to decrease the lost volts?

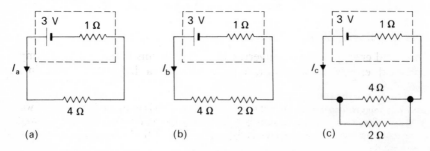

**Figure 3.16**

Lost volts = $Ir$. Hence to decrease the lost volts the current should be decreased. In circuit (*b*) in Figure 3.16, the total external resistance is increased so the current will decrease, but in circuit (*c*) the resistance decreases, so increasing the current. Hence the resistor should be placed in series.

*Note:* The word *voltage* is a term that is applied indiscriminately to both e.m.f. and p.d., since both these quantities are measured in volts. Care should be taken *not* to *confuse* the two quantities.

---

Use the equation
$$E = I(R + r)$$
for a *complete* circuit where $R$ is the *total* external resistance.

and
$$V = IR$$
between *two points* where $V$ is the p.d. *between* those points and $R$ the resistance between those points.

---

## 3:B.4 *Electrical Energy*

From the definition of potential difference,

$$\text{Energy} = \text{potential difference} \times \text{charge}$$
$$= VQ$$

---

$$\text{Energy} = VIt$$
$$\phantom{xxx}|\quad/\ |\ \ \backslash$$
$$\text{J}\quad\text{V}\ \ \text{A}\ \ \text{s}$$

---

Also using $V = IR$ and substituting one obtains

---

$$\text{Energy} = I^2Rt$$
$$= \frac{V^2}{R}t$$
$$\phantom{xxxxxx}\Omega$$

---

Electrical energy may be converted into other forms of energy, for example, mechanical energy in a motor, light energy in a light bulb, heat in an electric fire.

**Example:** An electrical heating element of resistance 7 Ω is immersed in 0.1 kg of water at 20 °C for 3 minutes. If the current is 4 A, what is the final temperature of the water? (The specific heat capacity of water is $4.2 \times 10^3$ J kg$^{-1}$ K$^{-1}$.) State any assumptions that are made.

$$\text{Electrical energy} = I^2Rt = 16 \times 7 \times 60 \times 3 \text{ J}$$
$$\text{Heat taken in by the water} = \text{mass} \times \text{specific heat} \times$$
$$\text{temperature rise.}$$
$$= 0.1 \times 4.2 \times 10^3 \times \text{temp. rise}$$

Assuming: (*a*) all the electrical energy is converted into heat,
(*b*) all this heat is absorbed by the water with no heat loss.

Then                      Electrical energy = heat taken in by the water
$$16 \times 7 \times 60 \times 3 = 0.1 \times 4.2 \times 10^3 \times \text{temp. rise}$$

Which gives a temperature rise of 48 °C.
Final temperature of the water = 68 °C.
   A **joulemeter** is an instrument which may measure electrical energy directly.

### 3:B.5   *Power*

This is the rate of converting energy, which in the electrical case will be given as

$$\text{Power} = \frac{\text{energy}}{\text{time}} = \frac{IVt}{t}$$

$$
\begin{array}{l}
\qquad\qquad\quad\ \text{A}\quad \text{V}\\
\qquad\qquad\quad\ \ \diagdown\ /\\
\text{Power} = I V\\
\ \ \ |\\
\ \ \text{W}\\
\qquad = I^2 R\\
\qquad = \dfrac{V^2}{R}\\
\qquad\qquad\qquad\diagdown\ \Omega
\end{array}
$$

   When purchasing electricity one must pay for the power and the time period for which it is used. The unit employed is the kilowatt-hour, that is a power of one kilowatt used for one hour will have a certain cost.

*Note:*   The kilowatt-hour has the same dimensions as energy, being a power multiplied by a time.

**Example:**   One kilowatt-hour on a certain meter costs 3p. How much does it cost to use a 10 A fire off 240 V mains for $1\frac{1}{2}$ hours?

$$\text{Power used} = 10 \times 240 \text{ W}$$
$$= 2.4 \text{ kW}$$
$$\text{Number of kilowatt-hours} = 2.4 \times 1\tfrac{1}{2}$$
$$= 3.6$$
Thus                          Cost $= 3.6 \times 3$
$$= 10.8 \text{ p}$$

**Problems**

**3.4**   A source has an internal resistance $r$ of 1 Ω. The current through the 3 Ω resistor in Figure 3.17 is 2 A, determine: (*a*) the p.d. across the 1.5 Ω resistor, (*b*) the current through the 2 Ω resistor, (*c*) the current through the source, and (*d*) the lost volts and e.m.f. of the source.

**3.5**   The heating element in an electric kettle is rated at 2 kW. How long does it take to bring 500 g of water at 20 °C to the boil if the specific heat capacity of water is $4.2 \times 10^3$ J kg$^{-1}$ K$^{-1}$? Assume 10% of the heat is lost to the kettle and the surroundings.

**3.6**   How much will it cost to use a 60 W light bulb off 240 V mains for 2 hours if the cost of electricity is 3p per kilowatt-hour? What is the current flowing through this bulb?

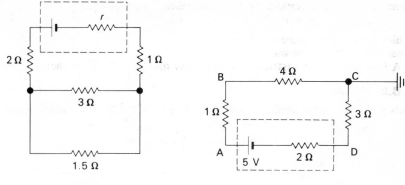

Figure 3.17                              Figure 3.18

**3.7**  Three cells, each of e.m.f. 2.6 V and internal resistance 1 $\Omega$, are supplying a current to an external resistor of 4 $\Omega$. Calculate the current through the resistor when: (*a*) the cells are in series, and (*b*) the cells are in parallel.

**3.8**  A cell of e.m.f. 5 V and internal resistance 2 $\Omega$ is connected to three resistors as shown in Figure 3.18. Point C is earthed (i.e. its potential is zero). Calculate the p.d. between B and C, the terminal p.d. across the cell, and state which point has a potential of $-1\frac{1}{2}$ V.

# C: Magnetic Effects of a Current, the Galvanometer, and Resistance Measurement

## 3:C.1  *Magnetic Field associated with a Current*

When two current-carrying wires are placed adjacent to each other they experience a force (see Section 3:B.1). This force is essentially due to the interaction of the magnetic fields associated with the currents in each wire.

For a single, straight, current-carrying conductor, the lines of magnetic field are circular around the conductor but in a plane perpendicular to the direction of the current $I$, as shown in Figure 3.19.

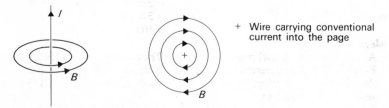

+ Wire carrying conventional current into the page

**Figure 3.19**  Lines of magnetic field

The direction of the magnetic field $B$ around the conductor may be determined by the **right-hand corkscrew rule**. Using the right hand, the thumb points in the direction of the current and the fingers, clenched round the thumb, will give the direction of the field.

With a solenoid a uniform magnetic field may be obtained along its axis, as shown in Figure 3.20.

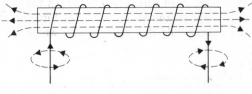

—————— Lines of magnetic field

**Figure 3.20** The magnetic field of a solenoid

The external field of a solenoid is similar to the external field of a bar magnet. The direction of the field may be determined by applying the corkscrew rule to the end turn of the solenoid wire.

## Force on a current-carrying conductor in a magnetic field

When a current-carrying conductor, with its own magnetic field, is placed in an *external* magnetic field, the magnetic fields will interact and there will be a *force* on the conductor.

The lines of magnetic field tend to straighten out, giving the force on the conductor shown in Figure 3.21.

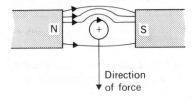

Direction
of force

**Figure 3.21** Force on a conductor in a magnetic field

**Fleming's left-hand rule** may be used to determine the direction of the *force*. The forefinger, second finger, and thumb are held mutually perpendicular to each other with:

> Forefinger in the direction of the field
> Second finger in the direction of **conventional current**
> Thumb gives the direction of the **motion**

*Note:* If the lines of magnetic field are in opposite directions attraction occurs. This is shown by the force of attraction *F* between two wires carrying currents in the same direction (Figure 3.22).

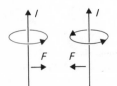

**Figure 3.22** Lines of magnetic field in opposite directions cause attraction

## 3:C.2 *The Principle and Use of a Moving-coil Galvanometer*

### Torque on a current-carrying wire loop in a magnetic field

Figure 3.23 shows a single loop of wire ABCD between the poles of a magnet. From the directions of the field and the current, the force on AB is outwards from the plane of the paper while that on CD is downwards into the paper.

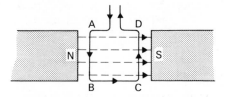

**Figure 3.23**  Current-carrying loop of wire in a magnetic field

This results in a turning effect, a **torque**, tending to turn the coil through a right angle. After turning through a right angle the forces would still be the same in magnitude but would be acting in opposite directions along the same straight line so that their torque would have become zero.

A coil with many loops or turns would follow the same pattern of movement, but the torque would be much greater.

### The moving-coil galvanometer

This instrument uses the coil described above, mounted on a spindle, but the turning effect is resisted by clocksprings attached to the spindle. Larger currents produce larger torques, thereby turning the coil, and the attached pointer, through larger angles. In this way the current passing may be measured from the angle through which the pointer turns.

*Note:* Currents of the order of mA may be measured by this instrument. Larger currents will tend to damage the galvanometer.

### The d.c. motor

This also uses a coil between the poles of a magnet (see Figure 3.24). Current is fed into the coil *via* two half circles of metal, called a **split-ring commutator,**

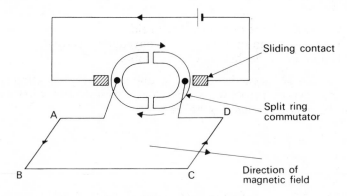

Sliding contact

Split ring commutator

Direction of magnetic field

**Figure 3.24**  A d.c. motor

mounted on the shaft carrying the coil. This arrangement automatically reverses the current after the loop has turned through a right angle and each successive half revolution thereafter. The coil is therefore kept constantly rotating.

### Use of a galvanometer to measure currents of several amperes

Consider a numerical example. A certain galvanometer has a resistance of 10 Ω and a maximum permitted current of $6 \times 10^{-3}$ A, that is a current of 6 mA will give a full-scale deflection, (f.s.d.). How may currents of up to 2 A be measured?

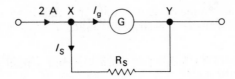

**Figure 3.25** Galvanometer with shunt $R_S$

A resistor $R_S$, termed a **shunt**, must be placed in *parallel* with the galvanometer so that only a small fixed fraction of the total current passes through the galvanometer.

For a maximum current of 2 A and f.s.d. of $6 \times 10^{-3}$ A,

$$I_g = 6 \times 10^{-3} \text{ A}$$
$$I_S = 2 - 6 \times 10^{-3}$$
$$= 1.994 \text{ A}$$

The p.d. XY across the galvanometer is equal to the p.d. XY across the resistor $R_S$. Using Ohm's Law between X and Y,

$$\text{p.d. XY} = I_g R_g = I_S R_S$$
$$6 \times 10^{-3} \times 10 = 1.994 \times R_S$$
$$R_S = 0.03 \text{ Ω}$$

Hence to use a galvanometer as an ammeter a shunt resistor is required in parallel. The value of the shunt depends on the currents to be measured, the larger the current the smaller the value of the shunt resistance, hence more current may then bypass the galvanometer.

### Use of a galvanometer as a voltmeter to measure a large p.d.

Using the same galvanometer as in the previous section, with f.s.d. $6 \times 10^{-3}$A and resistance 10 Ω, implies a maximum p.d. across the voltmeter of $6 \times 10^{-3} \times 10$ equal to $6 \times 10^{-2}$ V.

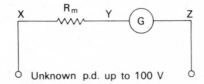

**Figure 3.26** Galvanometer with multiplier $R_m$

Now a resistor $R_m$, termed a **multiplier**, must be placed in *series* with the galvanometer in order that most of the external p.d. is dropped across $R_m$.

Consider a numerical example. How can this same meter be used to read up to 100 V?

For a maximum p.d. XZ of 100 V and p.d. YZ of $6 \times 10^{-2}$ V, the current through the galvanometer is $6 \times 10^{-3}$ A, which is also the current through $R_m$.

Using Ohm's Law between X and Z, $V = IR$

$$100 = 6 \times 10^{-3} (R_m + 10)$$
$$R_m = 1.67 \times 10^4 \ \Omega$$

Hence to use a galvanometer as a voltmeter a multiplier must be used in series. The multiplier will have a large resistance, especially if the p.d. to be measured is high.

*Note:* In general, a shunt has a low resistance and a multiplier has a high resistance.

### 3:C.3  *Methods of Measuring a Resistance $R_x$*

### (1) *Ammeter–voltmeter method*

In Figure 3.27, the ammeter will record the current and the voltmeter the potential difference across $R_x$. By using Ohm's Law, $V = IR$, the value of the resistance may be calculated. However, although the voltmeter measures the p.d. across $R_x$ correctly, the ammeter does *not* record the current through $R_x$ but the

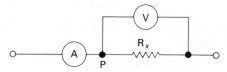

**Figure 3.27**   Voltmeter across $R_x$ only

total current entering P which is the sum of the currents through $R_x$ and the voltmeter. If the resistance of the voltmeter were the same as that of $R_x$, then only half the measured current would pass through $R_x$. On using $R = \dfrac{V}{I}$, $I$ would be twice the correct value giving a 50% error in the resistance of $R_x$! To obtain more accurate results a high resistance voltmeter must be employed. This method is therefore only of use in determining values of resistance which are small compared with the voltmeter resistance.

### (2) *Ammeter–voltmeter method:* alternative arrangement

To ensure an accurate measurement of the current the ammeter is placed directly in series with the resistor (Figure 3.28). Unfortunately the p.d. reading

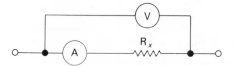

**Figure 3.28**   Voltmeter across both $R_x$ and ammeter

on the voltmeter is now in error, being the sum of the p.d. across the ammeter as well as across $R_x$. For this reading to be nearly the p.d. across $R_x$, the p.d. across the ammeter must be small. This may be achieved by choosing an ammeter with a low resistance, compared with $R_x$. This is the better method for measuring large values of resistance.

### (3) *Substitution method – ohmmeter*

This method employs a standard resistance box. With M joined to $S_1$ the current through the resistor $R_x$ is noted. M is then joined to $S_2$, bringing the resistance box into the circuit. The resistance box is adjusted until the *same* current as before is obtained. The value of the resistance on the box is then

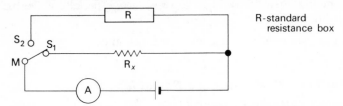

**Figure 3.29**   Substitution method

equal to the value of the unknown resistance $R_x$. As the e.m.f. of the source may vary slightly during the experiment, the current recorded with $R_x$ in the circuit should be checked again on completing the observations. This method may be used over a large range of resistances but is limited by the steps with which the resistances in the box may be altered.

   With the standard resistance box in the circuit the ammeter could be calibrated in terms of resistance and then used to measure unknown resistances directly. An ammeter calibrated in such a way *together* with its *steady* supply battery is termed an **ohmmeter**. Notice that the large values of resistance will be near the zero of the ammeter's 'current scale', and observe that the resistance scale is *non-linear*.

### (4) *The Wheatstone bridge*

The circuit is arranged as in Figure 3.30 with four resistors, $R_1$, $R_2$, $R_3$, and $R_x$. Current from the battery will flow from A to C through the two branches of the

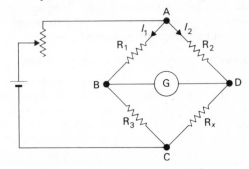

**Figure 3.30**   Wheatstone bridge

circuit. If the p.d. across $R_1$ and $R_2$ are the same, and that across $R_3$ and $R_x$ are also equal there will be *no* p.d. between B and D, hence *no current* will flow through the centre-zero galvanometer, giving:

$$V_{AB} = V_{AD} \quad \text{and} \quad V_{BC} = V_{DC}$$
$$I_1 R_1 = I_2 R_2 \quad \text{and} \quad I_1 R_3 = I_2 R_x$$

Dividing these equations,

$$\frac{I_1 R_1}{I_1 R_3} = \frac{I_2 R_2}{I_2 R_x}$$

$$\frac{R_1}{R_3} = \frac{R_2}{R_x}$$

or

$$R_x = \frac{R_2 R_3}{R_1}$$

Usually $R_3$ is a resistance box and $R_1$ and $R_2$ are resistors of known resistances in some simple ratio, for example $10:1$ or $1:1000$. The value of the resistance on the resistance box is varied until there is a *null deflection* on the galvanometer. The value of $R_x$ may then be determined from the above relationship.

The method may be made accurate by using a *sensitive* galvanometer. Since only the null point is required the accuracy of the calibration of the galvanometer is unimportant. The ratio of $\dfrac{R_2}{R_1}$ may be varied so that the full range of the resistance box may be utilized, enabling results to four significant figures to be obtained on a resistance box with resistances up to $9000\ \Omega$. For example, if $R_x$ is $2.574\ \Omega$ then the ratio $\dfrac{R_2}{R_1}$ may be made $1:1000$ giving a reading of $R_3$ as $2574\ \Omega$.

A wide range of resistances may be measured by this method, but if $R_x$ is small the resistance of the leads in the circuit will introduce errors.

### (5) The metre bridge

This is a special form of the Wheatstone bridge in which the resistors $R_1$ and $R_3$ are replaced by a uniform resistance wire AB, one metre in length, see Figure 3.31. Copper strip connectors are used to minimize connector resistance. A suitable resistance is removed from the resistance box R and the sliding contact touched on to the wire until the null point is obtained. As the wire is uniform, the resistances of AC and CB will be proportional to their lengths.

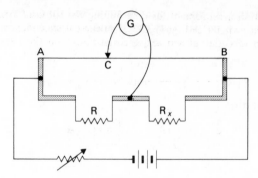

**Figure 3.31** Metre bridge

Hence at balance:

$$\frac{R}{R_x} = \frac{\text{resistance of AC}}{\text{resistance of CB}} = \frac{\text{length of AC}}{\text{length of CB}}$$

Again a *sensitive* galvanometer is required for greater accuracy. The null point C should be near the centre of the wire AB so that the percentage errors in measuring the lengths AC and CB are as small as possible. With the copper connecting strips errors due to the resistances of the leads are reduced, but at very small values of $R_x$ they will cause inaccuracies.

## Comparison of the five methods

| Method | Range of $R_x$ | Requirements | Errors |
|---|---|---|---|
| (1) | only small | high-resistance voltmeter | current through the voltmeter is neglected |
| (2) | only large | low-resistance ammeter | p.d across the ammeter is neglected |
| (3) | not small | steady source | limited by the steps and range of resistance box |
| (4) | wide range | sensitive galvanometer | resistance of the leads when $R_x$ is small |
| (5) | wide range | sensitive galvanometer, uniform wire AB, null point C near the centre of AB | resistance of the leads when $R_x$ is very small |

**Problems**
3.9 In the voltmeter–ammeter methods (1) and (2) for measuring a resistance $R_x$, would the measured values of $R_x$ tend to be greater or less than the true values?

**3.10** Using a substitution arrangement for determining the value of a resistance $R_x$ a pupil has only one switch (see Figure 3.32). The current was noted with the switch open. The switch was then closed and the resistances on the resistance box $R_B$

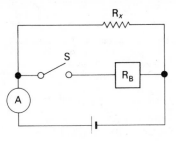

**Figure 3.32**

altered until the current was *twice* the previous reading. The resistance of $R_x$ was concluded to be the same as that on the resistance box. Is this correct? Does this method have any advantages or disadvantages over method (3) described on page 78?

# D: Measurement of e.m.f., the Potentiometer, and Alternating Current

## 3:D.1 Measurement of e.m.f.

The e.m.f. of a source is equivalent to the potential difference between its terminals when it is not supplying a current (see Section 3:B.3). A high-resistance voltmeter may be used to determine the e.m.f. of a cell by connecting it directly across the terminals (Figure 3.33).

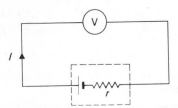

**Figure 3.33**  Voltmeter to measure e.m.f.

The e.m.f. of the cell is then the reading on the voltmeter. The error, due to the finite current flowing in the circuit, will equal the lost volts. As the resistance of the voltmeter is high the current will be small and this error, the lost volts, may be made small but *cannot* be eliminated.

## 3:D.2 The Potentiometer

This method of determining e.m.f. takes *no* current from the cell or source.

A supply battery is connected across a uniform resistance wire AB so that there is a uniform potential drop along the wire, as in Figure 3.34. For example, with a wire one metre long, if A is at $+10$ V compared to B there is a drop of

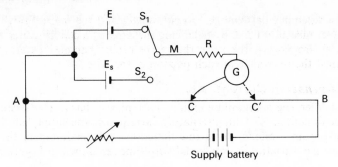

**Figure 3.34**  Potentiometer

$\frac{1}{10}$ V per cm along the wire. The unknown cell E is connected in by joining M to $S_1$ and a null point C is determined by touching the sliding contact on to the wire. At this null point there is no current through the galvanometer and hence *no* current through the cell E. The potential drop AC along the wire is then equal to the p.d. across the cell E, which is equal to the e.m.f. of the cell as no current is flowing.

$$\text{e.m.f. of E} = \text{p.d. AC}$$

This is repeated with the standard cell $E_s$ of known e.m.f. by joining M to $S_2$ and finding the new null point C′

$$\text{e.m.f. of } E_s = \text{p.d. AC}'$$

As the wire is of uniform resistance, and assuming the e.m.f. of the supply has not altered, the supply current remains constant and the p.d. AC of a portion of the wire will be proportional to its length AC.

$$\frac{\text{e.m.f. of E}}{\text{e.m.f. of } E_s} = \frac{\text{p.d. AC}}{\text{p.d. AC}'} = \frac{\text{length AC}}{\text{length AC}'}$$

To check that the supply e.m.f. has remained constant the determination of the null point C is repeated.

The resistor R is included to prevent a large current being drawn from the standard cell during the determination of null point C′, as this might cause damage to the cell. For example, the permitted current for a standard cadmium Weston cell is 10 $\mu$A. When close to the null point R may be safely short circuited to obtain a precise reading, as the current now flowing will be small.

*Note:*  The accuracy depends on:

(1) the *sensitivity* of the galvanometer,
(2) having a *uniform* resistance wire, and
(3) having a *steady* e.m.f. from the supply battery.

Observing these conditions the potentiometer may be employed in accurate measurements of both e.m.f. and p.d.

*Note:* The difference between the potentiometer and the metre bridge is: the potentiometer measures e.m.f. by balancing the e.m.f. of a cell or source against the potential drop down the wire; the metre bridge balances external resistances against the resistance of each portion of the wire.

### 3:D.3 *Alternating Current, a.c.*

A potential difference maintaining a direct current, d.c., has a steady value of $V$ volts in one direction. With an alternating current, a.c., the supply e.m.f. varies continuously from a maximum in one direction to a maximum in the other. The simplest a.c. variation is sinusoidal with time, as shown in Figure 3.35.

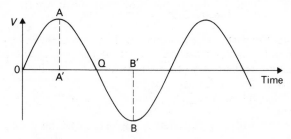

**Figure 3.35** Variation of $V$ with time (sine wave)

*Note:* Because the following discussion is concerned with a comparison between a.c. and d.c. the word voltage will be used for both p.d. and e.m.f. However, the distinction between the e.m.f. of an a.c. supply and the a.c. p.d. between two points in a circuit should be remembered.

From Figure 3.35, the maximum in either the positive or negative direction, AA′ or BB′, is termed the **peak voltage,** $V_m$.

The energy or power from an a.c. source will be the average over time of the instantaneous energy or power. For a peak voltage of $V_m$ the power at time A through a resistor of resistance $R$ will be $\dfrac{V_m^2}{R}$, but at time Q it will be zero. The average or **effective voltage** of an a.c. source may be defined as that d.c. voltage which gives the same power as the a.c. source.

**Experiment 3.2** *To determine the effective voltage of an a.c. source*

The brightness of the lamp in Figure 3.36 is observed when the a.c. source is connected

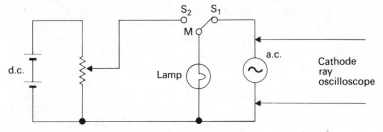

**Figure 3.36** Measurement of effective a.c. voltage

by joining M to $S_1$. A cathode ray oscilloscope (see Section 5:B.4) may be used to measure peak voltage and this value should be noted. M is then joined to $S_2$ and the resistance altered until the lamp has the same brightness. This can be checked by flipping the switch between $S_1$ and $S_2$, or more accurately by using a **light meter** placed next to the lamp. The d.c. voltage then provides the same power as the a.c. voltage.

This experiment shows:

$$\text{d.c. voltage} = \text{effective a.c. voltage}$$
$$= \frac{\text{peak voltage}}{\sqrt{2}}$$

This effective voltage is also termed the **root mean square** voltage, r.m.s. voltage.

$$\text{Effective voltage} = \text{r.m.s. voltage} = \frac{\text{peak voltage}}{\sqrt{2}} = \frac{V_m}{\sqrt{2}}$$

The effective value of an a.c. *current* is also equal to the peak current value divided by $\sqrt{2}$.

Hence
$$\text{Power} = \frac{\text{peak } I}{\sqrt{2}} \times \frac{\text{peak } V}{\sqrt{2}} = \frac{I_m V_m}{2}$$

a.c. voltages are usually quoted in r.m.s. values. For example, the 240 V mains have a r.m.s. value of 240 V.

The **frequency** of an a.c. source is the number of complete cycles which take place in one second. The unit is the **hertz**, Hz.

### Measurement of a.c. currents

(1) A **moving-coil galvanometer** (see Section 3:C.2) may not be used directly to measure an a.c. current as the coil will turn in the opposite direction when the current is reversed. However, if a rectifier (see Section 5:B.1) is used in conjunction with the galvanometer this instrument may be used to measure a.c. current.

(2) A **moving-iron ammeter** is usually less sensitive and less accurate than the moving-coil galvanometer, but it has the advantage of measuring a.c. current directly without rectifying circuits.

One design of this meter has a piece of soft iron suspended near a fixed coil through which the current to be measured is passed. The iron becomes a temporary magnet, due to the coil's magnetic field, and is attracted towards the coil. When the current changes direction the magnetic field inside the coil reverses together with the magnetic polarity of the iron. Hence the force on the iron remains attractive.

Another design has two pieces of soft iron placed side by side inside a coil, one of them being fixed. When the a.c. current is passed through the coil the pieces of iron become temporary magnets with the *same* polarity and repulsion of the movable piece occurs.

In both designs the magnitude of the repulsion or attraction will depend on the magnitude of the current and *not* on the alternating nature of the current. (3) A **hot-wire ammeter** has a wire AB which expands when it is heated by the a.c. current passing through it, see Figure 3.37. The slack is taken up by the spring, turning the pointer P across the scale.

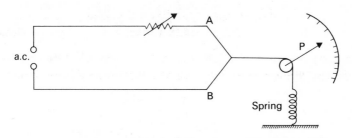

**Figure 3.37**   Hot-wire ammeter

(4) A **thermocouple ammeter** utilizes the a.c. current to be measured, to heat the hot junction H of a thermocouple. The d.c. current produced in the thermocouple is then measured by the sensitive galvanometer G, see Figure 3.38.

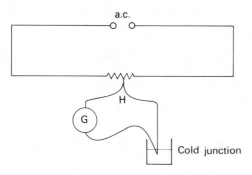

**Figure 3.38**   Thermocouple ammeter

*Note:* The ammeters (2), (3), and (4) have non-linear scales and require calibration.

## Measurement of frequency and a.c. potential differences

(1) A **c.r.o.** (see Section 5:B.3) may be used to measure both frequency and a.c., p.d., and e.m.f. Remember, the c.r.o. displays *peak* values $V_m$, the r.m.s. values must be calculated from $\dfrac{V_m}{\sqrt{2}}$. The c.r.o. has the advantage of having a very *high impedance* (see Section 4:C.1). Also notice that the inertia of the electron beam is negligible.

(2) The **moving-coil galvanometer** with a rectifier may also be used to measure a.c. potential difference.

**Problems**

**3.11** The e.m.f. of a 1.5 V cell of internal resistance 1 Ω is measured with a voltmeter of resistance 500 Ω. The voltmeter has 0.1 V graduations. State, with reasons, what reading will be observed on the voltmeter and what conclusions concerning the e.m.f. of the cell may be drawn from this experiment.

**3.12** A potentiometer has a one-metre uniform wire. A standard cell of 1.48 V gives a null point 37 cm along the wire. What is the potential drop per cm along the wire? State the potential difference between the ends of the wire. A second cell marked e.m.f. 2 V gives a null point 52 cm along the wire. Give an explanation of the result.

**3.13** What is the peak e.m.f. of the 240 V mains? The frequency of the mains is 50 Hz. How many times does the e.m.f. fall to zero in one second?

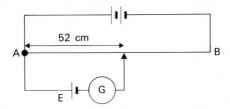

**Figure 3.39**

**3.14** The potentiometer wire AB is one metre in length (Figure 3.39). The standard cell E of e.m.f. 1.04 V gives a null point 52 cm along the wire. Determine the total potential drop AB. Draw a circuit diagram using an additional resistor to show how the potentiometer may be used to measure a small e.m.f., up to 10 mV. If the resistance of the wire AB is 5 Ω, calculate the value of this extra resistor. (The internal resistance of the supply battery may be neglected.)

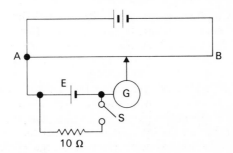

**Figure 3.40**

**3.15** The potential drop down the one-metre potentiometer wire AB is 0.024V cm$^{-1}$ (Figure 3.40). With S open a null point is obtained 75 cm from A. When S is closed the null point is obtained at 62.5 cm. Determine the e.m.f. and internal resistance of the cell E.

# 4 Capacitors and Inductors as Circuit Elements

## A: Capacitance

### 4:A.1 *The Electroscope*

Since a *conducting* solid has a large number of mobile electrons. a charge placed on it will be able to migrate throughout the bulk of the material. In a conducting solution, the charge carriers are the positive and negative ions.

A *semiconductor* has a smaller number of mobile charge carriers which may be either positive or negative, that is electrons or positive holes (see Section 5:A.1).

A non-conducting substance, an *insulator*, has effectively no mobile charge carriers and therefore a charge placed on an insulator will tend to remain in the region in which it is placed.

$$\text{Conductors: low resistivity} \sim 10^{-7}\ \Omega\text{m}$$
$$\text{Semiconductors: resistivity} \sim 10^{2}\ \Omega\ \text{m}$$
$$\text{Insulators: high resistivity} \sim 10^{10}\ \Omega\ \text{m}$$

### *The electroscope*

This instrument has a conducting plate P connected by a central spine to a gold leaf L. The spine is separated from the box, which is also a conductor, by an insulating stopper S. When the plate P is given a charge this will spread to both the end of the spine and the leaf, which will repel each other, causing the divergence of the leaf. If the box were given a charge of the same sign, its

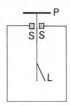

**Figure 4.1**   A simple electroscope

repulsion would oppose the divergence of the leaf. In most arrangements the box is earthed to obviate this effect, and the divergence of the leaf is an indication of the **potential difference** between the electroscope plate and earth.

*Charging by sharing and induction*

When a negatively charged conductor is touched on to the plate P of the electroscope some electrons will pass across to the plate and down to the leaf causing divergence. The electroscope has been charged by **sharing**.

A polythene rod may be given a negative charge by rubbing it with a woollen cloth. If instead of touching the plate, the rod is held *near* the plate as in Figure 4.2(a), the plate is touched by the finger (b), the finger removed (c), and then

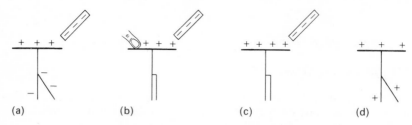

**Figure 4.2**   Charging by inductor

the rod removed (d), a positive charge is induced on the plate P, the electrons being repelled away down the finger to earth. This is called charging by **induction**.

*Note:* The charge obtained by induction has the opposite sign to the charging body. In sharing, charge of the same sign is obtained. Also a larger charge may be transferred by induction, usually equal to the charge on the charging body, whereas only a small part of the charge is transferred in sharing.

**Earth**

Symbol

Earth is some large conducting body which may supply or receive charges without a noticeable change in its own state of charge.

### 4:A.2   Capacitance and Capacitors

A simple **capacitor** is usually composed of two metal conducting plates separated by air or an insulator.

Symbol

Its function is to *store* charge.

(*a*) If a negative charge is put on one plate B in Figure 4.3, then electrons will be repelled off the other plate A leaving it with a positive charge.

**Figure 4.3** Charge on capacitor plates    **Figure 4.4** Battery charging a capacitor

(*b*) If the capacitor is connected to a battery, as in Figure 4.4, it will also store charge. The amount of charge stored now depends on the e.m.f. of the battery as well as the design of the capacitor.

## Capacitance
Unit: farad (F), scalar.
The capacitance of a capacitor is a measure of its ability to store charge.

The capacitance of a capacitor is the charge required to raise the potential difference between the plates to one volt.

$$\underset{\underset{\text{F}}{|}}{\text{Capacitance}} = \frac{\overset{\overset{\text{C}}{|}}{\text{charge}}}{\underset{\underset{\text{V}}{|}}{\text{potential difference}}}$$

$$C = \frac{Q}{V}$$

*Definition of the farad*

If one coulomb of charge is needed to provide a potential difference of one volt between the plates of a capacitor then the capacitance is one farad.

The farad is too large a unit for practical capacitors and smaller units are usually required:

$$\text{microfarad } \mu\text{F } 10^{-6} \text{ F}$$
$$\text{picofarad pF } 10^{-12} \text{ F}$$

**Example:**  A capacitor stores $8 \times 10^{-4}$ C of charge when the potential difference between the plates is 100 V. What is the capacitance?

$$C = \frac{Q}{V} = \frac{8 \times 10^{-4}}{100} = 8 \ \mu\text{F}$$

Notice in $8 \times 10^{-4}$ C, the C stands for the unit coulomb but in formulae or electrical circuits the symbol $C$ denotes capacitance.

## Factors affecting the capacitance of a capacitor
The ability of a capacitor to store charge, that is its capacitance, depends on its shape and size.

### Experiment 4.1   *Parallel plate capacitor*

One plate of the capacitor is connected to the disc of the electroscope and is given a positive charge by induction. The other plate of the capacitor is earthed and negative charges are drawn up on to it by the attraction of the positive plate. The divergence of the leaf indicates the potential difference between the positive plate and earth.

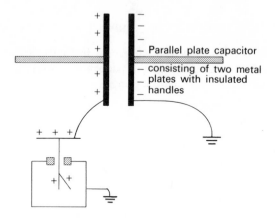

**Figure 4.5**   Capacitance of a capacitor

During the experiment the position of the earthed plate is altered, but care is taken not to touch the positive plate so that the charge $Q$ on it remains constant. Any change in the divergence of the leaves indicates a change in p.d. $V$ and since $C = \dfrac{Q}{V}$, this can only be caused by a change in capacitance $C$, $Q$ being constant.

*Note:* An *increase* in divergence means an increase in p.d. $V$ which in turn means a *decrease* in capacitance $C$.

The following table is completed by experiment:

| Alteration | Leaf divergence | Capacitance |
|---|---|---|
| Move plates together | decrease | increase |
| Move plates apart | increase | decrease |
| Decrease area of overlap | increase | decrease |
| Increase area of overlap | decrease | increase |
| Place glass between plates | decrease | increase |

This experiment shows that the capacitance is increased if the area of overlap $A$ of the plates is increased. Larger plates may store more charge, but if the plates are not opposite to each other less charge will be attracted on the other plate.

When the separation $d$ of the plates is small the attraction on one plate of charges of opposite sign on the other plate is increased, so helping to overcome the repulsion of neighbouring like charges on that plate. Again more charge may be stored.

The capacitance is also increased if material of a larger **dielectric constant** $\varepsilon_r$ is placed between the plates. ($\varepsilon_r$ is also termed the **relative permittivity**.)

It may be shown that:

$$C \propto A, \; C \propto \frac{1}{d} \text{ and } C \propto \text{relative permittivity, } \varepsilon_r$$

### Types of dielectric

The insulating material between the plates of a capacitor is called the **dielectric**. The dielectric constant of a material which fills the space between the plates of a capacitor is the factor by which it will increase the value of the capacitance compared with a vacuum between the plates.

**Example:** The dielectric constant of air is almost unity, the same as a vacuum. The capacitance of a capacitor is measured with air between the plates then observed to double when waxed paper is placed between the plates. The dielectric constant of waxed paper is therefore two.

*Examples of values of dielectric constants*

| Material | Dielectric constant |
|----------|---------------------|
| Air (vacuum) | 1 |
| Waxed paper | 2 |
| Mica | 7 |
| Ceramics | 6–4000 |

### Practical types of capacitor

(1) *Variable air capacitor*

This consists of a number of parallel, semicircular-shaped plates on a central spindle connected alternately together. The dielectric is air. This capacitor may be used as a tuning capacitor in radios.

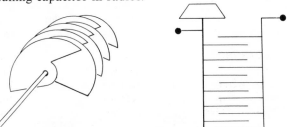

**Figure 4.6** Variable air capacitor

(2) *Electrolytic capacitor*

Symbol

A thin layer of aluminium oxide, the dielectric, is deposited on the positive plate by electrolysis. The negative plate consists of aluminium foil in contact with a piece of paper impregnated with the electrolyte. These capacitors must not be charged in the reverse direction or the oxide layer will decompose, their positive and negative terminals being marked. Notice the symbol for these

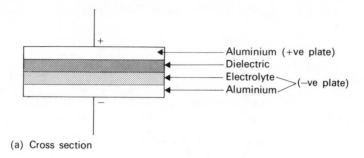

(a) Cross section

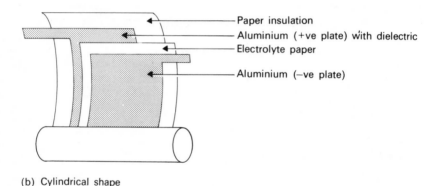

(b) Cylindrical shape

**Figure 4.7**   Electrolytic capacitor

capacitors. The dielectric layer is extremely thin hence high values of capacitance are possible without the capacitor being unduly large.

Notice that a number of practical capacitors are cylindrical in shape.

### Capacitors in parallel

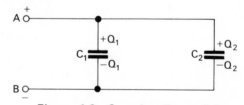

**Figure 4.8**   Capacitors in parallel

Let $C$ be the total capacitance between A and B.

If $V$ is the p.d. between A and B then

$$\text{p.d. across } C_1 = \text{p.d. across } C_2 = V$$

The total charge $Q$ is shared between the two capacitors,

$$Q = Q_1 + Q_2$$
$$CV = C_1V + C_2V \qquad \text{using } C = \frac{Q}{V}$$
$$C = C_1 + C_2$$

This result may be extended to any number of capacitors.

*Note:* The total capacitance of capacitors in parallel is the *sum* of their separate capacitances.

### Capacitors in series

Let $C$ be the capacitance of the single capacitor which may replace capacitors $C_1$ and $C_2$.

When charging the capacitors a charge of $-Q$ is induced on the left-hand plate of $C_1$ and $+Q$ on the right-hand plate of $C_2$. Thus charges of $+Q$ and

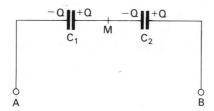

**Figure 4.9**  Capacitors in series

$-Q$ will be induced on the inner plates of $C_1$ and $C_2$ respectively. The *net* charge on the inner plates, which are connected, remains at zero.

If $V$ is the p.d. between A and B, $V_1$ is the p.d. AM across $C_1$ and $V_2$ the p.d. MB across $C_2$ then

$$V = V_1 + V_2$$
$$\frac{Q}{C} = \frac{Q}{C_1} + \frac{Q}{C_2} \qquad \text{using } C = \frac{Q}{V}$$
$$\frac{1}{C} = \frac{1}{C_1} + \frac{1}{C_2}$$

*Note:* The total capacitance of capacitors in series is always *less* than the capacitance of any one of them.

### 4:A.3  *Charging and Discharging a Capacitor*

**Experiment 4.2**  *Variation of p.d. across the capacitor*

A capacitor is connected to a d.c. supply through a resistor. Suitable values for the components are shown in Figure 4.10.

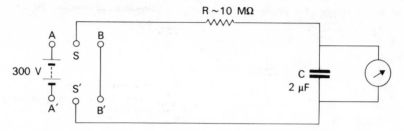

**Figure 4.10**   Charging and discharging a capacitor

*Note:*   Where values of components are given it should be understood that these values are only typical *not* essential.

After joining A to S and A′ to S′ the potential difference across the capacitor is recorded on the voltmeter as the capacitor C is charging up. This is repeated with other values of $R$ and $C$.

The supply is removed and the capacitor short circuited by joining B to S and B′ to S′. The potential difference across C is again recorded during discharging.

When charging, a capacitor *takes time* to build up its charge to a maximum potential difference. Also when discharging the charge *takes time* to flow off the capacitor plates reducing the potential difference to zero.

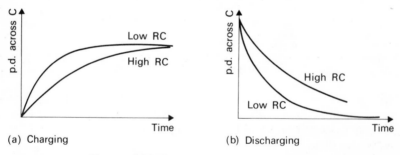

**Figure 4.11**   Variation of p.d. with time

As a larger capacitor is able to store more charge it takes longer to build up to its maximum potential difference, and longer to lose all its charge when discharging. A larger resistance only allows a smaller current to flow, hence more time is required for the charge to flow on and off the plates. Thus it is the product $RC$ which determines the *time taken* for the capacitor to charge up to its maximum p.d. For interest it may be mentioned that $RC$ is called the **time constant**. (The unit of $RC$ is the second; ohm $= \dfrac{\text{volt}}{\text{ampere}}$, farad $= \dfrac{\text{coulomb}}{\text{volt}}$ giving ohm $\times$ farad $=$ second.)

**Experiment 4.3**   *Variation of current in the circuit*

A capacitor is again connected to a d.c. supply through a resistor. Typical values are given in Figure 4.12.

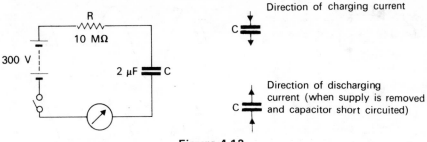

**Figure 4.12**

The current *I* flowing in the circuit as the capacitor charges up, after closing the switch, is recorded by the ammeter. This is repeated with different values of *R* and *C*.

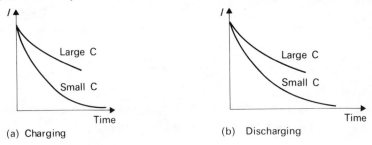

**Figure 4.13** Variation of current with time

When the switch is closed the full potential difference of the supply is across the circuit so that the maximum current will flow. As charge flows on to the capacitor plates the rate of flow of extra charge (the current) will decrease until the capacitor is fully charged, when the current will be zero.

If a larger capacitor is used, more charge must be put on its plates so that the current build up will be longer. As in Experiment 4.2, a larger resistance merely reduces the *size* of the current.

Similar graphs are obtained during discharging except that the current is now in the *reverse* direction as the charge flows *off* the capacitor plates.

### 4:A.4 *The Use of a Capacitor to Smooth Rectified a.c.*

#### Experiment 4.4

In this experiment a diode and various capacitors are used to endeavour to obtain a d.c. output from an a.c. supply. Again typical values are shown in Figure 4.14.

The Y-plates of a cathode ray oscilloscope are connected across the 1 kΩ resistor. The traces obtained are shown on the right of Figure 4.14.

In (a) an alternating voltage trace is obtained.

In (b) the diode allows current to pass only in one direction and therefore the negative half cycles are eliminated.

In (c) the capacitor charges up each half cycle, but as it takes time to discharge, the potential difference will not have time to fall to zero before the next charging half cycle.

In (d) a larger capacitor is used which has a slower rate of discharging and so will 'hold up' the p.d. and give better 'smoothing'.

This is an example of smoothed half-wave rectification (see Section 5:B.1).

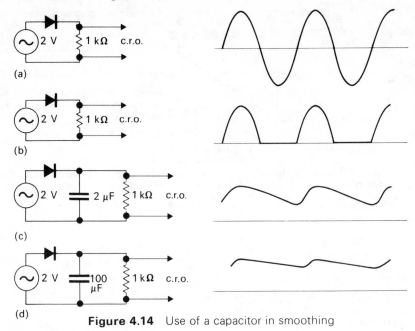

**Figure 4.14** Use of a capacitor in smoothing

## 4:A.5 *Energy Stored in a Capacitor*

A capacitor can store charge of opposite sign on its plates. If the plates are connected by a wire a current will flow and the stored energy will be dissipated as heat. A resistor can produce heat from electrical energy when a current flows, but if the current ceases no more heat is obtained. A resistor cannot store electrical energy.

If the plates of a capacitor, or the globes of a van de Graaff generator, are placed near each other a spark may be obtained as the energy stored by the capacitor is dissipated by ionizing the air molecules and as heat and light. These examples show that a capacitor may *store energy.*

To determine the energy stored by a capacitor, consider the work done to place a charge $Q$ on the uncharged capacitor plate. The initial p.d. between the plates is zero and the final p.d. is $V$. Hence the average p.d. is $\frac{1}{2}V$.

$$\text{Work done} = \text{charge} \times \text{p.d.}$$

hence    work done to charge capacitor $= Q \times$ average p.d.

$$\Rightarrow \text{energy stored by the capacitor} = \tfrac{1}{2}QV$$

*Note:* For a given capacitor the p.d. $V$ between the plates is directly proportional to the charge $Q$ stored, $(CV = Q \Rightarrow V \propto Q)$. Thus from the graph (Figure 4.15),

$$\text{Energy} = \text{charge} \times \text{p.d.}$$
$$= \text{area under the graph}$$
$$= \tfrac{1}{2}Q_0 V_0$$

Using $C = \dfrac{Q}{V}$

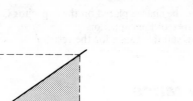

**Figure 4.15**

$$\text{Energy stored by a capacitor} = \tfrac{1}{2}Q_0V_0 = \tfrac{1}{2}CV_0^2 = \tfrac{1}{2}\frac{Q_0^2}{C}$$

where $Q_0$ is the charge stored and $V_0$ the final p.d. between the plates.

### Problems

**4.1**   The capacitor in Figure 4.16 is charged when the switch connects K to X.

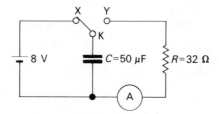

**Figure 4.16**

(*a*) Calculate the total charge placed on the capacitor C.
(*b*) Find the initial current during discharge when K is joined to Y.
(*c*) What is observed on the ammeter A?
(*d*) What difference would be observed on the ammeter if the value of $R$ was increased?

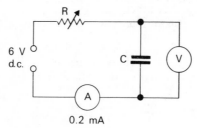

**Figure 4.17**

**4.2**   The resistance of resistor R is carefully adjusted during the experiment to keep a constant meter reading of 0.2 mA. The 6·V supply is connected and the p.d. across the capacitor, measured on the voltmeter V, is observed to increase from 1.6 V after 10 s to 5 V after 30 s (Figure 4.17).

(*a*) Calculate the charge placed on the capacitor C after 10 s and 30 s, and estimate the capacitance of the capacitor.

(*b*) Suggest a suitable range for the resistor R.

# B: Inductance

### 4:B.1 *Electromagnetic Induction*

An electric current may be produced in a circuit by *changes* in its magnetic environment.

(1) When a conductor moves relative to a magnetic field (either by moving the conductor or moving the magnetic field) so that the conductor cuts across the lines of the field, a current is produced in the conductor.

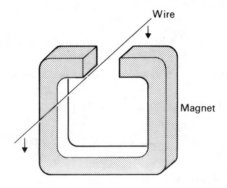

**Figure 4.18**

For example, if the wire is moved downwards between the poles of the magnet, as indicated in Figure 4.18, then a galvanometer connected to the ends of the wire would show a current.

Notice that the field, the direction of motion, and the direction of the current are all at right angles to each other.

**Fleming's right-hand (dynamo) rule** may be used to determine the direction of the current induced.

The forefinger, second finger, and thumb are held mutually perpendicular to each other with:

> Forefinger in the direction of the field.
> Thumb in the direction of the **m**otion.
> Second finger gives the direction of **c**onventional **c**urrent.

It may be observed that the direction of the induced current in the wire is such that the interaction of the magnetic field around the wire and the magnetic field of the magnet is repulsive so that work must be done to move the wire downwards. It is this work which is converted into electrical energy. (See also (2) and Lenz's Law below.)

*Note:* The current flows *only* while the motion is taking place; a conductor lying across a constant magnetic field but not moving will *not* produce a current.

The *magnitude* of the induced current will increase if

> the strength of the magnitude field increases,
> the relative movement increases, or
> the length of the conductor in the field increases.

(2) Current will also be produced in a conducting circuit if the magnetic field through the circuit changes.

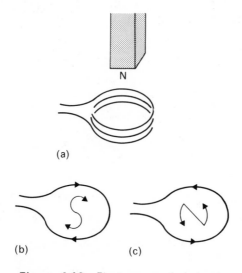

(a)

(b)          (c)

**Figure 4.19**   Electromagnetic induction

For example, Figure 4.19(a) shows the N pole of a magnet being pushed down into a coil of wire. The field through the conducting circuit is changing while the magnet is moving and current flows in the coil during this period. Figures 4.19(b) and (c) show the possible directions of the current. In Figure 4.19(b), the current is such that the top of the coil would be a S pole, whose attraction for the magnet's N pole would help the movement and no further pushing would be required! In Figure 4.19(c), the induced current makes the top of the coil a N pole which would tend to repel the magnet's N pole; this repulsion would require work to be done to overcome it and it is this work which is converted into electrical energy. Only the conditions in Figure 4.19(c) will satisfy the Law of Conservation of Energy, hence this direction of flow must be the *correct* one. This illustrates Lenz's Law (see below).

The *magnitude* of the induced current will increase if

> the speed of the magnet increases,
> the number of turns of the coil increases, or
> the strength of the magnet increases.

> *Lenz's Law*
>   The direction of an induced current is always such that it opposes the change causing it.
>
>   *Note:* This is a result of the Law of Conservation of Energy.

### The dynamo – a.c. generator

In a dynamo a coil is continuously rotated in a magnetic field producing an a.c. current because the direction of the induced e.m.f. will be reversed every half revolution. This principle has great importance in the generation of electricity.

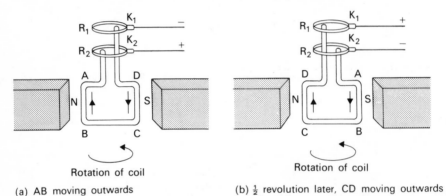

(a) AB moving outwards

(b) $\frac{1}{2}$ revolution later, CD moving outwards

**Figure 4.20**   a.c. generator

*Note:* The direction of the current induced in the coil ABCD is reversed every half revolution generating an alternating p.d. between $K_1$ and $K_2$. In many commercial generators the magnet is rotated, the coil remaining stationary.

### 4:B.2  *Transformer*

If a d.c. source is connected at PQ when S is closed, a deflection is obtained on the ammeter which quickly falls to zero. An induced current is only obtained in

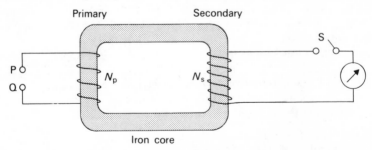

**Figure 4.21**   A simple transformer

the right-hand coil (secondary) when the current in the left-hand coil (primary) is *changing*.

If the d.c. source is replaced by an a.c. source at PQ, a continuously changing current flows in the primary and an a.c. ammeter shows a continuous a.c. in the secondary. The primary current has set up a changing magnetic field which produces an a.c. in the secondary, opposing the field which sets it up.

The main use of a transformer is to step-up or step-down an applied p.d. or e.m.f.

For an ideal transformer, with no magnetic leakage (that is all the lines of magnetic field threading the primary coil also thread the secondary), it may be shown that:

$$\frac{\text{Secondary p.d.}}{\text{Primary p.d.}} = \frac{\text{No. of secondary turns}}{\text{No. of primary turns}}$$

$$\frac{V_s}{V_p} = \frac{N_s}{N_p}$$

When there is *no* power loss:

Power in primary circuit = power in secondary circuit
$$V_p I_p = V_s I_s$$

Hence

$$\frac{V_s}{V_p} = \frac{N_s}{N_p} = \frac{I_p}{I_s}$$

However, few machines are perfectly efficient and the transformer has its own power losses.

(1) $I^2 R$ loss (Joule heating).
The current flowing through the wire tends to heat up the windings. This can be decreased by reducing the current and choosing wire of suitably low resistance.

(2) Eddy currents cause power loss.
Because the iron core is itself a conducting material in a changing magnetic field, induced currents will be produced. Since they have a complete return

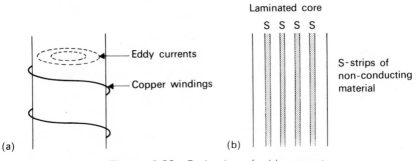

**Figure 4.22** Reduction of eddy currents

path, they too result in heat loss. This effect may be reduced by using a laminated core.

(3) Hysteresis loss.

In one cycle the core has to be magnetized, demagnetized, and remagnetized in the opposite direction. Energy is required to do this. This loss may be partly overcome by using special alloys for the core.

### Experiment 4.5

A number of experimental kits are available for demonstrating electromagnetic induction, Lenz's Law, the transformer, and its eddy currents.

### 4:B.3  *Inductors and Inductance*

An **inductor** is made of a coil of wire wound on a cylindrical frame. Inside the cylinder a **core** of magnetic material, e.g. soft iron, may be placed.

Symbol for an inductor:

With core    Without core

### *Back e.m.f. produced by inductors*

### Experiment 4.6

An inductor, in series with an ammeter (or a lamp), is connected to a d.c. supply. Figure 4.23(b) shows the magnetic field $B$ when a current $I$ flows through the inductor.

When the switch is closed the current is observed to build up from zero. The magnetic field $B$ will be increasing as the current builds up, and therefore an e.m.f. will be induced opposing $I$ and tending to *prevent* its build up. As this e.m.f. is in the opposite direction

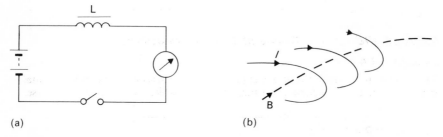

(a)                                    (b)

**Figure 4.23**   Back e.m.f.

to the applied voltage and current it is called the **back e.m.f.** (Also, if the supply is short-circuited, the current will fall to zero and the back e.m.f. will *oppose* this fall, tending to maintain the current $I$.)

*Note:*  A *changing* current produces a back e.m.f. when there is an inductor in the circuit.

The inductor will produce a *larger* back e.m.f. if the current through it is changing *more rapidly*.

## Inductance

Unit: henry (H), scalar.
The self inductance $L$ of a coil is a measure of the amount of back e.m.f. produced by a changing current.

> back e.m.f. = inductance × rate of change of current
>     |           |                        |
>     V          H                        $A\,s^{-1}$

### *Definition of the henry*

If a rate of change of current of one ampere per second is accompanied by an induced e.m.f. of one volt the inductance is one henry.

## Factors affecting the Inductance of a Coil

The back e.m.f. is increased if the *size* of the magnetic field is increased. The design of the inductor determines the size of this field for a given current. This determines its inductance.

Experiment may show that a coil with a large number of turns will produce a larger magnetic field. A core of strong magnetic material (high relative permeability $\mu_r$)* will also increase the magnetic field.

> The magnitude of the inductance $L$ of a coil will *increase* if
> the number of turns are *increased* or
> a magnetic core is present, ($\mu_r$ is increased).

## 4:B.4   *Build-up and Decay of Current in Inductors*

### Experiment 4.7

An inductor is connected to a d.c. supply through a resistor. $R$ denotes the total resistance of the circuit including the small resistance which every inductor possesses.

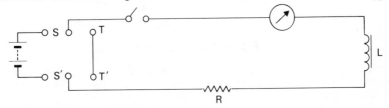

**Figure 4.24**   Build-up of current

With the battery connected at SS′ the current $I$ is recorded on the ammeter as the current builds up. In order to replace the battery by a short circuit, TT′ is joined to SS′ and then the battery removed. The current is again recorded as it decays to zero.

* $\mu_r$, the relative permeability, is not specifically asked for in the Higher syllabus.

This is repeated with other inductors of different numbers of turns and cores, that is different inductances $L$.

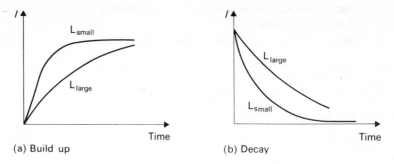

(a) Build up         (b) Decay

**Figure 4.25**   Variation of current with time

A large inductance produces a large back e.m.f. so in overcoming this, the current will take longer to build up. Also a large inductance will prevent the current falling quickly to zero, because the back e.m.f. is now in the same direction as the applied current, and it will tend to maintain the current.

Currents take *time* to build up or decay with inductors in the circuit. The larger the inductor the greater the time required.

**Problems**

**4.3** With S closed in Figure 4.26 the resistance of R is altered until the lamps are equally bright. S is then opened. Comment on the brightness of the lamps just after the switch S is closed. Is there any difference if the experiment is repeated after the core is removed from the inductor L?

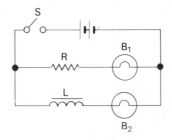

**Figure 4.26**

**4.4** A badly designed step-down transformer with a turns ratio of $6 : 1$ has a high power-loss due to eddy currents.

(*a*) If the primary p.d. is 240 V what is the value of the p.d. across the secondary circuit?

(*b*) The current in the primary is 2 A. What may be deduced about the value of the secondary current?

(*c*) How may these eddy currents be reduced and what effect would this have on the answers to (*a*) and (*b*)?

# C: Impedance

### 4:C.1 *Effects of the Three Circuit Components – R, C, and L – in d.c. and a.c. Circuits*

| Resistor | —⋀⋀⋀— | Resistance | ohms |
|----------|--------|------------|------|
| Capacitor | ⊣⊢ | Capacitance | farads |
| Inductor | —⌒⌒⌒— | Inductance | henries |

**Experiment 4.8** *Effects with d.c. supply*

The resistor, capacitor, and inductor are each connected to a d.c. source, as shown in Figure 4.27.

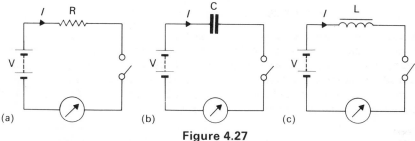

**Figure 4.27**

The steady current $I$ is recorded as the e.m.f. of the source is altered in each circuit.

In (a) the ratio $V/I$ is almost constant and equal to the resistance $R$ of the resistor providing that the internal resistance of the battery is negligible compared with $R$.

In (b) the current $I$ is zero, after the initial charging current had died away, for all values $V$ of the d.c. source. Hence $V/I$ is infinite showing that a capacitor is a break in a d.c. circuit.

In (c) the current $I$ is very large, after the initial build up, and therefore the ratio $V/I$ was very small. An inductor usually has a small associated resistance, but otherwise it does not oppose a d.c. current.

The only opposition to a d.c. current comes from a *resistor*. A capacitor acts as a break in a d.c. circuit.

**Experiment 4.9** *Effects with a.c. supply*

The d.c. sources in Figure 4.27 are replaced with a.c. sources (Figure 4.28).

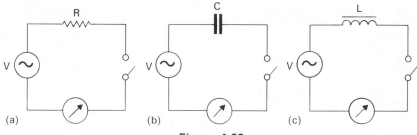

**Figure 4.28**

The current $I$ is recorded on the a.c. ammeter for different values of the a.c. supply $V$ in each circuit.

In (a) the ratio $V/I$ is again constant and equal to the resistance $R$.

In (b) finite current readings are obtained as charge is flowing continuously on and off the capacitor every cycle of the applied a.c. e.m.f. There is, however, some opposition to the current as any charge on the plates of the capacitor tends to repel subsequent charge. The ratio $V/I$ is found to be a constant for the given capacitor and is called its **reactance** $X_C$.

In (c) lower current readings than with equal values of d.c. e.m.f. are obtained, showing that an inductor opposes the current flow in a.c. circuits. A back e.m.f. is induced, as the current flow is continuously changing, which opposes the applied a.c. e.m.f. The ratio $V/I$ is a constant for the given inductor and is called its **reactance** $X_L$.

The general term for opposition to current flow is **impedance** $Z$. The impedance of a resistor is called **resistance** $R$, but the impedance of a capacitor or inductor is called **reactance** $X$.

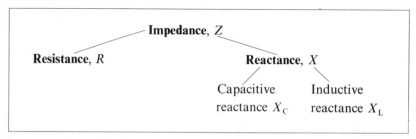

All the quantities $Z$, $R$, $X$ are measured in *ohms*, but resistances and reactances *cannot* be added together to give the overall impedance.

To summarize:

|  | | d.c. | a.c. |
|---|---|---|---|
| Resistor $R = \dfrac{V}{I}$ | | $Z = R$ | $Z = R$ |
| Capacitor $X_C = \dfrac{V}{I}$ | | $Z = \infty$ | $Z = X_C$ |
| Inductor $X_L = \dfrac{V}{I}$ | | $Z = 0$ | $Z = X_L$ |

Notice that for a pure inductor $Z$ is zero in a d.c. circuit but due to the resistance of the wire, small finite values of $Z$ will be obtained in practical experiments. For a capacitor in a d.c. circuit $Z$ is infinite, $\infty$, because the current flow is zero.

### 4:C.2 *Factors affecting Capacitive Reactance* $X_C$
**Experiment 4.10**

A capacitor is connected in series with an ammeter to an a.c. supply as in Figure 4.29.

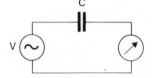

**Figure 4.29**

The a.c. e.m.f. of the source is maintained at a constant value $V$ and the current recorded for:

(a) different values of capacitance $C$ and
(b) different frequencies $f$ of the a.c. supply.

The reactance $X_C$ is equal to $V/I$. For a constant value of $V$ an increase in current $I$ implies a decrease of reactance $X_C$.

*Note:* A larger current means a smaller opposition to that current.

In (a) the current is observed to increase as the capacitance $C$ is increased, hence a larger capacitance has a smaller *opposition* to the current, therefore a smaller reactance $X_C$. This larger capacitance is able to accommodate more charge and the current can flow more easily on and off the plates.

In (b) the current $I$ also increases as the frequency is increased. At high frequencies the capacitor does not have time to become fully charged, hence larger charging currents are still flowing when the direction of the applied e.m.f. reverses. At low frequencies the capacitor may be charged with negligible currents flowing when the direction of the e.m.f. reverses. Thus at high frequencies the average current is large giving a small reactance $X_C$.

$$I \uparrow \text{ as } C \uparrow \qquad X_C \downarrow \text{ as } C \uparrow$$
$$I \uparrow \text{ as } f \uparrow \qquad X_C \downarrow \text{ as } f \uparrow$$
$$\text{It may be shown that } X_C = \frac{1}{2\pi f C}$$

$\uparrow$ increases $\downarrow$ decreases

## 4:C.3 *Factors affecting Inductive Reactance $X_L$*

**Experiment 4.11**

An inductor is connected to an a.c. supply, as in Figure 4.30.

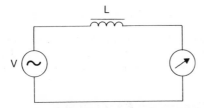

**Figure 4.30**

The a.c. e.m.f. is maintained at a constant value $V$ and the current recorded for:

(a) different inductances $L$ and
(b) different frequencies $f$ of the a.c. supply.

As in Experiment 4.10 a smaller current $I$ implies a larger opposition to that current, hence a larger value of $X_L$.

In (a) the current decreases as the inductance increases. A larger inductance produces a larger back e.m.f. hence more opposition to the current, that is a larger reactance $X_L$.

In (b) the current $I$ also ~~increases~~ decreases as the frequency increases. A more rapid *change* in applied current will increase the size of the back e.m.f. opposing the current, giving a larger reactance $X_L$.

$$I \downarrow \text{ as } L \uparrow \qquad X_L \uparrow \text{ as } L \uparrow$$
$$I \downarrow \text{ as } f \uparrow \qquad X_L \uparrow \text{ as } f \uparrow$$
$$\text{It may be shown that } X_L = 2\pi f L$$

$\uparrow$ increases $\downarrow$ decreases

### Experiment 4.12

Experiments with a slow a.c. generator, e.g. a hand generator, are useful to demonstrate, qualitatively, the dependance of $X_L$ and $X_C$ on $f$ and $L$ or $C$.

### 4:C.4   *Lagging and Leading*

#### *Resistor*

With a **resistor** there is no effect with an alteration of frequency of an a.c. source. The current and p.d. across a resistor reach their maximum values at the same time. They are **in phase**.

#### *Capacitor*

When the switch is closed the current falls from an initial maximum value to zero, while the p.d. across the capacitor rises from zero to a maximum.

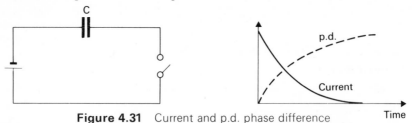

**Figure 4.31**   Current and p.d. phase difference

With an a.c. supply the same process is repeated every cycle.

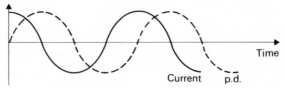

**Figure 4.32**   Current leads p.d.

For a pure capacitor:
　　The current **leads** the p.d. by 90° ($\frac{1}{4}$ cycle).*
　　The current and p.d. have a **phase difference** of 90°.

## *Inductor*

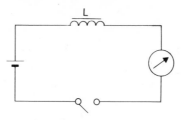

**Figure 4.33**

After the switch is closed the current takes time to reach its maximum value due to the back e.m.f., but the p.d. across the inductor attains its maximum value immediately.

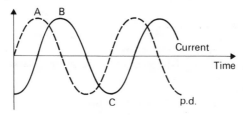

**Figure 4.34** Current lags p.d.

With an a.c. supply when the p.d. is increasing in the forward (+ve) direction there will be a back e.m.f. preventing the current reaching its maximum value. But when the p.d. is decreasing the induced e.m.f. will now tend to maintain the current in the forward direction (maximum at B). As the p.d. increases in the backward (−ve) direction the current will follow, but again due to the induced e.m.f. it will not reach its maximum until the p.d. falls to zero again (at C).

---

For a pure inductor:
    The current **lags** the p.d. by 90° ($\frac{1}{4}$ cycle).
    The current and p.d. have a **phase difference** of 90°.

---

*Note:*  It is because of these phase differences between current and p.d. with capacitors and inductors that reactances and resistances *cannot* be simply added to give impedances. (See Section 4:C.1.)

---

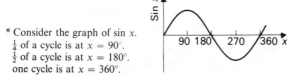

* Consider the graph of sin x.
$\frac{1}{4}$ of a cycle is at $x = 90°$.
$\frac{1}{2}$ of a cycle is at $x = 180°$.
one cycle is at $x = 360°$.
So for any oscillation $\frac{1}{4}$ of a cycle may be made equivalent to 90° by a suitable choice of axes.

### 4:C.5  *Energy dissipation in R, L, and C*

> Energy is dissipated in a resistor only.

### Resistor
Energy is always being taken from the source, either d.c. or a.c., and changed into another form of energy, heat for example.

### Capacitor
With an alternating supply, the positive and negative half cycles are similar. On average no energy is taken from the source. The capacitor is charged and energy stored but this is returned to the source during discharging.

### Pure inductor
With an alternating supply, energy is stored in the magnetic field during current build up and returns to the source of supply when the field collapses. Averaged over each cycle no energy is taken from the source.

### 4:C.6  *A summary of the Three Circuit Elements*

| | **Resistor**<br>Resistance $(R)$<br>ohm $(\Omega)$ | **Capacitor**<br>Capacitance $(C)$<br>farad (F) | **Inductor**<br>Inductance $(L)$<br>henry (H) |
|---|---|---|---|
| Symbol | —⋀⋀⋀— | ⊣⊢ | —⌒⌒⌒— |
| Factors affecting the value | $R = \dfrac{\rho l}{A}$ | $C \propto \dfrac{A\varepsilon_r}{d}$ <br>(parallel plate) | $L\uparrow$ with number of turns<br>$L\uparrow$ if a core is present |
| Impedance $Z$ in an a.c. circuit (unit: ohm) | $R$ | Reactance $X_C$ | Reactance $X_L$ |
| Dependence of $Z$ on a.c. frequency | $R$ independent of frequency | $X_C = \dfrac{1}{2\pi f C}$ | $X_L = 2\pi f L$ |
| Initial effects in d.c. circuit | $I$ attains full value immediately | $C$ takes *time* to charge up to full p.d. | $I$ takes *time* to build up, due to back e.m.f. |
| Phase | $V$ and $I$ in phase | $I$ leads $V$ by 90° | $I$ lags $V$ by 90° |

**Problems**

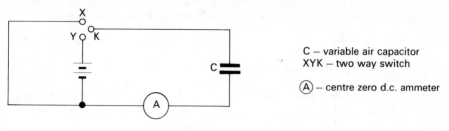

C – variable air capacitor
XYK – two way switch

(A) – centre zero d.c. ammeter

**Figure 4.35**

**4.5** Considering the above circuit, sketch graphs on the same axes to show how the current varies with time when the following are performed:
(*a*) K is joined to Y.
(*b*) K is joined to X.
(*c*) The vanes of the capacitor are adjusted to their positions of maximum overlap and K is joined to Y.
(*d*) the capacitor is immersed in a non-conducting liquid of dielectric constant $\varepsilon_r = 40$ and K is joined to Y.
Sketch similar graphs on another set of axes when:
(*e*) C is replaced by an inductor L with a core and KY is closed.
(*f*) the core is removed from the inductor and KY is closed.
Comment briefly on the graphs (*a*) to (*f*).

**4.6** In the circuit in Figure 4.36 *V* is a steady a.c. source. What is the effect on the current when the frequency is increased from 50 to 500 hertz with $S_1$ closed. What is the difference, if any, if both $S_1$ and $S_2$ are closed?

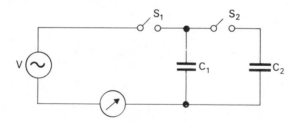

**Figure 4.36**

**4.7** The e.m.f. of the supply in Figure 4.37 is kept constant but the frequency is gradually increased. Is Z a resistor, a capacitor, or an inductor if:
(*a*) the reading on the ammeter is observed to decrease?
(*b*) the reading on the ammeter is observed to remain unchanged?

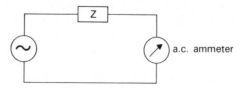

**Figure 4.37**

**4.8** Assume that the c.r.o.s in Figure 4.38 have been calibrated to give the same response to the same potential difference. Briefly explain the trace observed on each c.r.o. when the a.c. input is (*a*) a high frequency, (*b*) a low frequency.

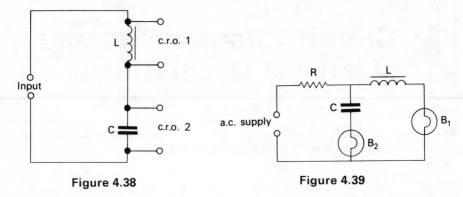

**Figure 4.38**          **Figure 4.39**

**4.9** Explain briefly which lamp in Figure 4.39 would be brighter at (*a*) low frequencies, (*b*) high frequencies.

# 5 Circuit Components and Electrical Oscillations

## A: Semiconductors and Transistors

### 5:A.1 Semiconductors

Semiconductors have a small number of mobile charge carriers and resistivities at room temperature of about $10^{-1} - 10^3$ $\Omega$ m.

Germanium and silicon, both of which are semiconductors, have four valence electrons per atom. In the crystal these valence electrons are linked to four adjacent atoms to give a tetrahedral lattice.

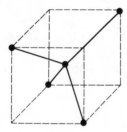

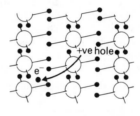

(a) Tetrahedral lattice

(b) Two-dimensional diagram showing the formation of a positive hole

**Figure 5.1**

In a pure crystal, if an electron breaks free from its position in the lattice a vacancy is left behind which has a positive charge. This position in the lattice, where there is a lack of an electron, is termed a positive **hole**. A hole may be filled by a neighbouring electron and although it is the electron which has moved in one direction the net result is a movement of the positive hole in the opposite direction. This hole may then be thought of as a **positive charge carrier**. Thus an electric current in this material consists of a drift of electrons in one direction and of positive holes in the other. This type of semiconductor is termed an **intrinsic** semiconductor. The number of electrons and positive holes are equal being released from the lattice of the pure crystal.

If the temperature is increased more electrons are released from their lattice positions producing electron/hole pairs and hence the number of mobile charge carriers is increased. This explains the *decrease* of resistance with temperature of such materials (see Section 3:B.2).

The more important semiconducting devices are made from **extrinsic** semiconductors which consist of a pure crystal of germanium or silicon to which a very small amount of a given impurity has been added. The impurity then provides the mobile electrons or holes.

### n-type germanium

This is germanium to which a very small amount of an element with *five* valence electrons (such as phosphorus, arsenic, or antimony), called a **donor**, has been added.

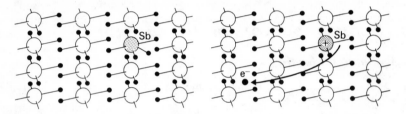

  (a) Germanium with antimony donor    (b) The extra electron is a negative charge carrier

**Figure 5.2**  n-type germanium

The atoms of these impurities fit into the germanium lattice without upsetting its electrical neutrality, but because the fifth electron is not essential in the lattice structure it is free to act as a charge carrier. When this electron moves away from the parent atom it leaves, for example, a positively charged antimony ion, but the crystal as a whole is electrically neutral.

*Note:* In this n-type semiconductor the charge carriers supplied by the donor are negative electrons.

### p-type germanium

This is germanium to which a very small amount of an element with *three* valence electrons (such as aluminium, gallium, or indium), called an **acceptor**, has been added.

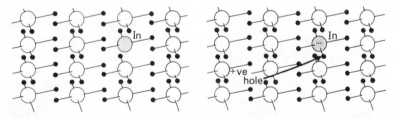

  (a) Germanium with indium acceptor    (b) A positive hole on a germanium atom becomes a positive charge carrier

**Figure 5.3**  p-type germanium

Again the atoms of the impurity fit into the germanium lattice without affecting its electrical neutrality, but the absence of a fourth electron leaves a vacancy in the lattice. An electron from another position requires little energy to move and occupy this vacancy giving, for example, a negative indium ion and leaving behind it a positive hole. This hole is then free to be moved about the crystal by other lattice electrons, becoming a positive charge carrier.

*Note:* In the p-type semiconductor the charge carriers supplied by the acceptor are positive holes.

The donor or acceptor concentrations are about one part in $10^8$.

Similar n-type and p-type semiconductors may be made using silicon with suitable impurities. It should be observed that the resistivity of the pure germanium or silicon is reduced by the addition of donor or acceptor impurities.

### Hall effect

A current-carrying conductor may be deflected by a magnetic field (see Section 3:C.1). A stream of electrons, in a cathode ray tube for example, may also be deflected along a curved path by a suitably applied magnetic field. In general any *moving charge* will be deflected by a magnetic field applied perpendicular to its direction of motion.

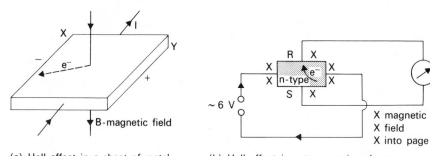

(a) Hall effect in a sheet of metal     (b) Hall effect in n-type semiconductor

**Figure 5.4**

If a magnetic field is applied perpendicular to a sheet of metal carrying a current $I$, as in Figure 5.4(a), some electrons will be deflected to the side X making this side negative with respect to the side Y. Hence a small transverse p.d. is generated across the sheet. This is known as the **Hall effect**.

In metals this p.d. is extremely small, but with semiconductors an appreciable Hall effect may be obtained. In Figure 5.4(b) mobile electrons will be deflected by the magnetic field to the upper side R and the Hall p.d. between the sides R and S may be detected on the meter.

Notice that this Hall p.d. is at right angles to both the magnetic field causing it and the applied p.d. between the left and right-hand faces. A p.d. in the opposite direction will be produced with p-type germanium where the migration of positive holes occurs under the influence of the magnetic field.

*Note:* The Hall effect enables the sign of the charge carriers and their density to be determined.

## p-n junction diode

A p-n junction is formed when p-type and n-type germanium or silicon are formed on a *single* continuous crystal. The normal random motion associated with the kinetic theory causes some of the holes ⊕ and the electrons ⊖ to

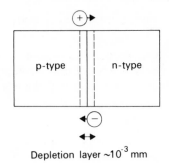

Depletion layer ~$10^{-3}$ mm

**Figure 5.5** p-n junction without bias

diffuse across the junction causing a p.d. to be established, and this prevents further migration. The barrier thus formed at the junction is called the **depletion layer**.

### Bias

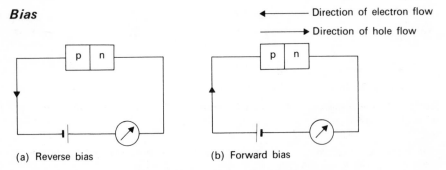

(a) Reverse bias

(b) Forward bias

**Figure 5.6** p-n junction with bias

### Reverse bias

A battery connected as in Figure 5.6(a) makes the n-type end more positive and the p-type end more negative, thereby effectively increasing the *width* of the depletion layer so that almost no current will flow. This way of connecting the battery is called **reverse bias**.

### Forward bias

This is an e.m.f. applied in the opposite direction, as shown in Figure 5.6(b), and is called **forward bias**. The depletion layer is now overcome and holes from the p-type material may now flow through the n-type, with the electrons flowing in the opposite direction, completing the circuit. Currents in the milliampere range are observed.

Thus this p-n junction acts as a **rectifier** as it preferentially allows the current to flow in the forward direction.

Symbol for the p-n junction diode

represents

Direction of conventional current which is the direction of hole movement

## 5:A.2 *Transistors*

A p-n-p transistor contains a thin section of n-type germanium or silicon between two p-type pieces on the same crystal. The n-p-n transistor, which is less common, has a thin section of p-type between two n-type pieces.

### Symbols for transistors

p-n-p transistor　　n-p-n transistor

b-base; c-collector; e-emitter (the arrow shows the direction of hole movement)

The **base** is the thin middle section of the p-n-p or n-p-n sandwich.

### Operation of the p-n-p transistor

For this transistor, emitter and collector refer to the 'emission' and 'collection' of positive holes. Notice that in the circuit shown in Figure 5.7 the emitter is common to both the base (input circuit) and the collector (output circuit), and therefore the transistor is said to be used in the **common emitter** condition.

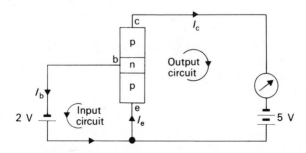

**Figure 5.7** Operation of p-n-p transistor

If a bias is applied only across the transistor, that is the 5 V of Figure 5.7, there is almost no current as the depletion layers are not removed. When the base is given a small negative potential with respect to the emitter as shown by the 2 V battery, the base-emitter depletion layer is removed and holes from the emitter pass into the base. A few combine with electrons of the base giving a small base-emitter current, but the majority pass through the thin base section into the p-type collector giving a larger collector-emitter current. If the base current ceases the depletion layer will reform; the input circuit to the base thus controls the output circuit to the collector.

> As small changes in current in the input circuit produce large changes in current in the output circuit this device acts as a **current amplifier**.

## Transfer characteristic of the transistor

The sets of graphs showing the variation of collector or base current with either the p.d. between the base and emitter $V_{bc}$, or the p.d. between the collector and emitter $V_{ce}$, are called the characteristics of the transistor.

The **transfer characteristic** is the graph showing the variation of collector current $I_c$ as the base current $I_b$ is altered.

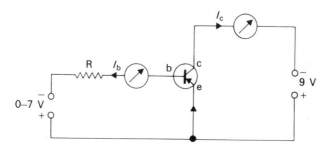

**Figure 5.8**  Circuit for obtaining characteristics

Using the circuit in Figure 5.8 the potential difference between the emitter and base $V_{be}$ is varied and readings of collector current are recorded by the milliammeter. Either $I_b$ may be calculated from the values of $V_{be}$ or measured directly on a meter in series with R.

*Results:*

| Collector current, $I_c$ | $V_{be}$ | $I_b = \dfrac{V_{be}}{R}$ $(R \sim 60\ \text{k}\Omega)$ |
|---|---|---|
|  |  |  |
|  |  |  |
|  |  |  |

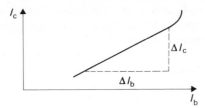

**Figure 5.9**  Transfer characteristic

A graph of $I_c$ against $I_b$ (Figure 5.9) gives the transfer characteristic.

$$\text{The current amplification factor} \ = \frac{\Delta I_c}{\Delta I_b} = \frac{\text{change in collector current}}{\text{change in base current}}$$

This is also termed the **current gain** or **forward current transfer ratio** of the transistor.

As uniform current amplification is required, only the straight part of the graph is considered and the transistor is not operated outside this range. Typical values of the current amplification factor are around 50, with base currents about 100 $\mu$A and collector currents about 5 mA.

When a transistor heats up, the graph shown in Figure 5.9 will alter, causing the amplification to vary. Additional components are required to prevent this and to maintain the transfer characteristic constant so that the input signal is accurately amplified.

### Transistor amplifier

The transistor in a common emitter condition with its base negative with respect to the emitter acts as a current amplifier.

The base may be maintained negative by:

(*a*) using a battery, as in Figure 5.7.

(*b*) using a potential divider method.

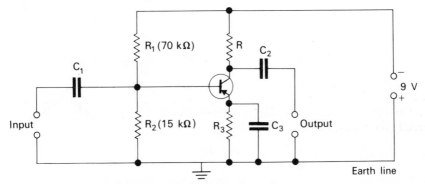

**Figure 5.10**  Transistor amplifier circuit

The bottom line of the circuit in Figure 5.10 is often earthed and is called the **earth line**. This implies that the battery maintains the upper end of the resistors R and $R_1$ at a negative potential of 9 V, and the positive terminal of the battery at earth potential. The potential divider consists essentially of the resistors $R_1$

and $R_2$ across the battery, the ratio of $R_1$ to $R_2$ determining the bias to the base. Notice that there is also a p.d. across $R_3$; the p.d. across $R_2$ minus the p.d. across $R_3$ is therefore the base bias.

With the base bias maintained either by a battery or by a potential divider, as shown in Figure 5.10, the input, usually an a.c. or varying current, is introduced through the capacitor as shown by $C_1$. The output is taken out via the capacitor $C_2$ to prevent short circuits in the d.c. supply. The resistor $R_3$ and capacitor $C_3$ assist in preventing any large build up of current in the output circuit, which would cause the transistor to heat up and its characteristics to alter.

### n-p-n transistor

The previous discussions may be applied to this transistor provided that the external battery connections are changed so that the base is maintained *positive* with respect to the emitter, hence the earth line should be connected to the negative terminal of the battery, as in Figure 5.11.

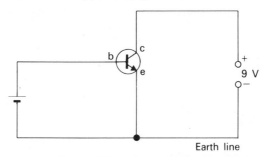

**Figure 5.11**   n-p-n transistor

*Note:*   It should be remembered, throughout this chapter, that where values of components are given on diagrams these are only typical *not* essential values.

**Problems**

**5.1**   An n-type semiconductor crystal contains a small amount of an acceptor, antimony for example, so that the crystal has an excess of electrons. Is this statement correct?

**5.2**   What is (*a*) the transfer characteristic of a transistor, (*b*) the current amplification factor?

# B:   Rectifiers, Valves and the Cathode Ray Oscilloscope

## 5:B.1   *Rectifiers*

A **rectifier** is a circuit component for producing a unidirectional current from an a.c. supply.

### (1) **The diode**

The diode is a valve with two electrodes, cathode, and anode, enclosed in an evacuated glass envelope. The heated cathode emits electrons which are attracted to the anode, only when the anode is positive with respect to the cathode.

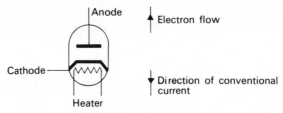

**Figure 5.12**   Diode

A current is thus allowed in one direction only, that is, from anode to cathode, with the electrons travelling from cathode to anode.

*Note:*   The emission of electrons from a heated metal is termed **thermionic emission**.

(2) **The p-n junction** may also be used as a rectifier (see Section 5:A.1).

*Note:*   Semiconductor devices, such as the p-n junction or transistor, are often termed 'solid-state' devices (in contrast to the valves with their glass envelopes).

### Half-wave rectification

For either (1) or (2) above the symbol ▬▶▮▬ will be used in circuit diagrams to indicate a rectifier.

With the circuit in Figure 5.13 the rectifier prevents the passage of the negative half-cycles and a pulsating unidirectional current is produced.

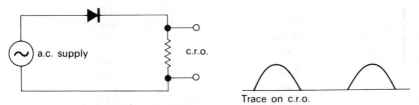

**Figure 5.13**   Simple rectifying circuit

### Full-wave rectification

(1) *Use of two diodes or p-n junctions*

The conventional direction of the current will be from B to A through the resistor. When X is positive, current flows through $D_1$, then from B to A back

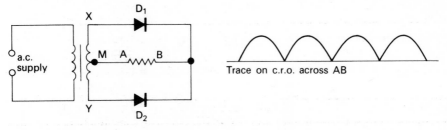

**Figure 5.14**   Rectifying circuit with centre tapped transformer

to M. When Y is positive, in the next half cycle, current flows through $D_2$, then from B to A back to M. Here both half cycles of the a.c. supply are utilized.

## (2) Bridge circuits

During one half cycle the current will flow PRA → BSQ and during the other half cycle the current direction is QRA → BSP. Notice that in both half cycles the current is A → B. This has the advantage that the total potential is applied

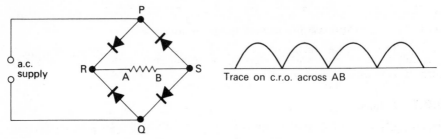

**Figure 5.15**  Rectifying bridge circuit

across the resistor in each half cycle whereas in the full-wave rectifier (1) only half the potential difference XM or MY is effective. Solid state rectifiers are usually employed to avoid separate heating circuits.

## Smoothing

Smoothing for half-wave rectification is explained at the end of Section 4:A.4. For full-wave rectification the capacitor has two charging half cycles and therefore achieves better smoothing.

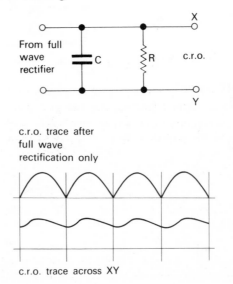

**Figure 5.16**  Smoothing circuit with capacitor only

A large value of C produces better smoothing as charge will flow off at a slower rate. To smooth out any remaining ripple a series of inductors and capacitors may be used.

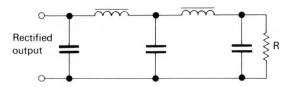

**Figure 5.17** Smoothing circuit to remove ripple

A full-wave rectifier with a smoothing circuit may produce a steady d.c. current from an a.c. supply.

### 5:B.2 *Triode*

The triode is a valve with three electrodes, cathode, anode and grid, enclosed in an evacuated glass envelope (Figure 5.18).

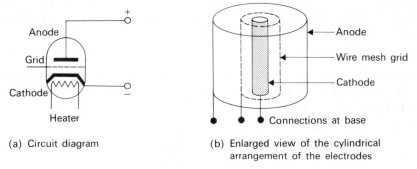

(a) Circuit diagram

(b) Enlarged view of the cylindrical arrangement of the electrodes

**Figure 5.18** Triode

The heated cathode emits electrons which are attracted to the positive anode. If a positive potential is applied to the grid, the grid will collect the emitted electrons and no cathode–anode current will flow. If a small negative potential is applied to the grid, its repulsive effect stops some of the electrons getting through and the more negative it is made, the fewer the number which will eventually reach the anode. Thus a small variation in the grid potential may cause a large variation in the number of electrons reaching the anode, and hence the magnitude of the anode current may be controlled.

### The triode amplifier

Small changes in grid potential produce large changes in the potential difference across the anode resistor. Hence the triode may amplify changes in *voltage*, providing the grid is biased negative with respect to the cathode.

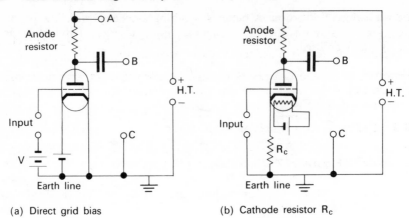

(a) Direct grid bias        (b) Cathode resistor R$_c$

**Figure 5.19** Triode amplifier

### (1) *Direct grid bias*

Here the grid is maintained negative by a battery V of around 3 V. A directly heated cathode is shown in the circuit in Figure 5.19(a). The output may be taken out between the points A and B or, more commonly, between B and C. The capacitor at B allows free passage to the a.c. output, but prevents short circuiting the d.c. HT supply.

### (2) *A cathode resistor* R$_c$

This may be used to maintain the grid bias. The cathode will have a potential of $IR_c$ *above* that of the grid, where $I$ is the current through $R_c$, so maintaining a negative grid. The output is taken out between B and C in Figure 5.19(b).

$$\text{Amplification factor } \mu = \frac{\Delta V_a}{\Delta V_g} = \frac{\text{change in anode voltage}}{\text{change in grid voltage}}$$

$\mu$ is of the order of 60.

The HT is chosen so that the amplification is uniform over the range of voltages desired, but the anode–cathode potential must be high enough to operate the valve. The grid bias is chosen to maintain the grid negative for all input values.

*Note:* The transistor is a current amplifying device but the triode is a voltage amplifying device.

### 5:B.3 *Comparison of Solid-state Devices and Valves*

Advantages of solid-state devices:

(1) cheaper to make and operate: a transistor requires ~6 V supply whereas the triode has ~400 V HT.
(2) smaller and less easily damaged: there is no glass envelope to break.
(3) do not require heater circuits or a warm up time.

Disadvantages of solid-state devices:

(4) may be permanently damaged if a large p.d. is applied in the wrong direction.

(5) operate incorrectly if the temperature becomes too high.

However, as (4) and (5) may be avoided by obeying operating instructions and including other subsidiary circuit components the solid-state devices clearly have great advantages over the valves.

## 5:B.4 *Cathode Ray Oscilloscope c.r.o.*

The cathode ray oscilloscope is an evacuated glass tube containing an electron gun and deflecting plates (Figure 5.20).

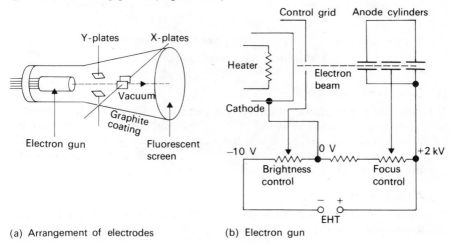

(a) Arrangement of electrodes     (b) Electron gun

**Figure 5.20**  c.r.o.

A beam of electrons emitted by the cathode is collimated by the cylindrical focusing anode. The beam may be deflected vertically by applying a p.d. between the Y-plates or horizontally by applying a p.d. between the X-plates, before impinging on a fluorescent screen. A **time base** is frequently applied to the X-plates so that the spot is swept across the screen at a uniform speed with a very fast 'fly back' return. This time base has a saw-tooth wave form.

An approximate saw-tooth wave may be obtained with the circuit shown in Figure 5.21. The capacitor C charges up to the striking potential of the neon

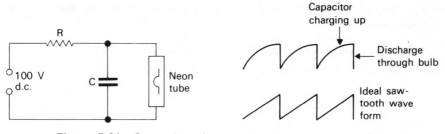

**Figure 5.21**  Generation of approximate saw-tooth wave form

tube which then ionizes and quickly discharges the capacitor giving the fast 'fly back' required. This process is then repeated. The values of C and R will determine the charging up time and hence the speed of the spot across the screen. A more complicated circuit is used in the c.r.o. to obtain a straight saw-tooth wave form. The number of sweeps per second is called the **time-base frequency**.

The wave form or p.d. to be examined is applied to the Y-plates via an amplifier. The **gain** control of the amplifier may therefore determine the **amplitude** of the Y-plate signal.

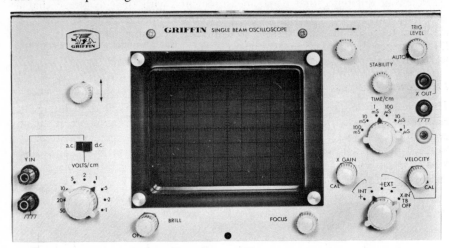

**Figure 5.22** c.r.o. controls (*Griffin and George,* single beam oscilloscope)

## Controls of the c.r.o.

The chief controls are described briefly below.

(1) **Focus**: to produce a collimated beam, see Figure 5.20.

(2) **Brilliance**: the control grid determines the number of electrons emitted, see Figure 5.20. Also, the power is turned on and off by this knob.

(3) **Y gain** or **Volts/cm**: to determine the amplitude of the vertical deflection.

(4) **a.c./d.c.**: switch for a high or low frequency input.

(5) ↕ **Y shift**: to move the display vertically up and down.

(6) **Y** and adjacent **earth sockets**: the input terminals for the application of a signal to the Y-plates.

(7) ←→ **X shift**: to shift the display horizontally.

(8) **X gain**: to expand the display horizontally.

(9) **Time/cm** or **T/B**: time-base switch to select the time-base frequency.

(10) **Velocity** control: for fine adjustment of the time base in the chosen range.

(11) **Trigger selector** switch: with positions for the internal INT ±, or an external EXT ± time-base signal to be connected to the X-plates. The time-base off position, X IN/TB OFF, allows an external signal to be applied to the X-plates.

(On some instruments there is not a separate selector switch but the T/B switch
(10) has an OFF position.)
(12) **EXT/X** and adjacent **earth sockets**: input terminals for an external signal to
the X-plates. (These sockets are at the rear of some instruments.)
(13) The **screen**, with a square grid.

The controls (7) and (8) are omitted on certain models.

## Applications of the c.r.o.

(1) Potential difference and e.m.f. measurements, with the advantage that a
c.r.o. takes almost no current, having a very high impedance.
(2) Wave form display, for example to examine smoothing circuits.
(3) Frequency display and measurement.
(4) Time measurement.

## Lissajous' figures

These result from the compounding of two wave motions at right angles to
each other. The time base of a c.r.o. is switched to the 'off' position and a signal
generator is connected to the X-plates. Another a.c. input signal is connected
to the Y-plates. The spot on the screen is now oscillating in both the X and
Y directions The frequency of the signal generator is adjusted to obtain
stationary patterns known as the Lissajous' figures.

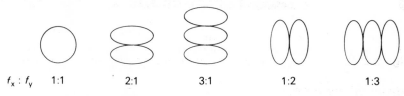

$f_x : f_y$    1:1              2:1                3:1                1:2                1:3

**Figure 5.23**  Lissajous' figures

From the patterns an unknown frequency signal to the Y-plates may be
determined.

*Note:*   The difference in the patterns $f_x{:}f_y = 1{:}2$ and $f_x{:}f_y = 2{:}1$.

**Problems**
**5.3**  Why are the diode and triode enclosed in evacuated glass envelopes?
**5.4**  With a triode of anode current 3 mA what value of cathode resistor is required to
maintain a grid bias of $-3$ V?
**5.5**  Give two advantages of the solid-state rectifier over the diode.
**5.6**  The input to the X-plates is 80 Hz and an unknown frequency $f$ is applied to the Y-
plates. The pattern in Figure 5.24 is obtained. What is the frequency of $f$?

**Figure 5.24**

# *C:. Oscillations and Electrical Oscillations*

## 5:C.1 *Oscillations*

A pendulum, such as that represented in Figure 5.25, executes a regular to-and-fro motion between positions A and B because the force on the bob is always directed towards O. The resulting acceleration causes the bob to attain a velocity at O which carries it through to the other side.

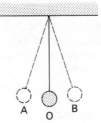

**Figure 5.25** Simple pendulum

The force and the acceleration are both zero at O, but the velocity and the kinetic energy $E_k$ are both at their maximum values. At A or B the velocity, and therefore the kinetic energy $E_k$ have become zero, this energy having been converted to potential energy $E_p$ which is then at its maximum value. The pendulum is thus a device in which there is a continual transfer of energy between the kinetic and potential forms.

> This regular motion is called an **oscillation** or a **vibration** and acts about a mean position O, with a continual interchange of potential and kinetic energy.

A **sonometer** wire may vibrate in various modes, depending where it is plucked or stimulated. The resulting frequencies are called the **fundamental** and **overtones**. Higher overtones may be obtained emitting correspondingly higher frequencies $4f_0, 5f_0, \ldots$

Fundamental frequency $f_0$      1st overtone $2f_0$      2nd overtone $3f_0$

**Figure 5.26** Modes of vibration of a wire fixed at both ends

**Experiment 5.1** *To investigate the frequency of oscillatory systems*

A number of vibrating systems are set up, as shown in Figure 5.27, and their frequencies determined as various physical properties are altered.

The frequency is observed when the following are altered:

In (a) the length of the pendulum.
In (b) the mass of an object vibrating vertically on the end of a spring.

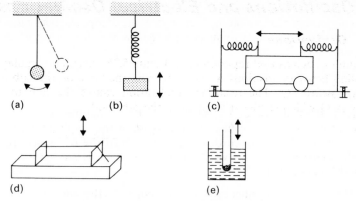

(a)  (b)  (c)

(d)  (e)

**Figure 5.27** Vibrating systems

In (c) the mass of a trolley vibrating between two springs.
In (d) the tension of a sonometer wire.
In (e) the mass of lead shot placed inside a test-tube vibrating vertically in a liquid.

The results of these experiments show firstly, that each system has a **natural** or **fundamental frequency** and secondly, that this frequency is only *changed* by *altering* the *physical properties* of that system. When any system is set into motion it will vibrate with its natural frequency, or possibly with a higher multiple called an overtone, as with the sonometer wire, but the amplitude of the natural frequency will be the greatest.

*Note:* In these systems the energy is continually converted from potential energy to kinetic energy to potential energy in each cycle.

### Damping

A system will continue to vibrate with the same amplitude, that is the displacement from the rest or mean position, providing no energy is lost from the system. If the amplitude decreases the oscillation is said to be **damped**. For example, air resistance will eventually cause the pendulum to come to rest. Most natural systems exhibit damping. The degree of damping of the systems of Experiment 5.1 should be observed.

The *energy losses* causing damping may be due to:
(1) internal or external friction: for example, energy lost internally through heating, or external air or water resistance.
(2) radiation: for example, a plucked string may emit a sound wave, or an oscillatory circuit may emit electromagnetic radiation (see Section 6:C.1).

To overcome these losses and *maintain* the oscillations, energy must be fed in, but at an appropriate frequency. If a pendulum were oscillating at 20 Hz an impulse could be given 20 times a second to coincide with its natural swing. Impulses given at the rate of 11 times a second would interfere with its natural vibration and cause damping. Impulses at the rate of 10 a second would assist every other oscillation but would be less effective than those at 20 a second.

> To maintain the oscillations and overcome damping, energy must be fed in at the *same* frequency as the natural frequency of the system.

### Resonance

Resonance is the response of a system, when the forcing frequency is equal to the natural frequency and results in an increase in the amplitude of the oscillation. The frequency at which this occurs is termed the **resonance frequency**. Forcing frequencies of $\frac{1}{2}$ or $\frac{1}{3}$ of the natural frequency may cause slight resonance in some systems.

*Note:* The resonance frequency is usually equal to the natural frequency of the system.

With the sonometer wire resonance is obtained for each overtone when the forcing frequency is equal to the overtone frequency, that is 2, 3, 4, ... times the fundamental frequency.

### 5:C.2 *Electrical Oscillations*

Electrical oscillations, that is a regularly varying electrical current or p.d. may occur when a *charged* capacitor is discharged through an inductor, as shown in Figure 5.28.

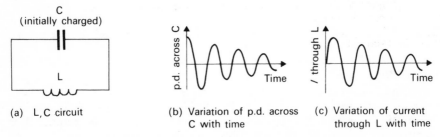

(a)  L,C circuit      (b) Variation of p.d. across     (c) Variation of current
                                     C with time                   through L with time

**Figure 5.28** Electrical oscillations in an L,C circuit

A charged capacitor has potential energy, but when it discharges through an inductor the current is a form of kinetic energy. While the current is flowing through the coil it produces a magnetic field which initially opposes the charge flowing. Because the flow of charge, the current, *decreases* when a capacitor is discharged, the magnetic field tends to collapse but the induced e.m.f. will tend to *maintain* the field and keep the current flowing. Therefore the capacitor is recharged with the opposite polarity (Figure 5.29).

*Note:* A back e.m.f. opposes the *change* in the current, hence in this case it *opposes* the current *decay*.

The energy is now once again potential energy on the capacitor. The process is repeated but with decreasing amplitude because some of the energy is converted into heat.

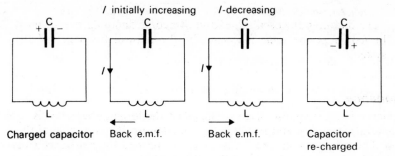

I initially increasing   I-decreasing

Charged capacitor   Back e.m.f.   Back e.m.f.   Capacitor re-charged

**Figure 5.29**   Back e.m.f. assists in recharging the capacitor

**Experiment 5.2**   *To study electrical oscillations*

M is first joined to B in the circuit in Figure 5.30, to charge the capacitor, and then to A when the milliammeter is observed to swing from side to side with decreasing readings showing the system to be damped. When the values of L and C are altered the natural frequency of the system changes.

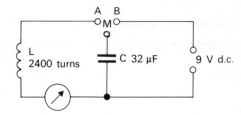

**Figure 5.30**   Simple oscillatory circuit

It is observed that:

$$f \uparrow \text{ as } C \downarrow$$
$$f \uparrow \text{ as } L \downarrow$$

↑ increases ↓ decreases

Let the natural frequency of an L,C circuit be $f_0$ then:

The natural frequency is such that the reactance of C equals the reactance of L.

$$\frac{1}{2\pi f_0 C} = 2\pi f_0 L$$

$$f_0^2 = \frac{1}{4\pi^2 CL}$$

To overcome damping, energy must be fed in at the resonance frequency to recharge the capacitor every cycle.

## 5:C.3 *Methods of Maintaining Electrical Oscillations*

(1) *Parallel tuned circuits*; where the L,C components are in parallel with the a.c. supply.

(2) *Series tuned circuits*; where the L,C components are in series with the a.c. supply.

(3) *Oscillators*; where an amplifier (transistor or triode) is used to feed back part of the oscillations.

### (1) *Parallel tuned circuit – rejector circuit*

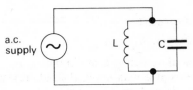

**Figure 5.31**   Simple parallel tuned circuit

In the circuit in Figure 5.31 the energy put in to maintain the oscillations is applied across the L,C components, which are in parallel.

*Note:*   At any frequency, the p.d. across L = p.d. across C = p.d. of the supply.

**Experiment 5.3**   *To study current variations with frequency in a parallel tuned circuit*

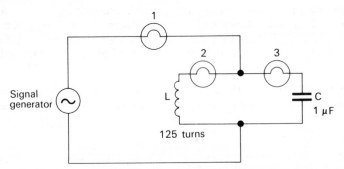

**Figure 5.32**   Parallel tuned circuit

Lamps 1, 2, and 3 are observed as the frequency is increased.

*Note:*   The brightness of the lamp indicates the magnitude of the current flowing.

At low frequencies lamp 2 is brighter. At a certain single frequency $f_0$ lamps 2 and 3 are at the same brightness, and above this frequency lamp 3 is brighter. Lamp 1 is only lit at low or high frequencies, indicating that for most of the range the current in the main circuit is small.

Lamp 1 is now replaced by an ammeter and the current $I$ in the main part of the circuit recorded for different input frequencies. Noting the steady p.d. $V$ of the supply, values of impedance $Z$, where $Z = \dfrac{V}{I}$, are calculated from each current reading and graphs of $I$ against $f$, and $Z$ against $f$ are plotted.

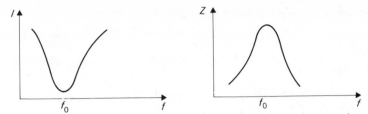

(a) Graph of current against frequency   (b) Graph of impedance against frequency

**Figure 5.33**   Variation of *I* and *Z* with *f* in a parallel tuned circuit

## For a parallel tuned circuit

*At $f_0$ the resonance frequency, $X_L = X_C$*

(*a*) The current in the main circuit is a minimum.

(*b*) The total impedance is at a maximum, the p.d. across L and C being constant. (The term rejector arises from the minimum current occurring at $f_0$. The impedance is at a maximum at this frequency hence the current is 'rejected' more at $f_0$ than at any other frequency.

(*c*) The currents through the inductor and capacitor are *equal* in magnitude. This is to be expected as their p.d. are the same and at resonance their reactances must be equal.   $X_L$

To understand how a large L,C current is obtained with a small current in the supply circuit the *phase* must be considered. At all frequencies $V_L = V_C$ and at resonance $I_L = I_C$ in magnitude. With a pure inductor *I* lags *V* by $\frac{1}{4}$ of a cycle and with a capacitor *I* leads *V* by $\frac{1}{4}$ cycle. This implies that the phase difference between $I_L$ and $I_C$ is $\frac{1}{2}$ cycle, i.e. they are 180° out of phase with each other.

*Below $f_0$, $X_L < X_C$*

More current flows through the *inductor* than the capacitor. Remember that the opposition, that is the reactance $X_L$, of an inductor to current is less at low frequencies.

*Above $f_0$, $X_L > X_C$*

More current flows through the *capacitor*. Remember that the opposition $X_C$ of a capacitor to current decreases at higher frequencies.

## (2) Series tuned circuit – acceptor circuit

In this circuit the energy input and the components are in series.

*Note:*   At any frequency the current through L = the current through C = current in the main circuit.

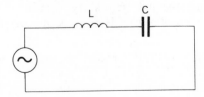

**Figure 5.34**   Simple series circuit

**Experiment 5.4**  *To study the current and p.d. variations with frequency in a series tuned circuit*

In the circuit of Figure 5.35 the two c.r.o.s are first calibrated so that traces of equal heights are obtained on each c.r.o. for a given p.d. These heights, being proportional to the p.d. across that component, are observed as the frequency increases. The results show that at a certain frequency $f_0$ the heights of the traces are the same. At lower frequencies the height of the trace across the capacitor is larger and above $f_0$ the height of the trace across the inductor is larger.

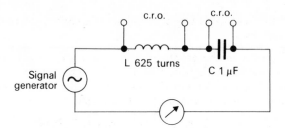

**Figure 5.35**  Series tuned circuit

Readings of current $I$ in the main part of the circuit and frequency $f$ are recorded. The impedance $Z = \dfrac{V}{I}$ is calculated for each reading, where $V$ is the steady p.d. of the supply. Graphs of $I$ against $f$ and $Z$ against $f$ are plotted.

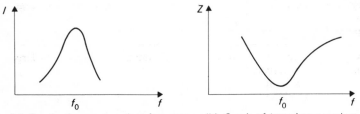

(a) Graph of current against frequency   (b) Graph of impedance against frequency

**Figure 5.36**  Variation of $I$ and $Z$ with $f$ in a series tuned circuit

## *For a series tuned circuit*

*At $f_0$ the resonance frequency, $X_L = X_C$*

(*a*) The current in the main circuit is at a maximum. (Because at this frequency $f_0$ the circuit 'accepts' current more readily than at any other frequency the series circuit is termed an **acceptor circuit**.)
(*b*) The impedance is at a minimum.
(*c*) The p.d. across the inductor equals the p.d. across the capacitor. At resonance the reactance of C equals the reactance of L, thus as the currents are the same, their p.d. must also be equal.

In this circuit the currents $I_L$ and $I_C$ are equal and in phase. At resonance $V_L = V_C$ but because $I_L$ leads $V_L$ by $\frac{1}{4}$ cycle and $I_C$ lags $V_C$ by $\frac{1}{4}$ cycle, the p.d. $V_C$ and $V_L$ must be $\frac{1}{2}$ cycle out of phase with each other. At resonance in a series circuit large potential differences are developed across the inductor and capacitor, 180° out of phase with each other, when the p.d. provided by the supply is quite low.

*Below $f_0$, $X_L < X_C$*
The p.d. across the *capacitor* is larger. For lower frequencies the reactance $X_C$ of the capacitor increases, thus as $V = IX_C$ if $X_C$ is larger the p.d. $V$ is also larger, the currents through $L$ and $C$ being equal.

*Above $f_0$, $X_L > X_C$*
The p.d. across the *inductor* is larger. At higher frequencies the reactance $X_L$ of an inductor increases.

*Note:* The difference in the graphs of $I$ against $f$ for the parallel and series tuned circuits as shown in Figures 5.33 and 5.36. They are of inverted shape. Notice also that because the circuits will have finite resistances, the phase differences mentioned above will *not* be exactly 180°.

*To summarize parallel and series L,C circuits*

| | At $f_0$, $X_L = X_C$ | | | | | $Below\ f_0$ | $Above\ f_0$ |
|---|---|---|---|---|---|---|---|
| *Type of Circuit* | $I_L > I_C$ | $V_L > V_C$ | $I$ main circuit | $Z$ | | $X_L < X_C$ | $X_L > X_C$ |
| Parallel | Equal in magnitude, 180° out of phase | Always equal | Minimum | Maximum | | $I_L > I_C$ $I_L$ larger | $I_L < I_C$ $I_C$ larger |
| Series | Always equal | Equal in magnitude, 180° out of phase | Maximum | Minimum | | $V_C$ larger | $V_L$ larger |

## (3) *Oscillators*

In an oscillator, part of the output of an amplifier is fed back to the input; in this way compensation is made for energy losses in the circuit. For example, in the oscillator shown in Figure 5.37, part of the alternating p.d. from the tuned L,C circuit, which is in the output of the amplifier, is fed back into the input circuit and re-amplified. Once started, the output will continue to be maintained, the energy for maintaining it coming from the steady d.c. potential across the amplifier. As with other systems the frequency of the oscillations produced depends only on the natural frequency of the L,C circuit, that is on the values of the inductance and capacitance, not on the value of the other components or type of amplifier.

### *Transistor oscillator*

The base bias is maintained by the potential divider $R_1$, $R_2$. Since $L_1$, $L_2$ are the windings of a transformer, part of the output is fed back into the input and amplified to maintain the oscillations, the 6 V battery providing the energy. The oscillations may be observed on a c.r.o. or detector D placed between the

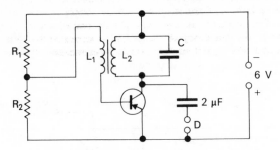

**Figure 5.37** Transistor oscillator

collector and emitter via a suitable capacitor, e.g. 2 $\mu$F. For $L_1$ and $L_2$ around 120 and 1200 turns respectively and $C$ about 0.05 $\mu$F audio frequency oscillations may be obtained and can be heard in an earphone placed at D. If $C$ is increased the pitch of the note decreases in accordance with the previous discussion that $f$ decreases as $C$ increases.

### Triode oscillator

The cathode resistor R and smoothing capacitor $C_R$ maintain the grid bias. The turns ratio of $L_1 : L_2$ is around 1 : 10. A c.r.o. may be connected across C to detect the oscillations, or very low frequency oscillations may be observed on a centre-zero ammeter in the L,C circuit. If the value of the capacitor is decreased the frequency of the oscillations will increase. Remember that a decrease in the inductance $L_2$ will also increase the frequency of the oscillation. For a suitable inductance $L_2$ and $C$ in the range 0.001 $\mu$F–0.004 $\mu$F audio frequencies may be detected on earphones placed between the inductor $L_2$ and the HT leads.

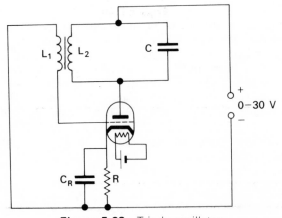

**Figure 5.38** Triode oscillator

**Problems**

**5.7** In a rejector circuit how does the p.d. across, and the current through, the inductor vary as the frequency is increased to the resonance frequency?

**5.8** In a series tuned circuit the frequency of the supply is adjusted to the resonance frequency. The capacitor is now replaced by one of a lower capacitance. What adjustment to the frequency of the supply is necessary to restore the resonance condition, and how may it be ascertained experimentally that resonance has been achieved?

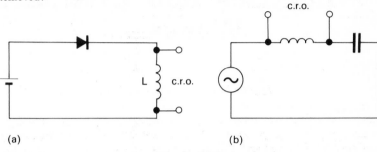

(a)　　　　　　　　　　　　(b)

**Figure 5.39**

**5.9** Sketch the trace observed on each c.r.o. in Figure 5.39. Show by means of another sketch if there is any change when the rectifier in (a) is reversed or the frequency in (b) is increased.

**5.10** After experiments with series and parallel tuned circuits a pupil discovers the graph shown in Figure 5.40. What quantity could he have plotted on the *y*-axis? Was he observing a parallel or series tuned circuit?

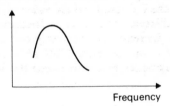

Frequency

**Figure 5.40**

# 6 Properties and Effects of Waves

## A: Wave Motion

### 6:A.1 Basic Wave Properties

When a 'source' vibrates about a mean position a disturbance, that is a wave, may travel away from the vibrating source. The particles along the path of the wave also tend to vibrate.

**Example:** A water wave can be generated by placing a vibrating pin, the 'source', in the surface of the water. The individual particles of water will vibrate up and down in a vertical direction but the wave travels horizontally across the surface of the water causing the particles of water in its path to vibrate, as shown in Figure 6.1(a).

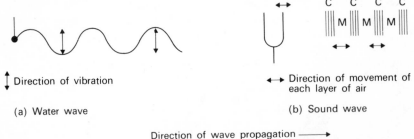

Direction of vibration

(a) Water wave

C C C C

Direction of movement of each layer of air

(b) Sound wave

Direction of wave propagation ⟶

**Figure 6.1** Waves

**Example:** A sound wave may be generated by a tuning fork which alternately compresses and rarefies the air adjacent to the prong. Each layer of air will vibrate about a mean position in a horizontal direction while the wave travels away from the source also in the horizontal direction, as shown in Figure 6.1(b). In this figure C denotes a compression while M denotes a rarefaction. At a slightly later time, of course, the high pressure will have moved outwards to the position at present marked M. The value of the pressure also varies periodically in the horizontal direction.

A **transverse wave** is one in which the vibration of the particles is perpendicular to the direction of propagation of the wave. For example: a water wave, a vibrating string or wire, electromagnetic radiation.

A **longitudinal wave** is one in which the vibration of the particles is in the same direction as the wave propagation. For example: sound waves, a slinky spring.

## Some basic terms

For both types of waves the above figure shows the instantaneous magnitude of the disturbance $x$ against the distance. $x$ may be the distance moved vertically by water particles, the pressure variation of air in sound waves or the magnitude of the electric field in light waves.

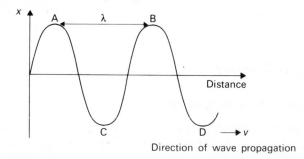

**Figure 6.2** Graphical representation of a wave

$\lambda$  The **wavelength** is the distance between two consecutive maxima or minima positions, that is the distance A → B or C → D. (Unit: metre, m)

$f$  The **frequency** is the number of complete waves passing any point in one second. (Unit: hertz, Hz)

$T$  The **period** is the time taken for one maximum to move to the position of the next maximum, that is the time taken for the wave to travel from A to B. (Unit: second, s)

$v$  The **velocity** is the rate at which the wave travels. (Unit: m s$^{-1}$)

*Note:*

$$v = \lambda f \qquad f = \frac{1}{T}$$

$a$  The **amplitude** is the maximum variation of the quantity $x$ of the vibrating particles from their mean or rest values. The unit of the amplitude depends on the chosen quantity $x$.

*Examples:*
(1) The distance from the top of a crest to the undisturbed surface in a water wave. (Unit of $a$: m)
(2) The maximum excess pressure of air in sound waves. (Unit of $a$: Pa)
(3) The maximum displacement of a particle of air in a sound wave. (Unit of $a$: m)

(4) The maximum value of the electric field in light or X-rays. (Unit of $a$: $V\ m^{-1}$)

These examples show that $x$ may be a variety of physical quantities.

## 6:A.2 *Interference, Diffraction, Reflection, and Standing Waves*

### Interference

If two waves of the same frequency and amplitude are brought together in such a way that their maxima coincide, that is they are *in phase*, the resultant wave will have the same frequency and wavelength but an increased amplitude.

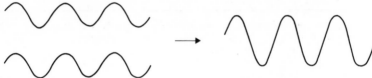

**Figure 6.3**   Constructive interference

This is termed **constructive interference**.

**Example:**   A resultant water wave with higher crests; a louder sound note of the same pitch.

If, however, the maxima of one wave coincide with the minima of the other then a null resultant is obtained.

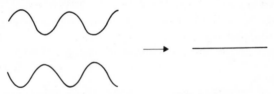

**Figure 6.4**   Destructive interference

This is termed **destructive interference**.

**Examples:**   A lack of movement on a water surface; silence from two sound waves.

> To prove the existence of a wave it is necessary to demonstrate destructive interference.

**Examples:**                              sound + sound = silence
                                           light  + light  = darkness

### Diffraction

Diffraction may be defined as a *bending* phenomena; that is the tendency for waves to 'go round corners' giving wave motion in the geometrical shadow of an obstacle or aperture.

(1) For a slit or aperture this diffraction effect is greater when the *aperture* is *small*. The greatest effect is obtained when the width of the aperture approaches the wavelength of the waves.

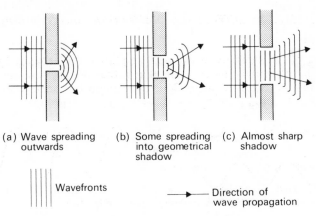

(a) Wave spreading outwards

(b) Some spreading into geometrical shadow

(c) Almost sharp shadow

||||| Wavefronts

⟶ Direction of wave propagation

**Figure 6.5** Diffraction

Notice that the plane wave spreads out in all directions after passing through the narrow aperture in Figure 6.5, compared with the sharp shadow obtained with the wide aperture. Also, the *longer* the *wavelength* the greater the diffraction effect.

*Note:* The direction of wave propagation is perpendicular to the wavefronts.

(2) When waves are incident on a single sharp edge the *longer* wavelength wave is bent to a greater extent into the geometrical shadow.

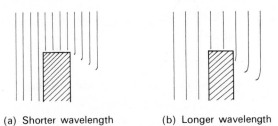

(a) Shorter wavelength

(b) Longer wavelength

**Figure 6.6** Diffraction around edges

(3) Diffraction effects are also observed when waves are incident on an obstacle.

Notice that for a large obstacle, as in Figure 6.7(a), almost no diffraction occurs and a sharp shadow is obtained. If the obstacle is very small compared with the wavelength, as in Figure 6.7(c), the wave appears to be unaffected.

*Note:* For light diffraction, effects are more noticeable for narrow gaps, small obstacles, and longer wavelengths, that is red light. The wavelengths for light are about $4 \times 10^{-7}$ m to $7 \times 10^{-7}$ m, and for water or sound waves about

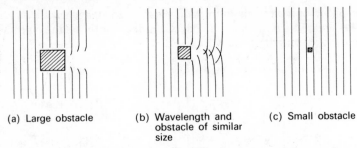

(a) Large obstacle     (b) Wavelength and          (c) Small obstacle
                           obstacle of similar
                           size

**Figure 6.7** Diffraction around objects

1 cm to 15 m. Thus a very fine slit must be used to show light diffraction, a hill may be required to provide a good shadow with sound waves, and a rock may offer little protection to an ocean wave.

Diffraction, that is the bending and distortion of the wavefront by an obstacle or aperture, results in the interference of individual segments of the waves giving dark and bright bands in the geometrical shadow, which are termed **fringes**. Fringe effects are most obvious when the wavelength of the waves is of the *same order of magnitude* as the obstacle or aperture. An example is provided by Figure 6.7(b) where the overlapping waves will interfere to give positions of maximum and minimum intensity. Fringes are also obtained when waves are diffracted through small apertures and round sharp edges.

## Reflection

If waves are incident on a large opaque barrier they will be reflected.

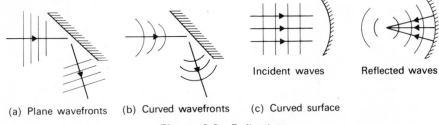

Incident waves          Reflected waves

(a) Plane wavefronts    (b) Curved wavefronts    (c) Curved surface

**Figure 6.8** Reflection

The wavelength, frequency, and velocity will *not* change as the incident and reflected waves are in the same medium, but the curvature of the wavefronts alters except in the case of plane waves incident on a plane barrier.

## Standing waves

When a wave is reflected back along the incident path interference may take place between the incident and reflected waves yielding **standing waves**.

**Example:** A vibrating wire, fixed at one end, F.

No movement is observed *along* the wire as the wave is **stationary**. The only movement is the vibration of segments of the wire in the vertical direction.

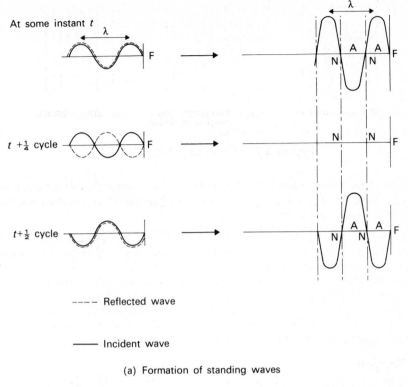

At some instant *t*

*t* +¼ cycle

*t*+½ cycle

- - - - Reflected wave

——— Incident wave

(a) Formation of standing waves

(b) Overall picture with intermediate positions

**Figure 6.9** Standing wave

The overall picture in Figure 6.9(b), of the instantaneous positions of the wire, shows that certain points N, called **nodes**, are stationary while other points A, called **antinodes**, vibrate from a maximum in one direction to a maximum in the other. All the intermediate points along the wire vibrate with amplitudes less than the maximum of the antinodes.

*Note:* For standing waves, all points along the wave reach their *different* amplitudes at the *same* time. In a travelling wave each point along the wave reaches the same amplitude but at different times.

> For standing waves the distance between two consecutive maxima, antinodes, is $\frac{1}{2}\lambda$, and the distance between consecutive nodes is also $\frac{1}{2}\lambda$, where $\lambda$ is the incident wavelength.

### 6:A.3  *Refraction*

Refraction is the change in *direction* of a wave when it passes obliquely from one medium to another. This change in direction arises because the *velocity* of a wave *alters* when it passes into different media.

The precise change in velocity depends on the type of wave as well as the media concerned. For example, light waves have their maximum velocity in a vacuum and travel faster in gases than solids; whereas sound waves travel slower in gases than in solids. The table on page 145 indicates velocity changes for different situations.

The frequency remains *constant* when waves are refracted from one medium

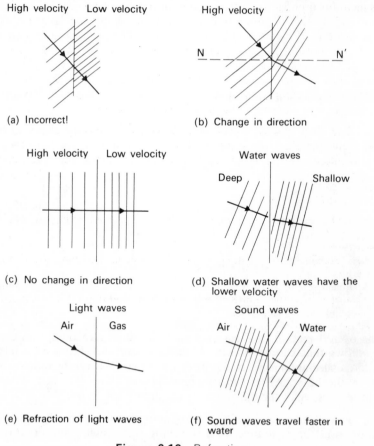

(a) Incorrect!

(b) Change in direction

(c) No change in direction

(d) Shallow water waves have the lower velocity

(e) Refraction of light waves

(f) Sound waves travel faster in water

**Figure 6.10**   Refraction

*Change in velocity trends for different media*

| Type of wave | Higher velocity | ——→ | Lower velocity |
|---|---|---|---|
| Water waves | deep water | | shallow water |
| Light | vacuum   air | water | glass |
| Sound | solids | liquids | gases |

to another; the frequency depending only on the number of waves emitted per second by the *source*. Remembering that $v = \lambda f$, if the velocity $v$ changes the wavelength $\lambda$ will change in the same proportion, the frequency $f$ remaining constant.

Hence when waves pass from a high velocity medium to a low velocity medium their wavelength will decrease. Because no extra waves are generated at the interface, Figure 6.10(a) must be incorrect! This implies that a change of direction must occur so that the wavefronts are continuous across the interface as shown in Figure 6.10(b).

As mentioned previously the direction of travel of a wave is perpendicular to the wavefronts, thus Figure 6.10(b) demonstrates that when a wave is refracted from a medium of high velocity to a medium of low velocity the wave is bent towards the normal. The **normal** NN' is a line drawn perpendicular to the interface. The converse is true for sound waves refracted from a low velocity medium into a high velocity medium, as in Figure 6.10(f). For plane waves incident perpendicular to the interface, as in Figure 6.10(c), each wavefront is in one medium only hence no change of direction occurs.

*Note:* The frequency of waves remains constant during refraction but the velocity and therefore the wavelength alter. However, if the frequency of the *source* is altered the refraction, that is the precise change in direction, will be different.

### Experiment 6.1

A ripple tank may be used to demonstrate the wave phenomena in this section.

### Problems
**6.1** Give examples of (*a*) stationary and (*b*) travelling longitudinal and transverse waves.

**6.2** A student sets up a longitudinal travelling wave in a slinky spring, estimates the distance between two consecutive compressions, and states that he has determined the amplitude. Is he correct?

**6.3** What is the distance between a node and neighbouring antinode of a standing wave in terms of the incident wavelength?

**6.4** In a ripple tank the wavelength is observed to alter from 5 cm at position A to 3 cm at position B. What might cause this change? What is the relative change in velocity and frequency from A to B?

# B: Interference of Sound and Light Waves – Quantitative

## 6:B.1 *Interference of Sound Waves*

### Experiment 6.2 *Interference of two sound sources*

A and B in Figure 6.11 are two loudspeakers connected to the same source, so that the emitted waves are of the same frequency, amplitude, and phase. (It is possible to use two similar generators tuned to the same amplitude and frequency but small differences in their power supply and construction could lead to small frequency variations.) The two

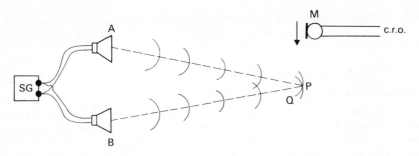

**Figure 6.11**   Interference with two sound sources

sources will interfere, a maximum being obtained at P when a crest from A coincides with a crest from B, that is the **path difference** between A and B is zero or a whole number of wavelengths. For a minimum at any position a wave crest must coincide with a wave trough, hence the path difference between AQ and BQ must be an odd number of half wavelengths. The 'crest' and 'trough' for a sound wave are the compressions and rarefactions of the air.

A microphone M will detect positions of maximum and minimum sound. (In practice silence is not obtained at minima positions as the source emits a narrow band of wavelengths not a single wavelength.)

> For a *maximum* the path difference is zero or an integral number of wavelengths. For a *minimum* the path difference is an odd number of half wavelengths.

*Note:*   The distance between two maxima, or two minima, is one wavelength as the two waves are both travelling waves.

### Experiment 6.3

Similar maxima and minima positions may be demonstrated by the interference of a direct sound wave and a reflected wave, as shown in Figure 6.12.
(1) The distance between two consecutive maxima or minima is one wavelength, as the direct and reflected travelling waves interfere (Figure 6.12(a)).

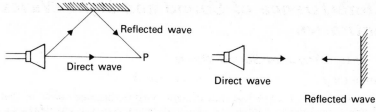

(a) Interference between direct and reflected waves

(b) Interference producing standing waves

**Figure 6.12** Interference of sound waves

(2) The incident and reflected waves are travelling in the *opposite* directions producing a *standing wave.* Hence, here the distance between maxima is *half* the incident wavelength. This experiment can be used to determine the velocity of sound.

## 6:B.2 *Interference of Light Waves*

### Coherent and incoherent waves

Light is produced from excited atoms returning to their ground state (see Section 7:C.3), a finite wave train of light being emitted by each atom. The light from one source, of excited neon atoms, for example, will not produce waves of identical amplitude and phase as light from another source of neon atoms, although both sources generate the same wavelengths. The waves from two such sources are said to be **incoherent** even though their frequencies, wavelengths, and average amplitudes may be the same. To obtain two **coherent** beams of light, that is beams which have identical amplitudes and phase at every instant, a *single* source must be used and divided into two beams.

### *Interference of two coherent light sources – Young's slits*

**Experiment 6.4** *Young's slits experiment*

Two sets of coherent waves are produced by passing a narrow beam of light through two small slits, as shown in Figure 6.13.

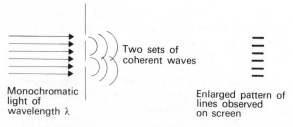

Monochromatic light of wavelength λ

Two sets of coherent waves

Enlarged pattern of lines observed on screen

**Figure 6.13** Young's slits experiment

Two narrow 'slits' are scratched on a blackened microscope slide. The width of each slit must be narrow as the wavelength of light is small. If red light is used, a series of black lines on a red background is observed. The black lines show positions of destructive interference.

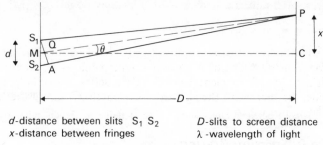

d-distance between slits $S_1$ $S_2$      D-slits to screen distance
x-distance between fringes               λ -wavelength of light

**Figure 6.14**

*Theory – Relationship between fringe separation and wavelength*

For a bright fringe on the screen the path difference between $S_2P$ and $S_1P$ in Figure 6.14 must be an integral number of wavelengths. If P is the first bright fringe then

$$S_2P - S_1P = S_2A = \lambda$$

(A is a point on $PS_2$ such that $PA = PS_1$.)

By geometry, $\Delta PMC$ and $\Delta S_1QM$ are similar and therefore

$$M\hat{S}_1Q = S_2\hat{S}_1A = \theta.$$

Since $D$ is very much larger than $d$ or $x$, $\theta$ is a small angle hence

$$\sin \theta = \tan \theta = \theta.$$

$$\theta = \frac{\lambda}{d} \quad \text{(from } \Delta S_1AS_2\text{)}$$

$$\theta = \frac{x}{D} \quad \text{(from } \Delta PMC\text{)}$$

Giving $$\frac{\lambda}{d} = \frac{x}{D}$$

It is useful to remember the formula

$$\lambda = \frac{xd}{D}$$

*Note:* The interference of the two waves gives constructive interference, a bright band, when the path difference is $\lambda$ or an integral multiple of $\lambda$. Hence a bright bringe is obtained at a position $x$, $2x$, $3x$, ..., $nx$ where $n$ is an integer. Similarly, a dark fringe is observed for a path difference of an odd number of *half* wavelengths.

For a given wavelength the distance apart of the fringes may be increased by reducing the distance between the slits $d$ or by increasing the distance to the screen $D$. If light of a shorter wavelength is used, say blue light, the path difference for the first bright fringe at P must still be one wavelength, hence P will be nearer to C, that is $x$ is decreased. This may be directly deduced from the formula $\lambda = \dfrac{xd}{D}$ if $\lambda \downarrow$ then $x \downarrow$ .

When a white light source is employed fringes will be obtained at different positions for each wavelength. A central bright patch at C, where the path difference is zero for all wavelengths, will have a series of overlapping spectra on either side; the blue, with the shortest wavelength, requiring the least path difference, being nearest to C.

### 6:B.3 *The Diffraction Grating*

With a diffraction grating, interference is obtained between a number of coherent waves. Instead of two slits, a diffraction grating has a large number of equally spaced slits, probably several thousand per centimetre. Interference takes place from all the coherent waves passing through these slits.

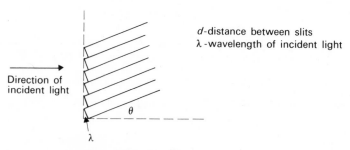

**Figure 6.15** Diffraction grating

Beyond the slit at an angle $\theta$ each wave is $\lambda$ ahead of the next. If all these waves are brought together by a convex lens then a bright resultant will be formed by constructive interference. At some other angles each wave will destructively interfere with some other wave giving darkness. A bright fringe will be obtained in a direction $\theta$ when

$$d \sin \theta = \lambda$$

Another bright line will be obtained for a larger angle $\theta'$ when $d \sin \theta' = 2\lambda$, each wave now being *two* wavelengths ahead of the next.

If white light is used then each wavelength $\lambda_1, \lambda_2, \lambda_3, \ldots$, that is each colour, will give a bright fringe in a slightly different direction $\theta_1, \theta_2, \theta_3, \ldots$, such that $d \sin \theta_1 = \lambda_1$, $d \sin \theta_2 = \lambda_2, \ldots$, for each colour. Thus the incident light will be split up into a spectrum (see Section 7:C.1) by the grating. This spectrum is called the **first order spectrum**. At larger angles $\theta'$, such that $d \sin \theta' = 2\lambda$ for each wavelength, another spectrum will be obtained called the **second order spectrum**. Higher order spectra are unlikely as $\sin \theta$ must be less than unity!

A diffraction grating is used in a spectrometer (see Section 7:C2), having the advantage over a prism that little light is lost on reflection or absorption.

**Problems**

**6.5** The generators SG in Figure 6.16 are tuned to a wavelength of 0.1 m and are connected to loudspeakers A, B, and C as shown. A microphone M is connected to

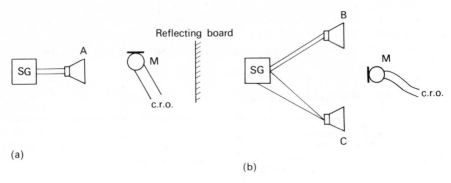

(a)

(b)

**Figure 6.16**

a c.r.o. which shows the strength of the signal at the position of the microphone. Comment on the distances between two neighbouring minima positions in (a) and (b).

**6.6** In a Young's slits experiment the distance $x$ between fringes was measured in order to determine the wavelength $\lambda$ used, from the formula $\lambda = \dfrac{xd}{D}$. State what $D$ and $d$ are.

(a) Considering each quantity $x$, $d$, and $D$, comment on the effect of their accuracy of measurement on the accuracy of determining $\lambda$.

What is the effect on the fringes of

(b) altering the distance $D$,

(c) altering the width of the slits,

(d) changing from yellow to blue light,

(e) using yellow and blue light together?

# C: Electromagnetic Radiation and Radio Communication

## 6:C.1 *Electromagnetic Radiation*

Light is electromagnetic radiation of certain wavelengths. The full range of electromagnetic radiation is given in Figure 6.17.

*Note:* A logarithmic scale has been used in Figure 6.17, that is the scale is in *powers* of ten.

*All* electromagnetic radiation has a velocity of $2.998 \times 10^8$ m s$^{-1}$ in a vacuum and lower velocities in other media. They show refraction, reflection, interference, and diffraction similar to other wave motions, but different wavelengths exhibit different degrees and effects in different media. Microwaves and light do not have the same refraction in water; X-rays and infra-red will not

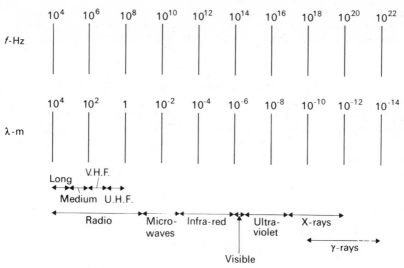

**Figure 6.17** The electromagnetic spectrum

show interference in the same apparatus as their wavelengths are not the same!

Previously it has been mentioned that electromagnetic wave motion is a transverse wave. The physical quantity or 'particle' which is varying will now be considered. In water waves the water droplets vibrate, in sound the excess air pressure periodically varies.

An electric charge has an associated electric field $E$. A moving charge, or charges, which constitutes an electric current will, in addition, have an associated magnetic field $B$. Charges moving with changing velocities, that is accelerating charges, will have *changing* magnetic and electric fields.

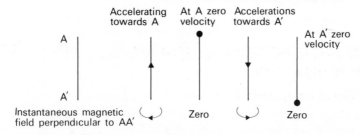

**Figure 6.18** Magnetic field around an oscillating electron

If a single electron oscillates in a wire AA' (Figure 6.18) the magnetic field varies from a maximum in one direction to a maximum in the other.

The overall picture of the variation in the magnetic field with time, as it spreads away from AA', is shown in Figure 6.19.

*Note:* The direction of the magnetic field is perpendicular to the page, that is perpendicular to AA'.

A

A′

○ Zero magnetic field

✕ Magnetic field into the page

● Magnetic field out of the page

**Figure 6.19** Variation of the magnetic field

As the electron is accelerating the electric field will also vary periodically but in a plane perpendicular to the magnetic field (Figure 6.20).

The electromagnetic wave will radiate outwards in all directions from the wire AA′ but perpendicular to AA′.

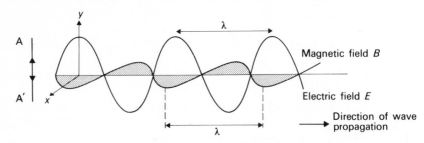

**Figure 6.20** Variation of *E* and *B*

*Note:* In electromagnetic radiation *two* physical quantities periodically vary, namely the magnetic field and the electric field. These fields *E* and *B* are perpendicular to each other and they are both at right angles to the direction of the wave propagation.

The frequency of the wave will depend on the frequency of oscillation of the electrons in the wire.

### 6:C.2 *The Electromagnetic Spectrum*

γ-**rays** may be emitted when excited **nuclei** return to a lower energy state (see Section 8:A.2). They are observed in radioactive decay and cosmic radiation.

**X-rays** may be generated when high velocity electrons are suddenly decelerated at a suitable target.

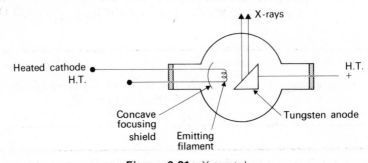

**Figure 6.21** X-ray tube

A high voltage, of the order of 300 kV, is applied between the cathode and anode in Figure 6.21 to accelerate the electrons and the anode is surrounded by a cooling system.

*Uses:*

(1) To produce ionization.
(2) In medicine and dentistry to photograph bones, teeth, and other organs.
(3) To measure crystal lattice spacing by diffraction, as the spacings are of the same order of magnitude as the wavelengths of X-rays.

When a diffraction grating is illuminated by light, dark and bright bands are observed. Because a crystal lattice has a regular array of nuclei in three dimensions, it acts like a series of diffraction gratings giving a pattern of spots, not lines. However, it is more usual to examine the diffraction pattern produced by the *reflection* of X-rays from the nuclei in the crystal planes. From examination of the diffraction pattern the lattice spacing may be determined.

**Ultra-violet radiation** may be emitted when certain excited atoms return to their ground state (see Section 7:C.3).

*Uses:*

(1) Produces vitamin D in the skin, but is harmful in large doses.
(2) Produces **fluorescence** effects. The fluorescent material absorbs the ultra-violet, then decays in microseconds to a lower energy state, thence to the ground state with the emission of radiation of a lower frequency, namely visible light. In some substances the decay to the intermediate state may take from seconds to hours, and light may be emitted after the ultra-violet has been removed, this latter phenomena is termed **phosphorescence**.
(3) Causes ionization of atoms in the atmosphere producing the ionosphere.

**Visible light** may also be produced by excited atoms returning to their ground state. Visible light is the relatively *small* range of wavelengths which can be detected by the human eye.

**Infra-red radiation** is usually emitted by excited molecules returning to lower energy states. This is a heat radiation.

*Uses:*

(1) Transmission of heat from the Sun, electric fires or radiators.
(2) In military and haze photography, as infra-red radiation penetrates cloud and darkness to a certain extent.
(3) In investigations of molecular structure (see Section 7:C.3).

**Microwaves** may be produced by a klystron or a magnetron, which are special types of valves causing electronic oscillations. (A triode cannot operate at these high frequencies.)

*Uses:*

(1) In radar when a short burst of microwaves may be reflected back by a metal object. The emitted and reflected waves are rectified and applied to the Y-plates

of a c.r.o. where each wave will cause a deflection. From the interval between deflections the distance of the object may be determined.

**Example:**  A burst of microwaves is deflected from an aircraft. A spot on a c.r.o. takes $\frac{1}{100}$ milliseconds to move 1 cm. A deflection due to the emitted wave occurs at the 0.5 cm mark and a second, due to the reflected waves, occurs at the 2.5 cm mark. How far away is the aircraft?

$$\text{Distance on c.r.o. between deflections} = 2 \text{ cm}$$
$$\text{Time taken for the spot to move 2 cm} = 10^{-5} \times 2 \text{ s}$$
$$\text{Velocity of microwaves} = 3 \times 10^8 \text{ m s}^{-1}$$
$$\text{Distance travelled by microwaves} = 3 \times 10^8 \times 2 \times 10^{-5} \text{ m}$$
$$= 6 \times 10^3 \text{ m}$$
$$\text{Distance to aircraft} = 3 \times 10^3 \text{ m}$$

Alternatively, a continuous beam of microwaves may be emitted from a rotating parabolic mirror and used to scan the surrounding area. For example, the mirror may be attached to the mast of a ship. Reflected waves from other ships or land masses may be detected and displayed on a screen. Microwaves have the advantage of penetrating fog and cloud.

(2) For determining molecular structure.

**Radio waves** cover a large range of wavelengths. They may be produced by the oscillations of electrons in an aerial. Their main use is in communications.

### Experiment 6.5

Certain microwave apparatus is very useful for demonstrating the wave properties of electromagnetic waves. Because the wavelengths are around 3 cm, diffraction may be observed behind a screen about 5 cm wide!

### 6:C.3   *Use of Radio Waves in Communications*

Radio waves have the important property of being refracted by the ionosphere, a layer of ions formed by the passage of ultra-violet radiation from the Sun. The waves will only be refracted back to the Earth if they are incident on the ionosphere at a certain angle, otherwise they will by lost (ray C in Figure 6.22).

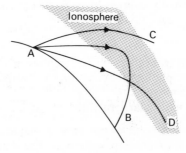

**Figure 6.22**

Rays emitted in an acute direction D will have a long path length and thus return weaker. The radio waves are usually beamed at a particular angle and secondary transmission stations pick up and reradiate them.

Very high frequency radio waves are not sufficiently refracted by the iono-sphere, which has different refractive indices for different frequencies, hence these radio waves, UHF, may be reflected back by artificial satellites.

Radio waves are required to transmit information, but audio frequencies are much lower than radio frequencies, so the audio frequency information is 'carried' by the radio waves.

## Modulation

A property of the carrier wave is varied at the audio frequency, as shown in Figure 6.23.

In **amplitude modulation** the amplitude of the radio wave, the 'carrier wave',

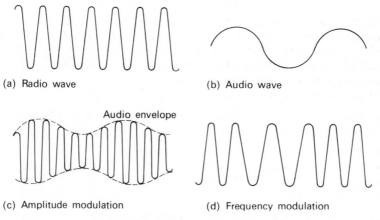

(a) Radio wave      (b) Audio wave

Audio envelope

(c) Amplitude modulation      (d) Frequency modulation

**Figure 6.23** Modulation

is altered to correspond to that of the low-frequency audio wave. In *frequency modulations* the frequency of the radio wave is varied, but this type of modulation will not be discussed further.

## Transmitter

This is an oscillator (see Section 5:C.3) connected to a suitable aerial system.

An **aerial** is essentially a straight conducting wire or system of wires in which the electrons may oscillate at the same frequency as the oscillatory circuit. Electromagnetic waves of this frequency will radiate outwards perpendicular to the aerial. The frequency of the transmitted radio waves will, however, depend *only* on the values of $L$ and $C$ in the oscillatory circuit.

In a triode oscillator, see Figure 5.38 on page 136, the amplitude depends on the HT supply, and the HT could therefore be varied at the audio frequency to produce amplitude modulation. In practice a more complicated method is used.

## Demodulation

The average value of the current from an amplitude modulated signal will be zero, but after rectification, as in Figure 6.24(b), the average value of the current will vary at the audio frequency.

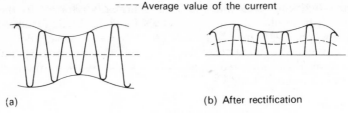

---- Average value of the current

(a)　　　　　　　　　　　(b) After rectification

**Figure 6.24**  Demodulation

## Receiver

A receiver must be designed to pick up the radio 'carrier' wave and obtain from it the audio frequency information.

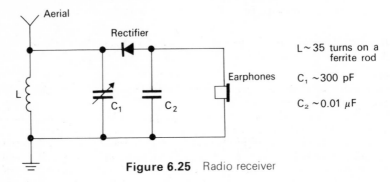

**Figure 6.25**  Radio receiver

L ~ 35 turns on a ferrite rod

$C_1$ ~300 pF

$C_2$ ~0.01 $\mu$F

## Summary of the function of the components of a receiver

Aerial — picks up a range of electromagnetic radio waves.

$C_1$ — the tuning capacitor, tunes the $L, C_1$ circuit to respond to the radio frequency of the required radio 'carrier' wave.

$L, C_1$ — acts as a resonating circuit.

Rectifier — provides an average value of the current varying at the audio frequencies.

Earphones — to convert the electrical variations into sound.

$C_2$ — capacitor to short out the higher frequency radio variations in the average value of the current.

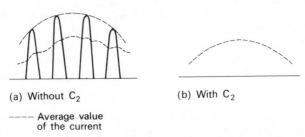

(a) Without $C_2$　　　　　　(b) With $C_2$

---- Average value of the current

**Figure 6.26**  Use of capacitor $C_2$

To improve the signal an amplifier may be added.

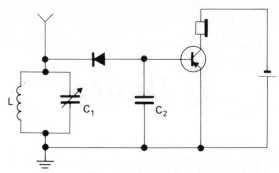

**Figure 6.27**   Receiver with amplifier

A number of further transistors may be used to increase the amplitude of the signal.

**Problems**

**6.7**   (*a*) Which type of electromagnetic radiation would you use to demonstrate diffraction with a 3 cm aperture?
(*b*) A clown's hat irradiated with ultra-violet light was found to shine in the dark after the ultra-violet was switched off. What is the term for this effect?

**6.8**   A parabolic rotating mirror emits microwaves of wavelength 4 cm. The receiving apparatus shows that reflection from an obstacle takes $10^{-5}$ seconds. What difference would be observed if the wavelength of the waves was increased to 8 cm?

**6.9**   In assembling a simple receiver, as shown in Figure 6.25, a pupil P places the rectifier in the opposite direction, pupil Q has $C_1$ and $C_2$ interchanged, and pupil R forgets to include $C_2$ altogether. Comment on the functioning of these receivers.

# 7 Optics

## A: Reflection and Refraction

### 7:A.1 Reflection

When a narrow, parallel beam of light, a **ray**, is shone on to a mirror the light is reflected such that the angle of incidence is equal to the angle of reflection, as shown in Figure 7.1.

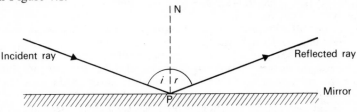

**Figure 7.1** Reflection

NP – normal at the point of incidence P (a normal is a line drawn at right angles to a second line or surface).

$i$    – angle of incidence between the incident ray and the normal.

$r$    – angle of reflection between the reflected ray and the normal.

### For reflection:

Angle of incidence $i$ = angle of reflection $r$

The incident ray, reflected ray, and the normal at the point of incidence are all in the same plane.

*Note:* If the light were replaced by a stream of ball bearings travelling in the direction of the incident ray and a hard board were substituted for the mirror, the balls would bounce off in the direction of the reflected rays. This suggests that a ray of light may also be regarded as a stream of 'particles', called **photons**, travelling in straight lines.

*Note:* Section 6:B.2 showed clearly that the wave nature of light may be adequately demonstrated by interference and diffraction at small slits and obstacles.

### 7:A.2 Refraction

Refraction, the change in direction of light at a boundary between two media, is due to the difference in the velocity of the light in the two media (see Section 6:A.3).

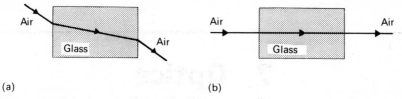

(a)  (b)

**Figure 7.2** Refraction

The light, that is the photons, travel *slower* in the glass than in the air. However, if the ray is perpendicular to the interface of the two media, there is no change in direction, although the light is still travelling slower inside the glass (Figure 7.2(b)).

**Experiment 7.1** *To investigate the relationship between the angle of refraction and the angle of incidence*

A semicircular block of glass or perspex is used to obtain refraction at one interface only, as shown in Figure 7.3(a).

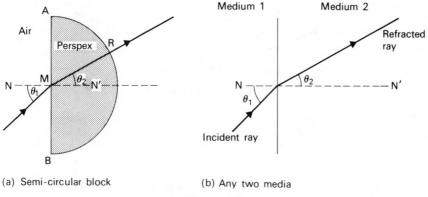

(a) Semi-circular block  (b) Any two media

**Figure 7.3**

NN′ – normal at the point of incidence.
$\theta_1$ – angle of incidence (angle between the incident ray and normal).
$\theta_2$ – angle of refraction (angle between the refracted ray and normal).

Light is directed to the midpoint M of the straight side AB. After refraction it traverses a radius of the block, hence there is no refraction at R.

Angles of refraction $\theta_2$ are measured for different angles of incidence $\theta_1$ and the following table is completed by experiment.

| $\theta_1$ | $\theta_2$ | $\sin \theta_1$ | $\sin \theta_2$ | $\sin \theta_1 / \sin \theta_2$ |
|---|---|---|---|---|
| | | | | |

The experiment shows that the last column, $\sin \theta_1 / \sin \theta_2$ is a constant within the limits of the experiment.

## Snell's Law

For light (or any wave motion) of a given frequency and any two media,

$$\frac{\sin \theta_1}{\sin \theta_2} = \text{a constant}$$

where $\theta_1$ and $\theta_2$ are the angles between the ray and the normal in each medium, as shown in Figure 7.3(b).

It may be demonstrated that this constant is the **relative refractive index** $_1n_2$ for the two media.

Thus, for the above experiment, the relative refractive index for air to perspex is given by:

$$_1n_2 = {}_{\text{air}}n_{\text{perspex}} = \frac{\sin \theta_1 \text{ (angle of incidence in air)}}{\sin \theta_2 \text{ (angle of refraction in perspex)}}$$

*Note:* The incident ray, the refracted ray, and the normal at the point of incidence are all in the same plane.

### Absolute refractive index, n

A ratio, no units.

The absolute refractive index $n$ of a medium (usually referred to simply as the refractive index) is defined as the ratio of the speeds of light in vacuum and in the medium. A larger refractive index indicates a slower speed of light.

$$n = \frac{\text{speed of light in vacuum } v_0}{\text{speed of light in medium } v}$$

$$n = \frac{v_0}{v}$$

*Note:* The refractive index varies with the frequency of the light.

### Relationship between speed of light in two media and the angles of incidence and refraction

Consider a beam of light refracted from a vacuum into a medium of refractive index $n$ and speed of light $v$.

In Figure 7.4, AC is perpendicular to XC and BD is perpendicular to CX'.

hence $\quad\quad\quad\quad A\hat{C}B = \theta_0 \quad$ and $\quad C\hat{B}D = \theta$

When ray Y travels the distance AB in vacuum ray X travels the distance CD in the medium.

Since the times taken to travel AB and CD are the same

$$\frac{AB}{v_0} = \frac{CD}{v}$$

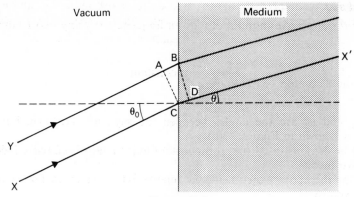

Vacuum                                      Medium

**Figure 7.4**

giving

$$\frac{v_0}{v} = \frac{AB}{CD} = \frac{AB/BC}{CD/BC} = \frac{\sin \theta_0}{\sin \theta}$$

hence

$$\frac{v_0}{v} = \frac{\sin \theta_0}{\sin \theta}$$

therefore

$$n = \frac{\sin \theta_0}{\sin \theta} \qquad \left( n = \frac{v_0}{v} \right)$$

The (absolute) refractive index is thus a measure of the amount by which the rays of light change *direction* when they enter a medium from a vacuum. The larger the refractive index the greater this change in direction.

The refractive index $n$ for a medium may be determined by measuring the refraction from a vacuum into that medium.

$$n = \frac{\sin \theta_0}{\sin \theta}$$

where $\theta_0$ is the angle of incidence in vacuum and $\theta$ is the angle of refraction in the medium.

The above results may be extended to refraction at the boundary between

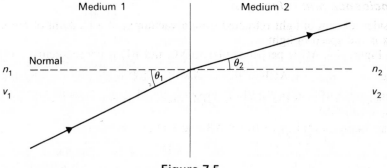

**Figure 7.5**

*any* two media with speeds of light $v_1$ and $v_2$, refractive indices $n_1$ and $n_2$, and angles between the rays and the normal of $\theta_1$ and $\theta_2$ respectively, Figure 7.5.

giving

$$\frac{v_1}{v_2} = \frac{\sin \theta_1}{\sin \theta_2}$$

From the definition of refractive index:

$$n = \frac{v_0}{v}$$

$$n_1 = \frac{v_0}{v_1} \quad \text{and} \quad n_2 = \frac{v_0}{v_2}$$

$$\Rightarrow \quad \frac{n_2}{n_1} = \frac{v_1}{v_2}$$

hence

$$\frac{n_2}{n_1} = \frac{v_1}{v_2} = \frac{\sin \theta_1}{\sin \theta_2}$$

These equations may be written in a symmetrical form and should be learnt.

$$n_1 v_1 = n_2 v_2$$
$$n_1 \sin \theta_1 = n_2 \sin \theta_2$$

It may now be observed that the relative refractive index $_1 n_2 = \dfrac{n_2}{n_1} = \dfrac{\sin \theta_1}{\sin \theta_2}$ as indicated at the end of Experiment 7.1.

*Note:*   Section 6:A.3 showed that the frequency $f$ remains unchanged during refraction but that the wavelength $\lambda$ alters. As $v = \lambda f$ then

$$\frac{n_1}{n_2} = \frac{v_2}{v_1} = \frac{\lambda_2}{\lambda_1} = \frac{\sin \theta_2}{\sin \theta_1}$$

also $v_1 = \lambda_1 f$ and $v_2 = \lambda_2 f$ for waves of speeds $v_1$ and $v_2$, and wavelengths $\lambda_1$ and $\lambda_2$ in media of refractive indices $n_1$ and $n_2$ respectively. These equations assist in the calculation of wavelengths when refraction occurs.

### Examples of absolute refractive indices

| | | | |
|---|---|---|---|
| Vacuum | $n = 1$ | Air | $n = 1.0003$ |
| Water | $n = 1.33$ | Glass | $n = 1.50$ to $1.65$ |
| Diamond | $n = 2.42$ | Perspex | $n = 1.5$ |

It should be noted that if the relative refractive index from air into a medium (which is comparatively easy to measure) is used instead of the absolute refractive index from vacuum to the medium, the error is very small because the refractive index of air is so close to unity.

### 7:A.3   Critical Angle

If light travels from a medium into air the angle of *refraction* in the air is greater than the angle of *incidence* in the medium, as the refractive index of a medium is larger than that for air (except for low pressure gases), see Figure 7.6(a).

If the angle of incidence is increased until the angle in air is 90°, as in Figure 7.6(b), the light can just emerge along the interface, and the angle in the medium is called the **critical angle C**.

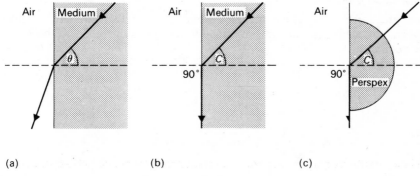

(a)                    (b)                    (c)

**Figure 7.6**   Critical angle $C$

From Figure 7.6(b),

$$n = \frac{\sin \theta_0 \text{ (angle of refraction in air)}}{\sin \theta \text{ (angle of incidence in medium)}}$$

or using     $n_1 \sin \theta_1 = n_2 \sin \theta_2$
$$n \sin C = 1 \times \sin 90°$$
$$n = \frac{\sin 90°}{\sin C}$$

$$n = \frac{1}{\sin C}$$

*Note:*   As the light is travelling *from* the medium into air the refraction angle, the angle in air, is in the numerator of the refractive index equation. Remember that in $n = \dfrac{\sin \theta_0}{\sin \theta}$, $\theta_0$ must be the angle in vacuum (air).

### Examples of critical angles:

Since $n = \dfrac{1}{\sin C}$ then using $\sin C = \dfrac{1}{n}$ the following critical angles should be calculated.

| | | |
|---|---|---|
| Diamond $n = 2.42$ | $C = 24.4°$ | |
| Perspex  $n = 1.5$ | $C = 41.8°$ | |
| Water    $n = 1.33$ | $C = 48.8°$ | |

The critical angle for perspex may be measured with a semicircular block as shown in Figure 7.6(c). Instruments have been designed which measure this critical angle accurately, thus providing reliable values for refractive indices. An instrument which measures refractive indices is called a **refractometer**.

### Total internal reflection

When the angle of incidence in the medium is greater than the critical angle, light cannot be refracted out into the air. All the light is then reflected back into the medium at the interface, as shown in Figure 7.7. This is termed **total internal reflection**.

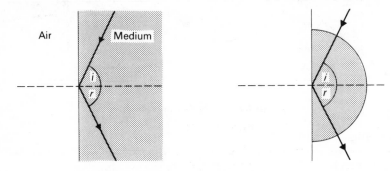

**Figure 7.7** Total internal reflection

By the law of reflection, $i = r$. (Remember that reflection also takes place to some extent when the angle in the medium is *less* than the critical angle.)

### Examples of total internal reflection

A 45° isosceles glass or perspex prism may be used as a mirror (Figure 7.8(a)) or as an erecting prism (Figure 7.8(b)). Erecting prisms are used in pairs in some binoculars.

In **fibre optics** light is shone into a transparent plastic fibre at a suitable angle so that total internal reflection occurs at the sides of the fibre throughout its length and the light cannot escape.

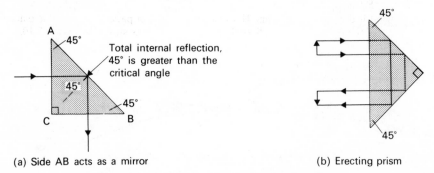

(a) Side AB acts as a mirror          (b) Erecting prism

**Figure 7.8** Total internal reflection in prisms

Diamonds and other precious stones have high refractive indices and therefore low critical angles. The light is often internally reflected and only emitted in certain directions, giving intense emitted beams and causing the stone to sparkle.

## 7:A.4 *Deviation*

If light is passed through a transparent rectangular block (Figure 7.9(a)) refraction occurs when the light enters and leaves the block but the emergent ray EE′ is *parallel* to the direction of the incident ray II′.

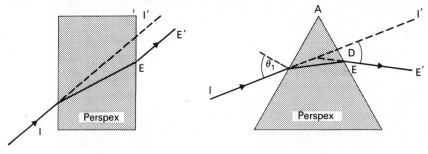

(a) Rectangular block, no deviation  (b) Deviation by a prism

**Figure 7.9** Deviation

When a prism is employed (Figure 7.9(b)) the refraction causes an overall change in direction which is termed **deviation**.

> The **angle of deviation** $D$ is the angle between the incident ray direction II′ and the emergent ray direction EE′.

The angle of deviation depends on: the angle of incidence $\theta_1$, the apex angle of the prism $A$, and the refractive index of the prism material.

*Note:* Because the refractive index varies with the frequency of the light used, the angle of deviation will also vary with the frequency.

### *Minimum angle of deviation*

#### Experiment 7.2

A ray of light is directed along a line II′ drawn on a sheet of paper. The prism is placed in the path of the light with a small angle of incidence $\theta_1$, as shown in Figure 7.10.

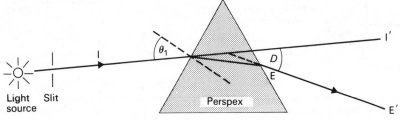

**Figure 7.10** Variation of angle $D$

The prism is slowly rotated, increasing the angle of incidence $\theta_1$. It is observed that the emergent ray EE′ approaches the line II′, *reducing* the angle of deviation D, and then moves away from II′, *increasing* the angle of deviation. The angle when the deviation is *least* is called the **minimum angle of deviation**. This position of minimum deviation is important when viewing spectra (see Section 7:C.2).

**Problems**

**7.1** The velocity of light is greatest in a vacuum. What does this imply about the possible values a refractive index may have?

**7.2** (a) A ray of light passes from glass, $n = 1.5$, into water, $n = 1.33$. Draw a sketch to show the relative sizes of the angles of incidence and refraction. No calculations are required.

(b) Determine the angles of refraction in the media shown in Figure 7.11, if the incident light is in air.

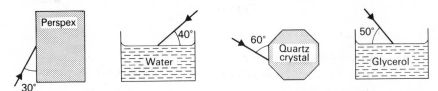

**Figure 7.11**

**7.3** Light of frequency $6 \times 10^{14}$ Hz travels from air into a block of glass of refractive index 1.5. (Assume the velocity of light in air is $3 \times 10^8$ m s$^{-1}$.) Calculate the velocity, wavelength, and frequency of the light in the glass.

# B: Lenses and the Telescope

## 7:B.1 Refraction through Lenses

Parallel rays of light are refracted by a convex lens in such a way that they converge to a **real principal focus F**. Such a lens is often called a **converging lens**.

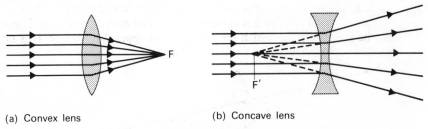

(a) Convex lens

(b) Concave lens

**Figure 7.12** Lenses

For a concave lens the parallel rays of light are refracted outwards by the lens in such a way that they appear to diverge from a **virtual focus F′**. This lens is termed a **diverging lens**.

## *Location and nature of images – by ray diagrams*

The **principal axis** is a line through the midpoint M of the lens (Figure 7.13). By convention the rays are drawn from left to right. O is the position of the object and I the image position.

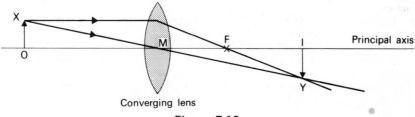

Converging lens

**Figure 7.13**

---

The following must be known:
  (1) A ray parallel to the principal axis passes through the focus after refraction.
  (2) A ray passing through the centre of the lens continues straight on undeviated.

---

In Figure 7.13 X is a point on the object. The two rays (1) and (2) above are constructed. They meet at point Y on the image. Y is the point on the image which corresponds to X on the object.

*Note:*  Any other ray passing through point X will also be refracted by the lens to Y.

The distance FM is called the **focal length** *f*.
The distance OM is called the **object distance** *u*.
The distance IM is called the **image distance** *v*.

The image is a **real image** if it may be shown on a screen placed at I, as in Figure 7.13. It will be on the *opposite* side of a single lens from the object.

The image is a **virtual image** if it cannot be obtained on a screen, as in Figure 7.14. It is the position from which the rays of light *appear* to diverge. It is not

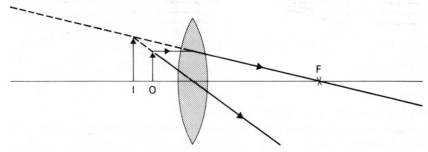

**Figure 7.14**  Ray diagram

essential for light to pass through the virtual image position in order to form such an image. The virtual image is on the *same* side of a converging lens as the object.

> Three facts should be stated about any image:
> (1) Real or virtual.
> (2) Erect or inverted.
> (3) Magnified or diminished.

The linear magnification of an image $= \dfrac{\text{size of image}}{\text{size of object}}$. It may be shown that this equals $\dfrac{\text{image distance}}{\text{object distance}}$.

$$\text{Magnification} = \frac{v}{u}$$

In the two arrangements above:
Figure 7.13 shows the image as real, inverted, and diminished.
Figure 7.14 shows the image as virtual, erect, and magnified.

By drawing a ray diagram *to scale* the nature of an image may be determined.

## Images formed by a converging lens

For any converging lens of focal length $f$:

| Object distance, $u$ | Type of image | Examples |
|---|---|---|
| (a)  $u > 2f$ | Real, inverted, diminished | Camera, objective lens of telescope |
| (b)  $u = 2f$ | Real, inverted, same size | Terrestrial telescope, photocopier |
| (c)  $f < u < 2f$ | Real, inverted, magnified | Projector, objective of microscope |
| (d)  $u = f$ | At infinity | Spotlight, eyepiece of telescope |
| (e)  $u < f$ | Virtual, erect, magnified | Magnifying glass, eyepiece of microscope and telescope |

## Images formed by a diverging lens

For *any* diverging lens a virtual, erect, and diminished image is obtained for *all* object positions (Figure 7.16). This type of lens is used in spectacles and certain telescopic arrangements.

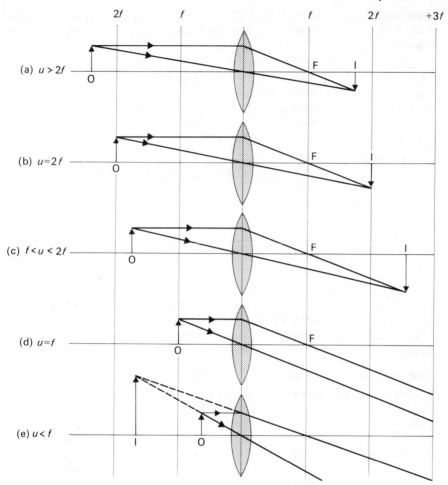

**Figure 7.15**  Ray diagrams showing the images formed by a converging lens

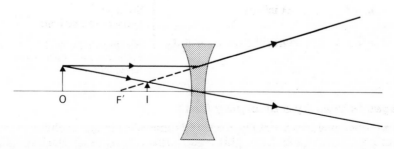

**Figure 7.16**  Ray diagram showing the image formed by a converging lens

### Experiment 7.3

Using ray boxes and cylindrical lenses the focal length of both convex and concave lenses and the formation of real and virtual images may be demonstrated. The nature of real images with spherical lenses may be shown on a screen using a simple optical bench.

*Note:* The foci and images are *blurred* when wide beams of light are used as only rays near the centre of a lens are brought exactly to the focus F or F'. This may be clearly shown with the ray boxes and five widely spaced incident rays. This effect may also be observed with thick lenses.

### *Lens formula*

Image distances may be calculated using the formula:

$$\frac{1}{f} = \frac{1}{u} + \frac{1}{v}$$

where $f$ is the focal length, $u$ the object distance, and $v$ the image distance.

This formula applies to any lens, converging or diverging, providing a 'real is positive' sign convention is used. This requires that:

(1) All distances are positive if actually traversed by the light, that is distances from real foci, images or objects.
(2) Distances to virtual foci or images are taken to be negative, these distances are only *apparently* traversed by the light. Thus, the focal length of a converging lens is positive and the focal length of a diverging lens is negative.

(There are other sign conventions which will not be discussed here.)

**Example:** Determine the position of an image of an object placed 30 cm in front of a converging lens of focal length 10 cm.

Using

$$\frac{1}{f} = \frac{1}{u} + \frac{1}{v}$$

then

$$\frac{1}{+10} = \frac{1}{+30} + \frac{1}{v}$$

giving

$$v = +15 \text{ cm}$$

The positive sign indicates a real image, situated 15 cm from the lens. The magnification $\dfrac{v}{u} = \dfrac{15}{30} = 0.5$, which indicates a diminished image.

**Example:** Determine the nature of an image of an object situated 20 cm in front of a diverging lens of focal length 10 cm.

Using

$$\frac{1}{f} = \frac{1}{u} + \frac{1}{v}$$

then

$$\frac{1}{-10} = \frac{1}{+20} + \frac{1}{v}$$

giving

$$v = -6.67 \text{ cm}$$

The image is therefore virtual, 6.67 cm from the lens, on the same side as the object, and diminished.

*Note:* The lens formula enables the image distance, and hence the magnification to be calculated. The sign associated with the image distance indicates if the image is real or virtual but the formula cannot yield information as to whether the image is inverted or erect. A ray diagram, drawn to scale, will give the three points needed to describe an image, which were specified on page 168.

### Power of a lens

The power of a lens is defined as the reciprocal of the focal length.

$$\text{Power} = \frac{1}{\text{focal length in metres}}$$

Unit: dioptre (D).

A converging lens has a positive power. A diverging lens has a negative power. Thus a converging lens of focal length 20 cm has a power of $+5$ D but a diverging lens of focal length 25 cm has a power of $-4$ D.

### 7:B.2 *The Telescope*

The telescope is a device designed to view distant objects. The astronomical telescope (Figure 7.17) has two convex lenses. The objective lens has a long focal length and the eyepiece a short focal length. The objective lens forms a real image of the object quite near to the eye. It is much *smaller* than the object, but as it is nearer to the eye it appears larger.

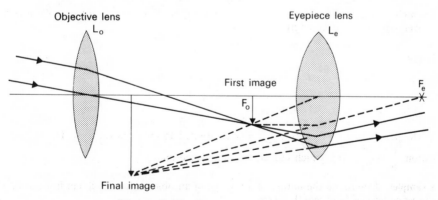

**Figure 7.17** Astronomical telescope

The eyepiece acts as a magnifying glass and magnifies the real image formed by the objective, producing a final image which is virtual and inverted.

Since the object is at a great distance, the first image will be formed very near to the focus $F_o$ of the objective lens $L_o$. As the eyepiece $L_e$ is acting as a magnifying glass, the distance of the first image (which is the object for this lens) from the eyepiece must be *less* than the focal length $f_e$ of the eyepiece, as in Figure 7.15(e) on page 169.

The distance between the lenses (i.e. the length of the telescope) is therefore *less* than the sum of the focal lengths of the two lenses.

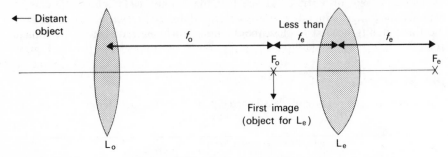

**Figure 7.18** Length of a telescope

## Final image at infinity (telescope in normal adjustment)

For a relaxed position of the eye, the final image position is at infinity. The object distance for the eyepiece lens $L_e$ must equal its focal length $f_e$, hence the first image is now at a distance $f_e$ in front of the eyepiece.

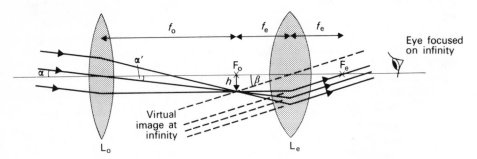

**Figure 7.19** Length of a telescope in normal adjustment

With a final image at infinity, the length of a telescope is *equal* to the sum of the focal lengths of the two lenses, as shown in Figure 7.19.

### Magnifying power of a telescope in normal adjustment

The **magnifying power (angular magnification)** *M* is defined as the ratio of the angle subtended by the image, $\beta$, to the angle subtended by the object, $\alpha$. Referring to Figure 7.19 and observing that angles $\alpha$ and $\beta$ are small:

$$\alpha = \alpha' = \frac{h}{f_o}, \quad \beta = \frac{h}{f_e}, \quad \text{and} \quad M = \frac{\beta}{\alpha}$$

Hence

$$M = \frac{f_o \text{ (focal length of objective)}}{f_e \text{ (focal length of eyepiece)}}$$

To increase the magnification of a telescope the focal length of the objective should be made as long as possible and the focal length of the eyepiece very short.

To convert an astronomical telescope to a terrestrial telescope, an extra lens is employed between the objective and eyepiece to invert the image, as shown in Figure 7.20. The final image is now *erect* but still virtual. (From Figure 7.15(b), the distance of this extra lens from its object, that is the first image at $F_o$, is twice the focal length of this extra lens.)

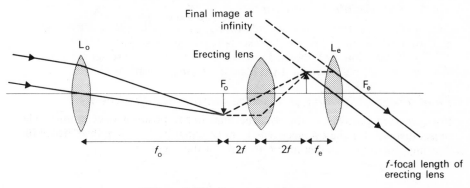

**Figure 7.20** Terrestrial telescope

**Problems**

**7.4** Two convex lenses A and B of the same shape are made of different glass. The refractive indices are 1.50 and 1.65 for A and B respectively. Which has the larger focal length?

**7.5** A virtual erect image of an object was obtained. Was a converging or a diverging lens used? Comment on your answer.

**7.6** For a final image at infinity, and an identical magnifying power, is a terrestrial or an astronomical telescope longer? What is the difference in their lengths?

**7.7** Complete the diagrams in Figure 7.21 to show refraction through the lenses.

**7.8** Draw a ray diagram to scale to determine the nature of the image of an object situated 15 cm from a converging lens of focal length 10 cm. State the range of object distances, which could be used with this lens in a projector, to produce a magnified image on a screen.

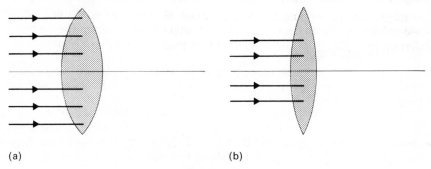

(a)                                       (b)

**Figure 7.21**

**7.9** A transparent slide 3.5 cm wide is placed 15 cm in front of a converging lens of focal length 20 cm. Draw a ray diagram to determine the position of the image. Check your answer by calculation and state the width of the image. Would this arrangement be of any use in either a slide projector or a slide viewer?

# C: The Spectrometer and Spectra

### 7:C.1 The Visible Spectrum

The visible spectrum consists of those wavelengths of electromagnetic radiation which are detected by the normal eye, $\lambda = 4 \times 10^{-7}$ m to $7 \times 10^{-7}$ m. If radiation of all these wavelengths overlap then white light is observed. A spectrum can be produced by a glass or perspex prism, as shown in Figure 7.22.

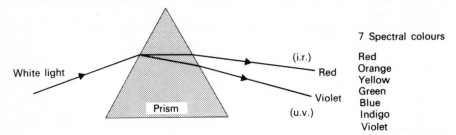

**Figure 7.22** Visible spectrum

The deviation produced by a prism depends on the refractive index (see Section 7:A.4) but because the refractive index varies with frequency the deviation of the blue light will be different to that of the red light. This difference in the deviation of the blue and red light (or of any two waves of different frequency) is called **dispersion**.

The **dispersive power** of a material is a measure of the dispersion and depends on the *difference* in the refractive indices for the blue and red light.

*Note:* Ultra-violet (u.v.) and infra-red (i.r.) radiation may be detected depending on the source and the properties of the prism material.

A spectrum may also be produced by the use of a diffraction grating (see Section 6:B.3).

### Chromatic aberration

A single lens may have **chromatic aberration** because the red light will *not* be brought to the same focus as the blue light. Hence the image of an object may have coloured edges.

This effect may be reduced by using an **achromatic** doublet which consists of a powerful convex lens of low dispersive power with a weak concave lens of high dispersive power. The overall effect is a converging lens with little dispersion. Achromatic doublets are used in optical instruments to reduce chromatic aberration.

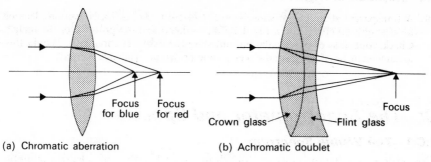

(a) Chromatic aberration

(b) Achromatic doublet

**Figure 7.23**

## 7:C.2 *The Spectrometer*

This is an instrument designed to produce, view, and study spectra. (A simpler version, which is often unsuitable for taking accurate measurements, is termed a **spectroscope**.)

There are three main parts and these are shown in Figure 7.24:

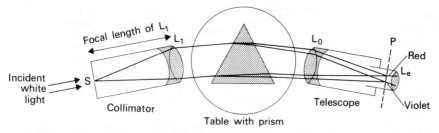

**Figure 7.24** Spectrometer

(1) The **collimator**

This has a slit S at one end and a lens $L_1$ at the other to produce a narrow parallel beam of light.

(2) The **prism** or **diffraction grating**

These split up the incident light into different wavelengths or colours. The important function here is *dispersion* to obtain different colours in different directions.

(3) The **telescope**

Here it is used to view each wavelength clearly. Each wavelength or colour is brought to a separate focus in the focal plane P of the objective $L_o$ and viewed through the eyepiece $L_e$. (The cross wires are also at the focal plane P.)

The prism or diffraction grating is placed on a central table which is adjusted into a horizontal position by means of levelling screws. This table can be rotated in a horizontal plane in order to bring a diffraction grating into a position perpendicular to the incident light or a prism to a position of minimum deviation. A locking screw ensures no change of position during the experimental investigation.

The telescope is joined by an arm to the central 'leg' of the table. It may rotate about the table which has a scale in degrees on its outer circumference, so that the position of a spectral line may be recorded. In this way the spectrometer may identify elements in a given sample of material by comparison of the spectrum formed from it with the known spectral lines of the pure elements.

## 7:C.3 *Spectra*

### *Light emission and absorption*

In an **atom** the electrons which move around the central nucleus are associated with particular energy levels. If the electrons are in the lowest possible energy levels the atom is said to be in its **ground state**. The electrons may occupy other higher energy levels, when the atom is said to be in an **excited state**. When an electron passes from an excited state energy level $E_i$ to a ground state energy level $E_j$ light is emitted of a particular frequency $f$ such that the energy difference

$$E_i - E_j = hf$$

where $h$ is Planck's constant ($6.63 \times 10^{-34}$ J s).

The energy levels can be represented by a series of horizontal lines (Figure 7.25).

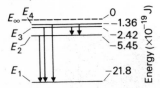

**Figure 7.25** Energy levels for the hydrogen atom

*Note:* The zero of energy refers to the condition of the atom when the electron has been completely removed, hence the negative values for the energy levels.

For any transition the frequency of the photon emitted can be calculated from the difference in the energies of the levels. For example:

$$E_3 - E_1 = (-2.42 - (-21.8)) \times 10^{-19} = hf_1$$

giving
$$f_1 = 2.92 \times 10^{15} \text{ Hz (in the ultra-violet)}$$

and
$$E_3 - E_2 = hf_2$$
$$= 4.57 \times 10^{14} \text{ Hz (in the visible region)}$$

These frequencies for electronic transitions may be in the ultra-violet, visible, or infra-red regions.

Conversely an electron may be excited to a higher energy level by absorbing radiation of this frequency $f$, that is absorbing a photon of light energy $E_i - E_j$.

---

The values of the energy levels depend on the individual atom. Therefore, the energy difference between levels and hence the frequencies which may be emitted or absorbed are **characteristic** of each atom.

A **molecule** also has vibrational and rotational energy levels. Transitions between these levels result in spectra lying in the *infra-red* and *microwave* regions respectively (compare with the electronic transitions opposite). In contrast to the line spectra for atoms, **band** spectra are observed for molecules.

## Types of emission spectra

### (1) Line spectrum

These are the specific frequencies or wavelengths emitted by excited atoms. A line spectrum may be obtained by passing an electrical discharge through the vapour of the atoms and viewing the emitted light with a spectrometer. Because a line spectrum is characteristic of a particular atomic species it can be used to detect small quantities of those atoms.

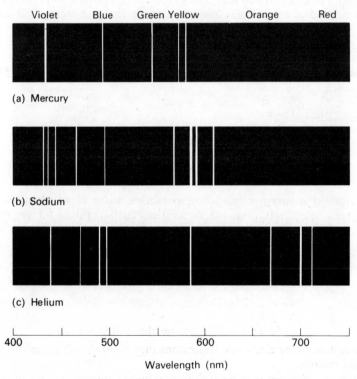

**Figure 7.26** Characteristic line spectra

### (2) Band spectrum

When a molecular species is excited a number of wavelength bands are observed, which are characteristic of that molecule.

### (3) Continuous spectrum

This is the spectrum of white light which has all, or nearly all, the wavelengths of the visible region. A gradually changing band of colour from red through to violet is observed. This may be produced by using a glowing tungsten lamp as a source and dispersing the light with a glass prism. Sunlight will give a continuous spectrum although with a few wavelengths absent.

### Absorption spectra

If white light illuminates the vapour of particular atoms then those wavelengths, or frequencies, corresponding to the line spectra of the vapour atoms will be **absorbed**. Any photon of light energy of frequency $f$ equal to the difference between two energy levels of that atom may be absorbed, resulting in an electron associated with a higher energy value. Light then reaching a spectrometer will have these wavelengths *absent*, hence dark lines will be observed on a continuous spectrum.

For example, if sodium vapour is used two dark lines will be observed in the yellow region.

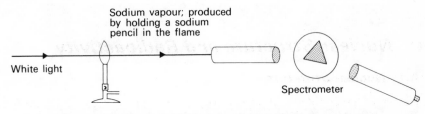

**Figure 7.27**   Absorption spectrum

The element helium was first detected in the absorption spectrum of the Sun, hence its name.

The infra-red *absorption bands* for molecules are used to identify certain groups within the molecule, as for example the carbonyl group $\diagdown C{=}O$.

**Problems**

7.10   What is the energy of a photon of the green spectral line of mercury whose wavelength is $5.46 \times 10^{-7}$ m? (Take the velocity of light as $3 \times 10^8$ m s$^{-1}$ and Planck's constant as $6.6 \times 10^{-34}$ J s.)

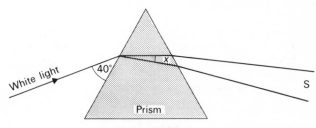

**Figure 7.28**

7.11   A ray of white light is dispersed by the prism in Figure 7.28, giving a spectrum at S. The angle $x$ is found to be 0.7°. If the refractive index of the prism material for red light is 1.51, what is its refractive index for the blue light?

# 8   Radioactivity and Wave Particle Duality

## A:   Nuclear Structure and Radioactivity

### 8:A.1   *Nuclear Structure*

An accepted model of the atom consists of a central nucleus with a nuclear radius of the order of $10^{-15}$ m surrounded by a cloud of electrons, giving an atomic radius of the order of $10^{-10}$ m. The nucleus contains **protons** and **neutrons**. Each proton has a positive charge equal in *magnitude* to the charge of an electron. The neutron is electrically neutral.

**Nucleon** is the collective name for protons and neutrons.

The **atomic number** $Z$ of an element is the number of protons in the nucleus, which is also equal to the number of electrons in the outer cloud.

The **mass number** $A$ is the total number of nucleons in the nucleus.

A **nuclide** is a particular nucleus with a specified number of protons and neutrons. Any nuclide may be represented by its chemical symbol X together with its atomic and mass numbers; $_{Z}^{A}$X, for example: $_{1}^{2}$H, $_{6}^{12}$C, $_{6}^{14}$C, $_{7}^{14}$N, $_{92}^{235}$U.

**Isotopes** are two or more nuclides of the same element, that is with the same chemical symbol X and atomic number $Z$, but with different numbers of neutrons hence different mass numbers $A$. For example $_{6}^{12}$C and $_{6}^{14}$C both have six protons but six and eight neutrons respectively.

**Isobars** are two or more nuclides of different elements with the same mass numbers, for example $_{6}^{14}$C and $_{7}^{14}$N.

### 8:A.2   *Radioactivity*

In 1896 Becquerel discovered that certain emanations from salts of uranium affected a photographic plate. Later Rutherford in 1899 distinguished between two types of emanation, one of low penetrating power, which he called $\alpha$-rays, and the other of high penetrating power, which he called $\beta$-rays. One year later Villard noticed a third type, even more penetrating, which he termed $\gamma$-rays.

## Absorption of radiation

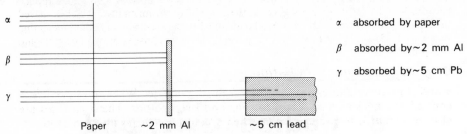

α    absorbed by paper

β    absorbed by ~2 mm Al

γ    absorbed by ~5 cm Pb

Paper     ~2 mm Al     ~5 cm lead

**Figure 8.1**   Absorption of α and β particles and γ-rays

## Deflection in a magnetic field

For the same magnetic field applied perpendicular to the direction of motion of the rays, γ-rays are observed to be unaffected, α-rays are deflected slightly in a direction indicating that they are positively charged, while β-rays are strongly deflected in the opposite direction suggesting a negative charge and a lighter mass (Figure 8.2). Measurements show that the β-rays are fast moving electrons and the charge on the α-rays is double that on the β-rays. Thus α- and β-rays are streams of charged particles.

**Experiment 8.1**   *Rutherford and Royds' experiment to show that α particles are helium nuclei*

Radon gas, which is observed to emit α particles, is introduced into the thin-walled glass tube. The α particles escape into the evacuated thick-walled glass envelope. After

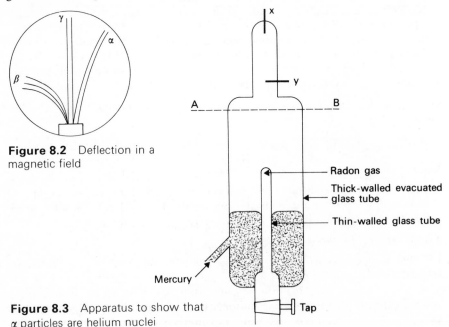

**Figure 8.2** Deflection in a magnetic field

**Figure 8.3**   Apparatus to show that α particles are helium nuclei

Radon gas

Thick-walled evacuated glass tube

Thin-walled glass tube

Mercury

Tap

several days the mercury is forced up to the level AB compressing the α particles, which have now captured stray electrons to become electrically neutral. A high p.d. is applied between X and Y to obtain a discharge in the gas. The spectrum emitted, which is viewed through a spectrometer, is observed to be identical to the spectrum of helium indicating that α particles are helium nuclei. An α particle therefore consists of two neutrons and two protons.

## Origin of α, β, and γ radiation

α and β particles and γ-rays *originate* from the *nucleus*. When an α *particle* is emitted, the nucleus loses two neutrons and two protons. The β *particles* are electrons emitted from the nucleus when a neutron *changes* into a proton.

$$n \rightarrow p^+ + e^-$$

*Note:* An electron from the outer electron cloud is *never* emitted as a β particle.

γ-*rays* are high-energy electromagnetic radiation emitted when a 'rearrangement' of the neutrons and protons occurs and the nucleus 'falls' from a high energy state to a lower energy state.

This difference in energy is equal to $hf$, where $h$ is Planck's constant and $f$ is the frequency of the γ-rays.

**Radioactivity** is the spontaneous disintegration of the nucleus of an atom from which α, β and γ radiation may be emitted with occasionally other particles or nuclear fragments. It is caused by an unstable nucleus tending to a stable condition and is *not* affected by chemical reactions or the outer electrons. Natural sources of radioactivity include cosmic rays and radioactive rocks.

*Properties of α and β particles and γ-rays*

| Property | α particle | β particle | γ-rays |
|---|---|---|---|
| Nature | Helium nucleus 2n + 2p | Electron | High-energy electro-magnetic radiation |
| Charge | $+2$ | $-1$ | Zero |
| Penetrating power | Low | Medium | High |
| Absorption | Paper or $10^{-2}$ mm Al | $\sim 2$ mm Al | $\sim 5$ cm lead |
| Ionization | High | Medium | Low |
| Velocity | Of the order of $10^{-7}$ m s$^{-1}$ | Up to $10^8$ m s$^{-1}$, but variable | At velocity of light $3 \times 10^8$ m s$^{-1}$ |
| Spread of Velocities | One or few definite velocities | Wide spread | All the same |
| Example of suitable source | $^{241}_{95}$Americium | $^{90}_{38}$Strontium | $^{60}_{27}$Cobalt |

For laboratory experiments a radioactive source emitting only one type of radiation is often required. The isotopes listed above are the most useful ones for each type, although $^{241}_{95}$Am does emit some $\gamma$-rays and $^{60}_{27}$Co gives a small $\beta$ emission which may be removed by absorption.

When these radiations travel through a gas they cause ionization along their path. Due to the heavier mass and lower speeds the $\alpha$ particles produce considerable ionization per mm of their path length and quickly lose their energy, hence their tracks are short and they are easily absorbed. The $\beta$ particles, with their higher velocities, cause less ionization per mm, and therefore produce longer tracks and penetrate further. The $\gamma$-rays produce very little ionization per mm, do not leave tracks and have high penetrating powers.

### 8:A.3 *Detection of Radioactivity*

### *Background radiation*

Cosmic rays and radioactive materials provide a general background of radiation, which can be detected by a suitable device. It is necessary therefore to take a count or reading before and after an experiment involving a radioactive source. The average of these readings is called the **background count**. This count must be subtracted from all experimental readings to obtain results due to the activity of the source alone.

### *Methods for detection of radioactivity*

#### (1) *Ionization chamber*

In the ionization chamber shown in Figure 8.4, radiation enters C, usually through a wire-mesh panel in the lid, causing ionization and therefore a small transient current between C and P. This may be detected on a milliameter, after

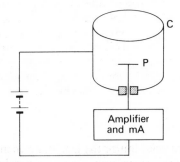

**Figure 8.4** Ionization chamber

amplification. If the radioactive source is gaseous it may be introduced directly into the chamber now fitted with a full lid with no mesh panel, and its activity observed. This instrument is most suitable for the detection of $\alpha$, $\beta$, and other charged particles which produce sufficient ionization along their path.

#### (2) *Geiger–Müller tube*

This is a sensitive ionization chamber which may be used to detect $\alpha$ and $\beta$ particles and $\gamma$-rays.

α or β particles enter the chamber through the thin mica end-window but γ-rays may penetrate the walls of the tube (Figure 8.5(a)). The radioactive particles ionize some of the neon atoms, which accelerated by the electric field undergo further collisions. These collisions produce more ionization in sufficient quantity to give a pulse on a meter connected to the output. To prevent sparking and to clear the tube for the next event, a quenching agent, such as a trace of bromine gas, is used.

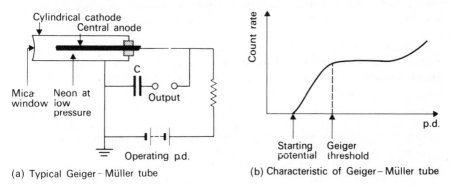

(a) Typical Geiger – Müller tube

(b) Characteristic of Geiger – Müller tube

**Figure 8.5** Geiger–Müller tube

*Note:* One pulse is recorded for each radioactive event regardless of the energy of the ionizing particle.

Before commencing an investigation a graph of count rate against operating p.d. is plotted for the Geiger–Müller tube (Figure 8.5(b)). Below a certain p.d., called the **starting potential**, no events are recorded. The central plateau region is stable for fluctuations in supply, hence a p.d. is chosen in this middle 'plateau' section ∼400–450 V in the type usually used in schools and colleges.

To count the total number of pulses a **scalar** may be used. A **rate meter** records the average value of the ionization current over a specified time interval, that is the average number of pulses per second, the **count rate**.

## (3) Cloud chamber

α, β, or other charged particles ionize the gas along their path. If this occurs in a liquid about to boil or in a vapour about to condense the ions will preferentially encourage the formation of droplets or bubbles giving a track. The path of the particle is then observed and can be photographed.

(*a*) **Wilson cloud chamber:** Water vapour in a closed chamber is expanded suddenly by a piston and thereby cools. This causes condensation on ions produced by any radioactive particle present. The expansion must be timed to occur when a charged particle enters the chamber. A photographic device can be linked to the piston and a photograph taken immediately after the expansion (see Figure 1.28 on page 30). An electric field is maintained across the chamber to clear the ions before the next expansion.

(*b*) **Bubble chamber:**   Liquid hydrogen at its boiling point fills a chamber and charged particles are revealed by a trail of bubbles. Lighting from beneath allows the trail to be photographed.

## (4) *Photographic emulsion*

$\alpha$ and $\beta$ particles and $\gamma$-rays will blacken photographic plates and hence leave lines on photographic emulsion plates. A number of plates may be placed on top of each other to obtain a three-dimensional track.

## (5) *Solid-state detectors*

The junction of a solid-state device is exposed to the radiation. The electrons and/or holes produced by the radiation will give rise to short currents which may be amplified and fed to a scalar or rate meter. By suitable choice of solid-state materials, $\alpha$ and $\beta$ particles or $\gamma$-rays may be detected.

## (6) *Scintillation counters*

Radiations produce a flash of light, a **scintillation**, when impinging on certain materials called **phosphors**, for example $\alpha$ particles cause zinc sulphide to scintillate. These weak flashes may be amplified by a photomultiplier. In modern scintillation counters liquid phosphors are used. By a suitable choice of phosphor most radiations may be detected by this method. This is one of the few devices which may be used to measure the *energy* of the incident radiation or particle.

## 8:A.4   *Disintegration*

Radioactivity is a *random* process. In a given time a certain number of parent nuclei will disintegrate into their daughter products but it is impossible to state when one particular nucleus will disintegrate.

The **activity** of a substance is the number of disintegrations per second and may be measured in **curies**.

$$1 \text{ curie} = 3.7 \times 10^{10} \text{ disintegrations per second}$$

Since the activity of a given sample of a nuclide is continuously varying as the nuclides decay, this concept is not always very useful.

### *Half life*

Unit: seconds (to years), scalar.

> The half life of a radioactive nuclide is the *time taken* for half the number of parent nuclei to disintegrate; or the time taken for the activity to fall to half of its initial value.

Although the decay is a random process the half life will be the same for all samples of the nuclide, providing that a very large number of atoms are used. Neither chemical combination of the nuclide nor changes in its physical surroundings will alter the half life.

Half lives range from over millions of years to less than microseconds.

## Decay series

Many parent nuclei decay into daughter products which are also radioactive.

**Examples**

$$^{238}_{92}U \rightarrow {}^{234}_{90}Th + {}^{4}_{2}He \qquad \alpha \text{ emission}$$
$$^{234}_{90}Th \rightarrow {}^{234}_{91}Pa + {}^{0}_{-1}e \qquad \beta \text{ emission}$$
$$^{234}_{91}Pa \rightarrow {}^{234}_{92}U + {}^{0}_{-1}e \qquad \beta \text{ emission}$$

$^{234}_{92}U$ then decays by repeated $\alpha$ emissions to an isotope of lead, which by various $\beta$ and $\alpha$ emissions yields another, stable, isotope of lead $^{206}_{82}Pb$. For any decay or radioactive transmutation the $A$ and $Z$ numbers of the daughter nuclei may be determined if the radiation emitted is known.

$\alpha$ **emission:** an $\alpha$ particle is two neutrons and two protons. For a parent nuclide $^{A}_{Z}X$ the daughter will be $^{A-4}_{Z-2}X'$.

$\beta$ **emission:** a $\beta$ particle is an electron emitted when a neutron changes into a proton. For a parent nuclide $^{A}_{Z}X$ the daughter will be $^{A}_{Z+1}X'$.

$\gamma$ **emission:** the parent and daughter nuclides will be identical in symbol, $^{A}_{Z}X$, but the energy state of the daughter will be lower.

## Measurement of half lives

The rate of disintegration of a radioactive specimen is experimentally determined at certain time intervals. The background count is also determined. A graph of activity due to the specimen against time is then plotted, which will have an exponential shape. From the graph the time taken for the activity to fall to half an initial value may be determined.

**Example:** From the graph in Figure 8.6 the counts per second will be the experimental readings minus the background count. The half life $T_{\frac{1}{2}}$ will be the time taken for the

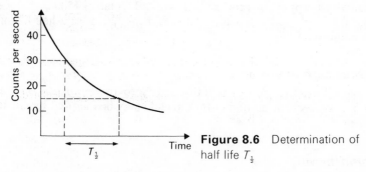

**Figure 8.6**  Determination of half life $T_{\frac{1}{2}}$

count rate to fall from 30 to 15, as shown in the graph, or may equally be the time taken to fall from 40 to 20 counts per second, both giving the same result.

*Note:* The background count must always be subtracted from experimental readings before a graph is plotted.

## Factors affecting the design of experiments to measure half lives $T_{\frac{1}{2}}$

If the daughter nuclides are radioactive, care must be taken to measure only the activity due to the parent nuclides. This may be achieved if:

(1) The daughter product is removed by chemical combination.
(2) The half life of the daughter product is much longer than that of the parent so that the activity due to the daughter may be neglected.
(3) The daughter emits a different type of radiation so that either an instrument sensitive to the parent's radiation may be chosen, or if the daughter's radiations are more easily absorbed they may be shielded from the detection apparatus.

**Examples:**

$$^{216}_{84}\text{Po} \rightarrow {}^{212}_{82}\text{Pb} + {}^{4}_{2}\alpha \qquad \text{half life} = 0.2 \text{ s}$$
$$^{212}_{82}\text{Pb} \rightarrow {}^{212}_{83}\text{Bi} + {}_{-1}^{0}\beta \qquad \text{half life} = 10 \text{ hours}$$

An ionization chamber more sensitive to $\alpha$ than $\beta$ particles may be used to measure $T_{\frac{1}{2}}$ of $^{216}_{84}\text{Po}$. In addition, the half life of the daughter is much longer and therefore the number of $\alpha$ particle events is so much larger than any $\beta$ particle events that the latter may be neglected.

To measure $T_{\frac{1}{2}}$ of the $^{212}_{82}\text{Pb}$ a paper shield may be used to absorb the $\alpha$ particles, or a scintillation counter with a $\beta$-sensitive phosphor may be chosen as a detector.

*Note:* When the half lives are measured the intensity or energy of the radiations emitted are not considered.

### 8:A.5 Uses of Radioactivity

#### (1) Radioactive dating

If the half life of the radioisotope is known, the ratio of parent to daughter nuclides in a rock may yield the time elapsed since the rock was laid down or the time passed since an animal or plant died. The isotope chosen must have a half life comparable to the age of the object being studied. For example, to determine the age of ancient rocks $^{238}_{92}\text{U}$, with a half life of $4500 \times 10^6$ years, is used, but for fossils and archaeological specimens $^{14}_{6}\text{C}$, with a half life of 5600 years is employed.

#### (2) Tracer techniques

A suitable radioactive isotope is introduced into the biological or chemical system. The subsequent motion of that nuclide may be followed by a detection instrument.

#### (3) Radiotherapy

$^{60}_{27}\text{Co}$ with its $\gamma$-rays is used to treat cancer patients. Radium needles are implanted in some cancers.

## (4) *Industrial uses*

The ionization produced by $\alpha$ and $\beta$ radioactive sources prevents the build-up of static charge hence the accumulation of dirt. Radiation may kill germs and may be used for sterilization. Reflection, refraction or scattering of radiation beams may detect flaws in materials. Thicknesses may be measured by noting the reduction in count rate from a $\beta$ source.

## (5) *Nuclear power*

This may be generated from suitable isotopes.

### Problems

**8.1** Which of the following nuclides are isotopes or isobars?

$$^{40}_{19}K, \quad ^{40}_{18}Ar, \quad ^{206}_{82}Pb, \quad ^{207}_{82}Pb, \quad ^{208}_{82}Pb.$$

**8.2** Which of the following may be deflected by an electric field: $\alpha$ particles, neutrons, $\gamma$-rays, $\beta$ particles?

**8.3** From a sample of uranium which is radioactive, 100 g of uranium chloride and 100 g of uranium nitrate were prepared. How will their half lives differ?

**8.4** A radioactive nuclide has a half life of 2 hours. What percentage of its original activity remains after 8 hours?

**8.5** The activity from a radioactive source was measured every day and the following results were obtained:

| Time in days | 0 | 1 | 2 | 3 | 4 | 5 |
|---|---|---|---|---|---|---|
| Activity | 137 | 92 | 63 | 44 | 31 | 22 |

The background count was found to be 7. Plot a graph and determine the half life of this source.

# B: Atomic Models, Mass-energy Equivalence, and Nuclear Reactions

## 8:B.1  *Models of the Atom*

### Thomson's model

In this model of the atom, discussed by Thomson in 1904, the electrons were thought to be embedded in a sphere of diffuse positive material, this material filling the *whole* atomic volume. At this time some properties of the electron were known but the proton had not yet been observed.

### Rutherford's model

As Rutherford was dubious of Thomson's model, Geiger and Marsden conducted the following 'scattering' experiment in 1911.

The experiment was performed in a vacuum to prevent other collisions by the $\alpha$ particles. The $\alpha$ particles were directed at a very thin gold foil target, as shown in Figure 8.7. Most $\alpha$ particles passed to the detector at position A but

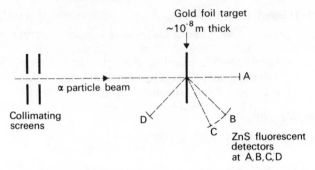

Gold foil target
~$10^{-8}$ m thick

α particle beam

A

Collimating screens

D

B

C

ZnS fluorescent detectors at A, B, C, D

**Figure 8.7** Rutherford's scattering experiment

some are deviated through various angles and detected at positions B to C. Occasionally (about once in 8000 cases) an α particle was repelled back and detected around position D. If the mass and charge of each gold atom were distributed throughout its volume *none* of the α particles should have been deflected backwards. This brought about a proposal by Rutherford for a new model of the atom (Figure 8.8).

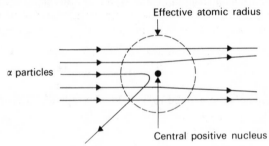

Effective atomic radius

α particles

Central positive nucleus

**Figure 8.8** Rutherford's atomic model

In this model the positive charge and most of the mass of each atom is concentrated in a small central nucleus, with a radius of around $10^{-15}$ m. The electron cloud is around this nucleus and accounts for the volume of the atom, the atomic radius being about $10^{-10}$ m. This dense central nucleus could then produce the large deflections when the occasional α particle passed close by.

From similar experiments values were obtained for effective nuclear and atomic radii.

### 8:B.2 Mass-energy Equivalence

Einstein's equation relating mass $m$ to energy $E$ is

$$E = mc^2$$

where $c$ is the velocity of light in a vacuum.

In some nuclear transformations it is observed that the total mass of the products does *not* equal the mass of the initial nuclides.

**Example:** In $\beta$ emission a neutron gives rise to a proton and a $\beta$ particle

$$_0^1n \; \rightarrow \; _1^1p \; + \; _{-1}^0e$$

Rest mass    16 748    16 725     9    $\times \; 10^{-31}$ kg

Total mass of left-hand side $= 16\,748 \times 10^{-31}$ kg
Total mass of right-hand side $= 16\,734 \times 10^{-31}$ kg
Mass difference $= 14 \times 10^{-31}$ kg

Using Einstein's equation,

Energy due to this mass difference $= 14 \times 10^{-31} \times 9 \times 10^{16}$
$$= 1.26 \times 10^{-13} \text{ J}$$

Most of this energy appears as the kinetic energy of the very fast moving $\beta$ particles but a small amount is accounted for by nuclear recoil and heat.

*Note:* The law of conservation of mass does not apply but the law of conservation of energy still holds when the equivalence of mass and energy is taken into account.

## 8:B.3 *Nuclear Reactions*

### Nuclear fission

Nuclear fission is the splitting of a nuclide into smaller nuclides or particles. When some large nuclides are split into fragments it is observed that the mass of the products is *less* than the mass of the starting nuclides, thus again energy is emitted.

**Example:** If uranium-235 captures a slow neutron it may split into two smaller nuclides with a net gain in energy.

$$_0^1n + _{92}^{235}U \rightarrow _{36}^{92}Kr + _{56}^{141}Ba + 3\,_0^1n + \text{energy}$$
(mass $_{36}^{92}Kr$ + mass $_{56}^{141}Ba$ + mass $3\,_0^1n$) is *less than* (mass $_{92}^{235}U$ + mass $_0^1n$)

Spontaneous fission of this nuclide of uranium also occurs but the above artificial transformation yields higher energies.

Nuclear fission occurring under controlled conditions provides atomic power which may be converted into electricity. The principle of the atomic bomb is the uncontrolled nuclear fission reaction of a certain critical sized piece of uranium or plutonium with the subsequent emission of a large amount of energy.

### Nuclear fusion

Nuclear fusion is the building up of elements from smaller nuclides or protons and neutrons. The mass of the products may be *less* than the mass of the starting elements giving a net gain in energy.

**Examples:**
$$_0^1n + _1^1p \rightarrow _1^2H + \text{energy } (2.7 \times 10^{-13} \text{ J})$$
$$2\,_1^2H \rightarrow _1^3H + _1^1p + \text{energy } (6.5 \times 10^{-13} \text{ J})$$
$$_1^3H + _1^2H \rightarrow _2^4He + _0^1n + \text{energy } (2.8 \times 10^{-12} \text{ J})$$

$_1^3H$ a hydrogen isotope with two neutrons is called **tritium**.
$_1^2H$ a hydrogen isotope with one neutron is called **deuterium**.
For the reaction

$$_0^1n \; + \; _1^1p \; \rightarrow \; _1^2H$$

Mass of nuclide     1.6748    1.6725    3.3442     $\times \; 10^{-27}$ kg

Mass of n + p = $3.3473 \times 10^{-27}$ kg

Mass difference between n + p and deuterium = $0.0031 \times 10^{-27}$ kg

The **mass defect** of any nuclide is the difference between the total mass of the individual nucleons making up the nuclide and the mass of that nucleus, the nucleons now being bound together. Thus the mass defect of deuterium is approximately $3 \times 10^{-30}$ kg. Using $E = mc^2$ the energy is $3 \times 10^{-30} \times 9 \times 10^{16}$ J which is $2.7 \times 10^{-13}$ J. This energy is called the **binding energy** of deuterium. (The binding energy per nucleon of a nuclide gives an indication of the stability of that nuclide.)

The last example, viz $^3_1\text{H} + {}^2_1\text{H} \rightarrow {}^4_2\text{He} + {}^1_0\text{n}$ + energy, is of more practical importance with an energy yield of $2.8 \times 10^{-12}$ J per fusion. Thus the fusion of one mole of helium containing $6 \times 10^{23}$ atoms yields ($6 \times 10^{23} \times 2.8 \times 10^{-12}$) = $1.7 \times 10^{11}$ J, which is a large amount of energy from a few grams of fuel! This is equivalent to a power of 5.6 MW being used continuously, day and night, for one week.

Although high energies may be obtained from these nuclear fusion reactions, to initiate the reaction the two nuclides must *collide*. In many cases the starting nuclides are both positive and repel each other. However, if the temperature is considerably increased their mean velocities will increase (see Section 2:C.2) and more collisions will take place enabling the reaction to proceed. These **thermonuclear** reactions occur naturally in the stars where the temperatures are very high, the temperature on the Sun being around 6000 °C. This principle is also used in the hydrogen bomb where the detonator must provide the high temperature.

*Note:* In nuclear fusion small elements are built up into larger elements with the release of energy. With nuclear fission large elements are broken into smaller elements with energy release. For elements with atomic number ~30–80 there is usually little gain in energy for either fission or fusion reactions.

### Artificial transformations

Certain radioactive nuclides occur naturally. Artificial radionuclides may be manufactured by bombarding stable nuclides with small nuclear particles such as $\alpha$ or $\beta$ particles or neutrons.

**Examples:**

(1)   $^7_3\text{Li} + {}^1_1\text{H} \rightarrow {}^4_2\text{He} + {}^4_2\text{He}$

(2)   $^{27}_{13}\text{Al} + {}^1_0\text{n} \rightarrow {}^{24}_{11}\text{Na} + {}^4_2\text{He}$

the daughter $^{24}_{11}\text{Na}$ decays spontaneously

$$^{24}_{11}\text{Na} \rightarrow {}^{24}_{12}\text{Mg} + {}^{\ 0}_{-1}\text{e} \quad (\beta \text{ particle})$$

(3)   $^{27}_{13}\text{Al} + {}^4_2\text{He} \rightarrow {}^{30}_{15}\text{P} + {}^1_0\text{n}$

the daughter also decays

$$^{30}_{15}\text{P} \rightarrow {}^{30}_{14}\text{Si} + {}^{\ 0}_{+1}\text{e} \quad (\text{positron})$$

The bombardment may cause a nuclide to be split, as in Example (1) or produce a nuclide of a higher atomic number as in Example (3). Also notice that the product depends on the bombarding particle; in (2) and (3) the same isotope of aluminium is used.

In these artificial transformations particles other than $\alpha$ and $\beta$ may be emitted. In Example (3) a neutron then a positive electron, the positron, are emitted which do not usually occur in natural radioactive decay. In nuclear fission and fusion artificial transformations are often involved as these may yield higher energies. In tracer techniques artificial isotopes are often required if the element has no naturally occurring radioisotope.

## Nuclear particles emitted in nuclear reactions

$\alpha$ *and* $\beta$ *particles* are emitted in both natural radioactive decay and artificial nuclear reactions.

The **neutron** was first discovered by Chadwick in 1932 when he bombarded beryllium with $\alpha$ particles.

$$^9_4\text{Be} + ^4_2\text{He} \rightarrow ^{12}_6\text{C} + ^1_0\text{n}$$

It has since been observed in many artificial nuclear reactions.

The **positron** is a positive electron with the same mass as the electron but a positive charge equal in magnitude to the electronic charge. The positron is the **antiparticle** to the electron and was first discovered in cosmic rays.

### Production of the positron

(1) In artificial nuclear reactions, when a proton is converted to a neutron.

$$^{30}_{15}\text{P} \rightarrow ^{30}_{14}\text{Si} + ^0_{+1}\text{e}$$

One proton of the phosphorus nucleus has been converted into a neutron giving a silicon nucleus.

(2) When a $\gamma$-ray is converted into an electron/positron pair.*

$$\gamma \rightarrow ^0_{-1}\text{e} + ^0_{+1}\text{e}$$

This is another example of mass–energy conversion.

$$\text{Mass of electron} = 9.1 \times 10^{-31} \text{ kg} = \text{mass of positron}$$
$$\text{Mass of electron/positron pair} = 18.2 \times 10^{-31} \text{ kg}$$
$$\text{Energy equivalent} = 18.2 \times 10^{-31} \times 9 \times 10^{16} \text{ J}$$
$$= 1.64 \times 10^{-13} \text{ J}$$

The energy of a photon of $\gamma$-rays is $hf$, where $h$ is Planck's constant of $6.6 \times 10^{34}$ J s. Hence if the energy of the photon is converted into the rest mass of the electron/positron pair

$$1.64 \times 10^{-13} = 6.6 \times 10^{-34} f$$

giving the frequency $f$ of approximately $2 \times 10^{20}$ Hz, which is in the $\gamma$-ray range of the electromagnetic spectrum.

This is the *minimum* frequency as the electron/positron pair are usually produced with high kinetic energies so that a higher frequency would be required.

As momentum must be conserved the electron and positron will have equal velocities in opposite directions. They may be identified in a cloud chamber by applying a magnetic field perpendicular to the chamber and observing the curvature of their tracks, which will be equal but in opposite directions.

---

* This example and the section on the neutrino are given for interest only. They are not required for examination purposes.

Conversely if an electron and positron combine the two $\gamma$-rays produced are termed the **annihilation radiation**.

$$e^+ + e^- \rightarrow 2\gamma$$

In a cloud chamber the electron and positron will leave tracks which will terminate where they meet and the $\gamma$-rays are produced.

The **neutrino** and **anti-neutrino** are involved in positron emission and $\beta$ decay to ensure there is conservation of **energy** and **angular momentum**. It is observed that the electrons emitted in $\beta$ decay have a *range* of velocities, which implies that they are emitted with *different* kinetic energies. But, the example on page 189 indicates that the energy available is *constant* at $1.26 \times 10^{-13}$ J. Hence another particle must be involved, which is also emitted with a variable amount of kinetic energy. The total energy of the *two* particles will be constant. Further, if the $\beta$ particle has an angular 'spin' in one direction there must be another particle with an equal 'spin' in the complementary direction for the angular momentum to be conserved.

The complete reaction for $\beta$ decay should be written:

$$_{1}^{0}\text{n} \rightarrow {}_{1}^{+1}\text{p} + {}_{0}^{-1}\text{e} + \bar{v}$$

Neutrinos have zero mass (or a mass too small to detect). Notice that it is the anti-neutrino $\bar{v}$ which is involved in $\beta$ decay, and the neutrino $v$ in positron emission.

A large number of other fundamental particles have been discovered in recent years. For example, the pions ($\pi$ mesons), postulated by Yukawa in 1935 to account for the strong nuclear forces between protons and neutrons, were observed later in cosmic radiation.

**Problems**

**8.6** Why is Thomson's model of the atom inadequate to explain Rutherford's scattering experiment, on page 188?

**8.7** Which of the following are conserved: momentum, current, energy, power, mass, charge? State clearly any conditions applicable.

**8.8** Is the following radioactive transformation an example of nuclear fission, nuclear fusion or neither?

$$_{7}^{14}\text{N} + {}_{2}^{4}\text{He} \rightarrow {}_{8}^{17}\text{O} + {}_{1}^{1}\text{H}$$

What is the name for the particle emitted?

# C: Wave Particle Duality

## 8:C.1 *Particle Aspect of Electrons and Electromagnetic Radiation*

In Chapter 5 the wave nature of light was discussed; interference and diffraction being demonstrated. The particle aspect of light was introduced in Chapter 7; a photon of light of a certain energy being emitted when an electron passes between two energy levels. The electron has been treated as a particle but it may show wave properties such as diffraction.

The particle aspect of both electrons and light, or other electromagnetic radiation, will be considered first.

## Particle aspect of electrons

(1) In a cathode ray tube the electron beam may be deflected and observed by the spot the electrons produce on a luminescent screen. The motion of the electrons is found to obey the equations of classical mechanics.

(2) In collisions involving electrons in a cloud chamber, the changes in energy and momentum of the particles are found to obey the laws of conservation of energy and momentum in the same way as the colliding vehicles, balls, and pucks discussed in mechanics.

## Particle aspect of electromagnetic radiation

### (1) *Line spectra*

When an electron falls from an excited energy level $E_i$ to a lower energy level $E_j$ light, or other electromagnetic radiation, of frequency $f$ is emitted such that $E_i - E_j = hf$ (see Section 7:C.3). A packet of light energy, a **photon**, is emitted, the frequency $f$ depending only on the energy difference. The intensity of the radiation is determined by the *number* of transitions taking place, that is on the *number* of photons emitted.

*Note:* The 'particles' of electromagnetic radiation, **photons**, have zero mass and energy $hf$ where $f$ is the frequency and $h$ is Planck's constant. It may also be shown that they have momentum, see (3) below.

### (2) *Photoelectric effect*

This is the emission of electrons from a substance when illuminated by electromagnetic radiation. The particular case of electron emission from the surface of a metal when illuminated by light or ultra-violet radiation will be discussed here.

*Note:* Compare the terms **photoelectric emission,** which is the emission of electrons under the action of light, and **thermionic emission**, which is the emission of electrons from a heated cathode (see Section 5:B.1).

**Experiment 8.2** *To demonstrate the photoelectric effect*

A clean zinc plate is attached to the plate of a negatively charged electroscope and illuminated by ultra-violet radiation, as shown in Figure 8.9. The leaf is observed to *fall* indicating that negative charge has been lost, which suggests that the zinc plate has emitted electrons.

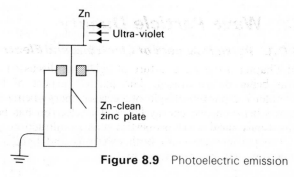

Zn

Ultra-violet

Zn-clean
zinc plate

**Figure 8.9** Photoelectric emission

## Experiment 8.3

When the zinc plate in the apparatus shown in Figure 8.10 is illuminated by ultra-violet radiation, the milliammeter shows a deflection, even when there is no p.d. between P and the zinc plate, in a direction confirming that electrons are emitted by the zinc plate.

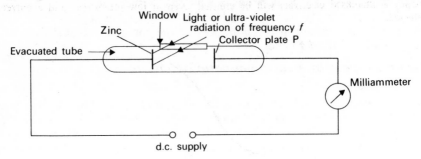

**Figure 8.10**

(1) Using constant intensity radiation of frequency $f$ the potential $V$ of plate P is gradually increased from a negative value below 2 volts and the current $I$ is recorded. A graph of $I$ against $V$ is plotted, as shown in Figure 8.11.

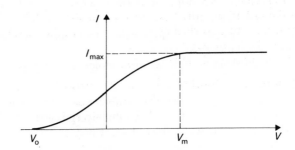

**Figure 8.11** Variation of $I$ with $V$

Below a certain potential $V_0$ (called the stopping potential) no electrons reach P and therefore no current flows in the circuit. At $V_m$ almost all the emitted electrons are collected on P so that further increases in potential above $V_m$ cannot increase the current ($I_{max}$). This implies that the electrons leave the zinc surface with energies ranging from zero which require the high potential $V_m$ to be collected by P up to a maximum energy (which are only prevented from reaching P by the retarding potential $V_0$). Hence for the maximum kinetic energy of an emitted electron

$$\tfrac{1}{2} m v_{max}^2 = V_0 e$$

where $e$ is the electronic charge.

Using the same frequency $f$ the intensity of the radiation is altered and the maximum current $I$ is observed to increase but the value of the stopping potential $V_0$ remains the same. This implies that the *number* of electrons emitted depends on the intensity but the energy of the emitted electrons is *not* affected.

(2) With the potential of P maintained above $V_m$, to ensure that any emitted electron is

collected, the frequency $f$ of the radiation is varied and the current $I$ is recorded. A graph of $I$ against $f$ is plotted as shown in Figure 8.12.

For frequencies below a certain frequency $f_0$, termed the **threshold frequency**, no current is recorded, that is no electrons are emitted. Even if the intensity of this radiation $f_0$ is considerably increased the current remains at zero. However, as the frequency is increased electrons will be emitted, even at low intensities, and a current detected.

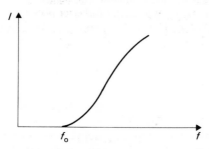

**Figure 8.12** Variation of $I$ with $f$

A certain amount of energy is required to eject the electron from the metal. The results of Experiment 8.3 imply that this energy *cannot* be *continuously* absorbed from the radiation, otherwise intense radiation below $f_0$ would eject an electron, but it must be absorbed in packets, *photons*, the energy of a photon depending *only* on the frequency $f$.

For the electrons most easily able to escape,

$$\text{Energy of photon absorbed} = \text{minimum energy to escape from the metal, } W_{\text{min}}$$
$$+ \text{ kinetic energy of the electron, } \tfrac{1}{2}\,mv^2_{\text{max}}$$
$$hf = W_{\text{min}} + \tfrac{1}{2}\,mv^2_{\text{max}}$$

Therefore there will be a minimum frequency $f_0$ such that $hf_0 = W_{\text{min}}$ and the electrons will just escape from the metal with zero velocities. Below $f_0$ the photon has insufficient energy to release an electron. Substituting $hf_0 = W_{\text{min}}$ in the above equation yields

$$hf - hf_0 = \tfrac{1}{2}\,mv^2_{\text{max}}$$

which is Einstein's photoelectric law.*

It may be shown that the minimum energy required to eject an electron from a clean zinc surface is about $6.1 \times 10^{-19}$ J.

The energy of a photon of red light, $hf_{\text{red}}$ is $3.4 \times 10^{-19}$ J.

The energy of a photon of blue light, $hf_{\text{blue}}$ is $5.4 \times 10^{-19}$ J. Hence ultraviolet radiation is required to obtain photoelectric emission for zinc.

---

* The equations are not required by the Higher Physics syllabus but the photoelectric *effects* should be clearly understood.

Different metals will have different threshold frequencies.

The photoelectric effects below are explained by considering the particle aspect of light.

> *No* electrons are emitted below a certain threshold frequency $f_0$ which depends on the metal irradiated.
>
> The electrons are emitted with kinetic energies ranging from zero to a certain maximum, this maximum depending on the *frequency f* of the incident *photons*.
>
> The number of electrons emitted depends on the *intensity* of the incident radiation, that is on the *number* of incident *photons*.

### (3) *Compton effect*

In 1924 Compton observed that a beam of X-rays of frequency $f$ scattered by electrons through an angle $\theta$ had a reduced frequency $f'$. The recoil electron, which was effectively at rest before collision, acquired energy and momentum (Figure 8.13).

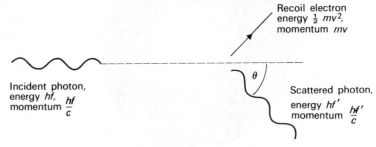

Recoil electron energy $\frac{1}{2}mv^2$, momentum $mv$

Incident photon, energy $hf$, momentum $\frac{hf}{c}$

Scattered photon, energy $hf'$ momentum $\frac{hf'}{c}$

**Figure 8.13** Compton effect

The conservation laws of momentum and energy were found to be obeyed if the momentum of a photon was taken as $\frac{hf}{c}$, where $c$ is the velocity of light. The photons may thus be treated like particles with the collision being similar to that between two pucks on a frictionless surface!

### 8:C.2 *Wave Aspect of Electromagnetic Radiation and Electrons*

### *Wave aspect of electromagnetic radiation*

(1) Interference of light may be demonstrated by Young's slits experiment, (see Section 6:B.2).

(2) Diffraction of light is shown by the diffraction grating (see Section 6:B.3) and by diffraction patterns obtained around sharp edges or small apertures.

(3) X-rays may be diffracted by crystals (see Section 6:C.2). When the crystal is in a powdered form the diffraction pattern may be a series of concentric rings, as shown in Figure 8.14.

**Figure 8.14** X-ray diffraction rings produced by a crystal (*National Chemical Laboratory*)

## Wave aspect of electrons

### (1) Electron diffraction

When a beam of electrons is fired at a thin gold film a **diffraction** pattern similar to X-ray diffraction in crystals is obtained, see Figure 8.15. Compare Figures 8.14 and 8.15.

**Figure 8.15** Electron diffraction rings produced by a sheet of thin gold foil (*Science Museum, Prof. Sir G. Thomson F.R.S.*)

To explain the distribution of the electron pattern it is necessary to consider that the electrons have associated wave properties. It is observed that if the velocity, and therefore the momentum $p$ of the electrons is increased the associated wavelength $\lambda$ decreases, $p\uparrow$ as $\lambda\downarrow$. The relationship between the momentum $p$ and the wavelength $\lambda$ is found to be

$$p = \frac{h}{\lambda}$$

This relationship was originally proposed by Louis de Broglie in 1924, hence the wavelength $\lambda$ is called the **de Broglie wavelength**. If $p = \frac{h}{\lambda}$ then $p = \frac{hf}{c}$ which is identical to the equation for the momentum of a photon in the Compton effect!

Figure 8.16 shows the similarities between electron and light diffraction. The

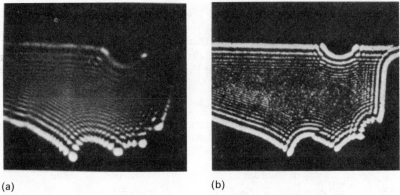

(a)                                        (b)

**Figure 8.16** (a) Diffraction pattern produced by electrons emitted from a sharp point and passing through an aperture between tiny opaque crystals. (b) Diffraction of light passing through an opening in a metal plate cut to the same shape as the gap in the crystal in (a). (*Prof. Sir B. Pippard F.R.S., Cavendish Laboratory*)

beam of electrons passes through an aperture between tiny crystals. The light is diffracted through a similarly shaped opening in a metal plate.

As the wavelength associated with a particle depends on its momentum diffraction effects are unlikely to be observed with particles of large mass!

## (2) *Electron microscope*

An **electron microscope** is used to study minute objects such as cell nuclei. Electric fields are used for focusing the electrons but the principle and theory of the microscope may be treated in the same manner as the light microscope. The

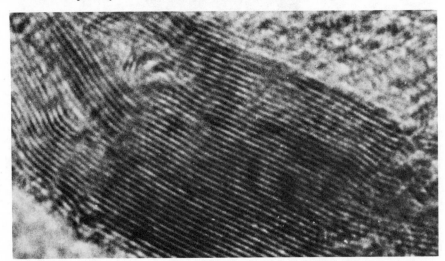

**Figure 8.17** An electron microscope study of a carbon fibre. The separation between the graphite layers of 0.34 nm is readily observed. (*Dr. J. R. Fryer, Glasgow University*)

small wavelengths associated with the electron beams give the electron microscope its ability to resolve at high magnification ~one million (see Figure 8.17).

It may be mentioned that the electron may not be directly 'seen'; only its properties and effects may be observed. Some of the observations are explained by treating the electron as a particle with energy and momentum, other observations are interpreted by considering the de Broglie wavelength.

*Summary: wave particle duality*

|                    | Light                                            | Electron                                       |
| ------------------ | ------------------------------------------------ | ---------------------------------------------- |
| Particle<br>aspect | (1) line spectra<br>   photon emission<br><br>(2) photoelectric effect<br>   photon absorption<br><br>(3) Compton effect<br>   photon deflection | (1) cathode ray tube<br>   electron deflection<br><br>(2) cloud chamber<br>   electron collision |
| Wave<br>aspect     | (1) interference<br>(2) diffraction of light<br>(3) X-ray diffraction | (1) electron diffraction<br>(2) electron microscope |

**Problems**

**8.9**  Why must the zinc plate in Experiment 8.2 be clean?

**8.10**  In photoelectric emission why do the kinetic energies of the emitted electrons vary, even though monochromatic light is used?

**8.11**  Would it be possible to demonstrate diffraction with particles or objects other than electrons?

# Answers to Problems

## Chapter 1

**1.1**  Force: $[M][L][T]^{-2}$.
Power: $[M][L]^2[T]^{-3}$.

Potential difference $\left(\text{p.d.} = \dfrac{\text{energy}}{\text{charge}}\right): \dfrac{[M][L]^2[T]^{-2}}{[I][T]}$

dimensions of p.d are $[M][L]^2[T]^{-3}[I]^{-1}$.

Frequency is measured in cycles per second: $[T]^{-1}$.
Focal length of a lens is a length: $[L]$.
Linear magnification of an object is the ratio of the image size to the object size, therefore as with all ratios it has *no* dimensions.
Half life of a radioactive substance is the time taken for half the number of atoms to disintegrate: $[T]$.

**1.2**  (a) The time taken for one slit to replace the previous one must be $\frac{1}{50}$ second. $\frac{1}{5}$ of a revolution takes $\frac{1}{50}$ second. Hence one revolution takes $\frac{1}{10}$ second. Number of revolutions per second $= 10$.
(b) The highest single viewing frequency is 60 Hz. The strobe has 6 slits so that the motion is viewed six times every revolution of the disc. Frequency of the water waves $= 6 \times 60 = 360$ Hz.

**1.3**  $u = 0, v = 30$ m s$^{-1}, t = 2$ s, $a = ?, s = ?$.
Consider the acceleration first. Equation required is

$v = u + at, a = \frac{30}{2} = 15$ m s$^{-2}$.

To determine $s$ either of the other equations may be used.
Using $s = ut + \frac{1}{2}at^2, s = 0 + \frac{1}{2} \times 15 \times 4 = 30$ m.

**1.4**  From A to B the velocity is increasing therefore the object is accelerating. BC the velocity is constant. CD the velocity is decreasing, but CD is a curve hence the object has a non-uniform deceleration. (Notice that the object did not start from rest.)

1.5    (a)

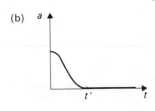

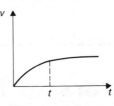

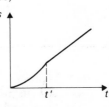

(Downward direction positive)

(b)

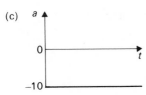

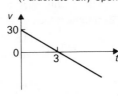

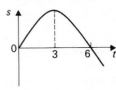

(Parachute fully open at $t'$)

(c)

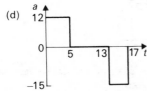

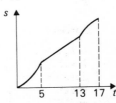

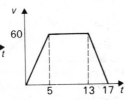

(Upward direction positive)

(d)

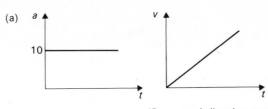

1.6    (a) Front of train (motion to signal box): $s = 50$ m, $a = 1$ m s$^{-2}$, $u = 0$, $v = ?$.
Using $v^2 = u^2 + 2as$, $v = 10\sqrt{3} = 17.3$ m s$^{-1}$.
Back of train: $s = 150$ m, $a = 1$ m s$^{-2}$, $u = 0$, $v = ?$.
Using $v^2 = u^2 + 2as$, $v = 20$ m s$^{-1}$.
(b) Time for the whole train to pass the signal: $a = 1$ m s$^{-2}$, $u = 17.3$ m s$^{-1}$,
$v = 20$ m s$^{-1}$, $t = ?$.
Using $v = u + at$, $t = 2.7$ s.

1.7    In the horizontal direction, velocity $= 40 \cos 30$
$= 34.6$ m s$^{-1}$
This horizontal velocity remains unchanged.
In the vertical direction the velocity $= 40 \sin 30°$
$= 20$ m s$^{-1}$
The vertical velocity, initially directed upwards, will decrease to zero, because of
gravity, then increase in the downward direction. The initial vertical velocity is 20
m s$^{-1}$ upwards, hence after 2 s the vertical velocity will be zero and the ball will
start to fall. After the remaining 8 s the ball will acquire a downward velocity of
80 m s$^{-1}$ just before hitting the rock.

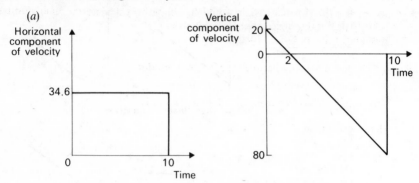

(*a*) Horizontal component of velocity

Vertical component of velocity

(*b*) The horizontal velocity remains constant.
Distance of the rock = 34.6 × 10 = 346 m.
(*c*) Horizontal velocity just before landing = 34.6 m s$^{-1}$
Vertical velocity just before landing = 80 m s$^{-1}$

$$\text{Resultant velocity} \quad OR = 87.2$$

$$\tan \alpha = \frac{34.6}{80} \quad \alpha = 23.3°$$

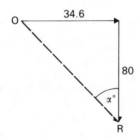

Velocity before landing = 87.2 m s$^{-1}$ at an angle of 23.3° to the vertical (66.7° to the horizontal).

**1.8**  Horizontal distance travelled  = velocity × time
                                          = 1000 × 40 = 4 × 10$^4$ m.
Vertical velocity when released = $u = 0$, $a = +10$ m s$^{-2}$, $t = 40$ s, $s = ?$.
Using $s = ut + \frac{1}{2}at^2$, $s = 0 + \frac{1}{2} \times 10 \times 16\,000$
Height of aircraft, $s = 8000$ m.
Vertical velocity before impact $v = ?$.
$a = +10$ m s$^{-2}$, $t = 40$ s, $u = 0$.
Using $v = u + at$, $v = 10 \times 40 = 400$ m s$^{-1}$.
The resultant of the two velocities may be obtained by construction as shown in

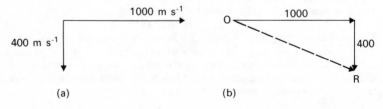

(a)

(b)

the Figure (b). (In this case it would be simple to calculate the final resultant velocity as a right-angled triangle is involved.)

Resultant velocity OR $= 1080$ m s$^{-1}$

**1.9** (a) The mean velocity between the 4th and 5th dot is $\dfrac{0.05}{1/50} = 2.5$ m s$^{-1}$.

The mean velocity between the 5th and 6th dot is $\dfrac{0.06}{1/50} = 3.0$ m s$^{-1}$.

Hence velocity at X $= 2.75$ m s$^{-1}$.

(b)     dots
       velocities at the
       midpoints between
       successive dots
       in m s$^{-1}$           1      1.5      2        2.5            3

The velocity increases by 0.5 m s$^{-1}$ in every $\frac{1}{50}$ second. This is a uniform increase in velocity and so the acceleration is constant and $= \dfrac{0.5}{1/50} = 25$ m s$^{-2}$.

In practical experiments, once the acceleration has been checked to be constant, the velocity near the beginning and end are determined and the time interval between them calculated from the number of dots. In the example above:

Initial velocity $= 1$ m s$^{-1}$ (midway between 1st and 2nd dot)
Final velocity $= 3$ m s$^{-1}$ (midway between 5th and 6th dot)
Time interval is the time taken for 4 dots (NOT 5!)
$$= 4 \times \tfrac{1}{50} \text{ s}$$

$$a = \frac{\text{change in velocity}}{\text{time taken}}$$

$$= \frac{3 - 1}{4/50}$$

$$= 25 \text{ m s}^{-2}.$$

**1.10** (a) At rest the balance will record the force on the mass due to the gravitational attraction of the Earth. Reading on balance $= 20$ N. ($g = 10$ m s$^{-2}$.)

(b) There are no extra *forces* on the mass when the lift moves with a constant velocity. Reading $= 20$ N.

$W = 20$ N

(*c*) A diagram (page 203) is drawn and the forces are marked on it. *T* is the tension in the string holding the mass to the balance. By Newton's third law – reading on the balance equals *T* N. From Newton's first and second laws – the tension *T* will *not* equal the weight of the mass as the lift is accelerating upwards. There must be an unbalanced force on the mass.

Unbalanced upward force causing acceleration

$$= ma$$
$$T - 20 = 2 \times 2.5$$
$$T = 25$$
$$\text{Reading} = 25 \text{ N.}$$

*Note:*  If the lift were accelerating downwards the tension would be less than the weight and so the reading would be less than 20 N.

**1.11**  (*a*) (i) Initial momentum $= 5 \text{ kg m s}^{-1}$.
(ii) Total final momentum must also equal $5 \text{ kg m s}^{-1}$.
Momentum of A after collision $= 8 \times 0.5 = 4 \text{ kg m s}^{-1}$. The angle between the final momenta is given as 90°.

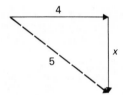

From above, $5^2 = 4^2 + x^2$.
Therefore *x*, the final momentum of B
$$= 3 \text{ kg m s}^{-1}$$
and the final velocity of B
$$= 6 \text{ m s}^{-1}$$
As the masses of A and B are equal the velocities alone could have been considered.

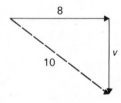

From above, the final velocity *v* of B is $6 \text{ m s}^{-1}$.
(*b*) Consider the kinetic energy before and after collision.
Initial $E_k = \frac{1}{2} \times 0.5 \times 10^2$
Final $E_k = \frac{1}{2} \times 0.5 \times 8^2$
$$+ \frac{1}{2} \times 0.5 \times 6^2$$
$$= \frac{1}{2} \times 0.5 \times 10^2.$$

As the kinetic energy was the same before and after the collision, it was conserved, showing that the collision was elastic.

*Note:* The example serves to illustrate that if the collision is elastic then the initial and final kinetic energies are equal:

Initial $\frac{1}{2}mv^2$ for A = final $\frac{1}{2}mv^2$ for A + final $\frac{1}{2}mv^2$ for B

and also that if the masses of A and B are equal the $\frac{1}{2}m$ terms cancel so that:

Initial $v^2$ for A = final $v^2$ for A + final $v^2$ for B

This can only happen if the final velocities are at *right angles* to each other.

**1.12** For both (*a*) and (*b*) the collisions are elastic and therefore momentum and kinetic energy are conserved as in **1.11**. For (*a*) the angle will be 90° as the masses of the particles are equal, but for (*b*) the masses are not equal and therefore the angle will *not* be 90°.

**1.13** (*a*)

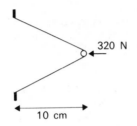

$$F = ma \quad \text{so} \quad 320 = 0.02 \times a$$
$$\therefore \quad a = 16\,000 \text{ m s}^{-2}.$$

(*b*) When the ball is about to leave the catapult the force on it is zero. When the catapult is fully extended the force is 320 N.
Assuming the force is proportional to the extension.

$$\text{Average force} = \tfrac{1}{2}(320 + 0)$$
$$= 160 \text{ N}$$
$$\text{Average acceleration} = 8000 \text{ m s}^{-2}.$$

(*c*) Assuming the average acceleration acts over the entire 10 cm distance, $u = 0$, $s = 0.1$ m, $a = 8000$ m s$^{-2}$, $v = $ ?.
Using $v^2 = u^2 + 2as$,

$$v^2 = 0 + 2 \times 8000 \times 0.1$$
$$= 1600$$
$$v = 40 \text{ m s}^{-1}.$$

(*d*) If the force is doubled the acceleration will double as $F = ma$, but it is the *square* of the velocity which doubles, $v^2 = 2as$ ($u = 0$).
$$\text{So } v^2 = 3200 \text{ and } v = 40\sqrt{2} \text{ m s}^{-1}.$$
The velocity is increased by a factor of $\sqrt{2}$ when the force increases by a factor of 2.

**1.14** (*a*) Initial momentum = $2 \times 20 = 40$ kg m s$^{-1}$.
(*b*) Impulse = change in momentum
$$= -8 - 40$$
$$= -48 \text{ kg m s}^{-1} \text{ or } -48 \text{ N s.}$$
(*c*) Impulse = $F \, \Delta t$. Force $F = \dfrac{-48}{3} = -16$ N (against the direction of motion of the ball).

(d) Using $F = ma$, $a = -8$ m s$^{-2}$. $u = 20$ m s$^{-1}$, $v = -4$ m s$^{-1}$, $s = ?$.
Using $v^2 = u^2 + 2as$, $s = 24$ m.
Observe that the final velocity is negative, $-4$ m s$^{-1}$. Also notice that the ball travelled 25 m in the original direction and 1 m backwards giving a nett displacement of 24 m.

**1.15** (a) Component of the weight $W$ down the plane
$$= W \cos 60°$$
$$= 2 \times 10 \times \tfrac{1}{2} = 10 \text{ N}.$$
Resultant force on the trolley $= 10 - 4 = 6$ N.

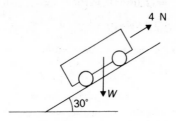

(b) Using $F = ma$, $a = \tfrac{6}{2} = 3$ m s$^{-2}$. $s = 6$ m, $u = 0$, $v = ?$.
Using $v^2 = u^2 + 2as$, $v = 6$ m s$^{-1}$.
(c) $F = 4$ N and, using $F = ma$, $a = 2$ m s$^{-2}$. $u = 6$ m s$^{-1}$, $v = 0$, $s = ?$.
Using $v^2 = u^2 + 2as$, $s = 9$ m.

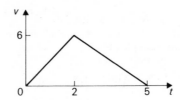

(d) Down the plane the time taken to acquire 6 m s$^{-1}$ with an acceleration of 3 m s$^{-2}$ is 2 s. Along the plane the time taken to decelerate to rest is 3 s.

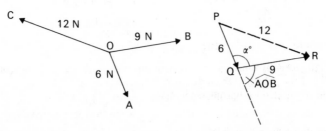

**1.16** Because the forces are in equilibrium the vector addition of the 6 N and 9 N forces must equal 12 N.
The angle $\alpha$ may be determined either by construction using compasses or by using the cosine rule.
This gives $\alpha = 104.5°$ and angle AOB $= 75.5°$.

**1.17** The acceleration due to gravity on this planet $= \tfrac{10}{4} = 2.5$ m s$^{-2}$
Velocity after 6 s $= 15$ m s$^{-1}$

Increase in $E_k = \frac{1}{2} \times 3 \times 15^2 = 337.5$ J

Hence decrease in $E_p = 337.5$ J.

# Chapter 2

**2.1**  Volume of one atom $= (2.3)^3 \times 10^{-30}$ m$^3$

Mass of one atom $= (2.3)^3 \times 10^{-30} \times 9.10^3$ kg

$= (2.3)^3 \times 9 \times 10^{-27}$ kg

One mole of copper has a mass of $63 \times 10^{-3}$ kg

$(2.3)^3 \times 9 \times 10^{-27}$ kg is the mass of one atom

$63 \times 10^{-3}$ kg is the mass of $\dfrac{63 \times 10^{-3}}{(2.3)^3 \times 9 \times 10^{-27}}$

$= 5.8 \times 10^{23}$ atoms.

It has been assumed that the distance between centres is equal to the side of a 'cubic cell'. The calculation shows that there are $5.8 \times 10^{23}$ atoms in a mole of copper. This is a reasonable experimental value compared with the accepted value for Avogadro's Constant of $6 \times 10^{23}$ mol$^{-1}$.

**2.2**  One mole of tin, that is $118.7 \times 10^{-3}$ kg contains $6 \times 10^{23}$ atoms.

From the density $7.28 \times 10^3$ kg  occupy 1 m$^3$.

$$118.7 \times 10^{-3} \text{ kg occupy } \frac{118.7 \times 10^{-3}}{7.28 \times 10^3} \text{ m}^3$$

This is then the volume occupied by $6 \times 10^{23}$ atoms.

$$1 \text{ atom occupies } \frac{118.7 \times 10^{-3}}{7.28 \times 10^3 \times 6 \times 10^{23}}$$

$$= 2.72 \times 10^{-29} \text{ m}^3.$$

Separation of the atoms $= \sqrt[3]{2.72 \times 10^{-29}}$

$\simeq 3 \times 10^{-10}$ m or 0.3 nm.

**2.3**  (a) Pressure $= hdg$ $= 0.8 \times 13.6 \times 10^3 \times 10$

$= 1.09 \times 10^5$ Pa.

(b) Pressure $= 5 \times 10^3 \times 10$ $= 5 \times 10^4$ Pa.

**2.4**  'Height' $= \dfrac{\text{pressure}}{\rho g}$

Height of an alcohol barometer $= \dfrac{10^5}{0.79 \times 10^3 \times 10} = 13$ m.

Height of a water barometer $= \dfrac{10^5}{10^3 \times 10} = 10$ m.

*Note:* The 'heights' of these barometers are large compared with a mercury barometer of 0.76 m.

**2.5**  (a) Root mean square velocity $c_{\text{r.m.s.}}$

$$= \sqrt{\frac{3p}{\rho}} = \sqrt{\frac{3 \times 10^5}{9 \times 10^{-2}}} = \sqrt{3.3 \times 10^6} = 1.8 \times 10^3 \text{ m s}^{-1} \text{ at s.t.p.}$$

(b) Average kinetic energy of the hydrogen molecule

$$= \tfrac{1}{2}\,\overline{mc^2}$$
$$= \tfrac{1}{2} \times 2 \times 1.67 \times 10^{-27} \times 3.3 \times 10^6$$
$$= 5.5 \times 10^{-21} \text{ J at s.t.p.}$$

Assuming the molecular mass of hydrogen is twice the atomic mass.

(c) The average kinetic energy of *all* molecules is the same at the same temperature, $E_k \propto T$. Therefore the average kinetic energy of oxygen is also $5.5 \times 10^{-21}$ J at s.t.p.

(d) The average kinetic energy is proportional to temperature. $\dfrac{E_{k1}}{E_{k2}} = \dfrac{T_1}{T_2}$.

$E_{k1} = 5.5 \times 10^{-21}$ J, $T_1 = 273$ K, $T_2 = 300$ K,

$$E_{k2} = \frac{5.5 \times 10^{-21} \times 300}{273} = 6 \times 10^{-21} \text{ J}.$$

The kinetic energy of the nitrogen molecules at 27 °C is $6 \times 10^{-21}$ J.

**2.6**   Mean square velocity of hydrogen $= 3.3 \times 10^6$ at 0 °C.

For any gas, $\tfrac{1}{2}\,\overline{mc^2} \propto T$.

For hydrogen $m$ remains constant, hence $\overline{c^2} \propto T. \dfrac{\overline{c_1^2}}{\overline{c_2^2}} = \dfrac{T_1}{T_2}$,

so for $\overline{c_1^2} = 3.3 \times 10^6$ m s$^{-1}$, $\overline{c_2^2} = 10^{10}$ m s$^{-1}$, $T_1 = 273$ K,

$$T_2 = \frac{273 \times 10^{10}}{3.3 \; 10^6} = 9 \times 10^5 \text{ K}.$$

*Note:*   High temperature is required to increase the velocities of the molecules.

**2.7**   Heat required    $= 10 \times 120 + 0.4 \times 4.2 \times 10^3 \times 10$
$= 1200 + 16800$
$= 18000$ J.

$$\text{Power} = \frac{\text{heat}}{\text{time}} = \frac{18\,000}{60} = 300 \text{ W}.$$

**2.8**   Heat supplied by the heater $= 20 \times 2 \times 60$ J.

Heat absorbed by the water $= 0.3 \times 4.2 \times 10^3 \times (T - 20)$, where $T$ is the final temperature.

Assuming no heat loss,

$$T - 20 = \frac{20 \times 2 \times 60}{0.3 \times 4.2 \times 10^3}$$
$$= 1.9$$

Final temperature $= 21.9$ °C.

The final temperature would be lower in a copper container.

**2.9**   Heat supplied by the heater in one minute
$= 0.6 \times 4.2 \times 10^3 \times 10$
$= 25.2 \times 10^3$ J.

Heat required
$=$ heat to raise temperature $+$ heat to evaporate

$= 0.03 \times 4.2 \times 10^3 \times 20 \quad + 0.03 \times 23 \times 10^5$

$$= 2.52 \times 10^3 + 69 \times 10^3$$
$$= 71.52 \times 10^3 \text{ J.}$$
Time taken
$$= \frac{71.52 \times 10^3}{25.2 \times 10^3} \simeq 3 \text{ minutes.}$$

# Chapter 3

**3.1** Considering the energy changes:

(a)   $eV = \frac{1}{2}mv^2$   

$V$ = electric field × distance
$$= 3000 \times 0.05 = 150 \text{ V}$$

$$1.6 \times 10^{-19} \times 150 \qquad = \frac{1}{2} \times 9.1 \times 10^{-31} \times v^2$$

$$v^2 = \frac{1.6 \times 15 \times 2 \times 10^{-18}}{9.1 \times 10^{-31}}$$

$$= 52.75 \times 10^{12}$$

$$v = 7.3 \times 10^6 \text{ m s}^{-1}$$

(b) If there is no electric field there will be no force on the electron hence its velocity will not change. Velocity at the screen = $7.3 \times 10^6$ m s$^{-1}$.
(c) From cathode to anode the electron is accelerating.
$u = 0$, $v = 7.3 \times 10^6$ m s$^{-1}$, $s = 0.05$ m, $a = ?$, $t = ?$.

Notice that as $u = 0$, $v^2 = 2as$ and $v = at$, $v = \dfrac{2s}{t}$.

$$t = \frac{2 \times 0.05}{7.3 \times 10^6} = 1.36 \times 10^{-8} \text{ s.}$$

From anode to screen the electron is travelling with a steady velocity so time
$$= \frac{\text{distance}}{\text{velocity}} = \frac{0.1}{7.3 \times 10^6} = 1.36 \times 10^{-8} \text{ s.}$$

(d) The velocity given by $v^2 = \dfrac{2eV}{m}$ will be increased if the electric field is increased. If the velocity increases the transit time will decrease when the distance between the plates remains constant.

**3.2** One electron has a charge of $1.6 \times 10^{-19}$ coulombs.

One coulomb contains $\dfrac{1}{1.6 \times 10^{-19}}$ electrons = $6.25 \times 10^{18}$ electrons.

**3.3** (a) The terminal velocity is measured to enable the *radius* of the drop to be calculated. From the radius the effective mass may subsequently be determined.
(b) A likely value is $1.6 \times 10^{-19}$ coulombs.

| result | 3.18 | 12.80 | 4.79 | 6.41 | 8.01 |
|---|---|---|---|---|---|
| no. of electronic charges | 2 | 8 | 3 | 4 | 5 |

Assuming the results are accurate to one decimal place. A value of $0.8 \times 10^{-19}$ is also consistent with this set of results but implies that the reading 12.80 has 16 electrons which is rather high.

**3.4** (a) p.d. across $1\frac{1}{2} \Omega$ resistor = p.d. across $3 \Omega$ resistor
$$= 3 \times 2 = 6 \text{ V, using } V = IR.$$
(b) current through $1\frac{1}{2} \Omega$ resistor = 4 A.
$\therefore$   total current through $2 \Omega$ resistor = 6 A.

(c) 6 A is also the current through the source.

(d) lost volts = current × internal resistance = 6 V.

e.m.f. of source, $E = I(R + r)$

Total $R = 2 + 1 + 1 = 4 \, \Omega$

$E = 6(4 + 1) = 30$ V.

**3.5**   Electrical energy $= 2 \times 10^3 \times t$ J, where $t$ is the time taken.

Heat required $= 0.5 \times 4.2 \times 10^3 \times 80$ J. 10% of the heat is lost, so

$$\tfrac{90}{100} \times 2 \times 10^3 \times t = 40 \times 4.2 \times 10^3$$

$$t = \frac{40 \times 4.2 \times 10^3 \times 100}{2 \times 10^3 \times 90}$$

$$= 93 \text{ s.}$$

**3.6**   Kilowatt hours used $= 60 \times 10^{-3} \times 2 = 120 \times 10^{-3}$

Cost $= 0.12 \times 3 = 0.36$ p

$$\text{Current} = \frac{\text{power}}{\text{p.d.}} = \frac{60}{240} = \tfrac{1}{4} \text{ A.}$$

**3.7**   (a)

Total e.m.f. $= 3 \times 2.6 = 7.8$ V

Internal resistance $= 3 \, \Omega$

Using $E = I(R + r)$,

$7.8 = I(4 + 3)$

$I = 1.1$ A.

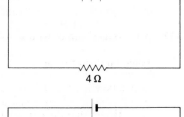

(b)

Total e.m.f. $= 2.6$ V

Internal resistance is $r$.

$$\frac{1}{r} = \tfrac{1}{1} + \tfrac{1}{1} + \tfrac{1}{1}; r = \tfrac{1}{3} \, \Omega$$

Using $E = I(R + r)$,

$2.6 = I(4 + \tfrac{1}{3})$

$I = 0.6$ A.

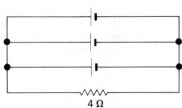

$4 \, \Omega$

**3.8**   The p.d. across a particular component may not be calculated until the current has been determined.

Using $E = I(R + r)$ for the whole circuit,

$5 = I(8 + 2)$

$I = 0.5$ A

p.d. BC $= 4 \times 0.5 = 2$ V (using $V = IR$ between BC)

t.p.d. = e.m.f. − lost volts

$= 5 - 2 \times 0.5$

$= 4$ V

Potential of C is zero; p.d. CD $= 3 \times 0.5 = 1\tfrac{1}{2}$ V.

⇒ potential of D $= -1\tfrac{1}{2}$ V.

Notice that the potential of A $= -1\tfrac{1}{2} + 4 = +2\tfrac{1}{2}$ V; potential of B $= +2$ V.

**3.9**   (a) With the ammeter recording the total current through $R_x$ and the voltmeter, the current $I$ is too high, using $R_x = \dfrac{V}{I}$ a value of $R_x$ *less* than the correct value will be obtained.

(b) The p.d. reading is too high so the value calculated for $R_x$ will be *greater* than its true value.

**3.10** Yes, this method is correct. The second ammeter reading implies an equal current through $R_x$ and the resistance box. Hence the two resistances are equal. As the second current is twice the first current the lost volts will be higher for the latter, so the p.d. across both $R_x$ and the resistance box will decrease as the t.p.d. is less. This will introduce errors when the current is large, that is when $R_x$ is small. In method (3) this error is eliminated.

*Note:* It is often useful to consider possible effects of the internal resistance of a cell or source, in questions which ask for sources of errors.

**3.11** Using $E = I(R + r)$, $1.5 = I(500 + 1)$ $I = 0.003$ A.

$$\text{Lost volts} = 0.003 \text{ V.}$$
$$\text{True p.d. across voltmeter} = 1.5 - 0.003$$
$$= 1.497 \text{ V.}$$

This is the expected reading on the voltmeter, but the graduations are only every 0.1 V, therefore assuming a reading to half a graduation (that is to 0.05 V) may be estimated, the reading observed is 1.5 V. The conclusion drawn from this experiment is

$$\text{e.m.f. of cell} = 1.5 \pm 0.05 \text{ V.}$$

**3.12** p.d. along 37 cm of wire $= 1.48$ V.

$$\text{potential drop per cm} = \frac{1.48}{37} = 0.04 \text{ V.}$$

$\Rightarrow$ p.d. between the ends of the wire $= 4$ V.
A null point at 50 cm would be expected with the 2 V cell. The higher value of 52 cm indicates that the potential drop along the wire has decreased, suggesting that the supply battery is running down. Alternatively the cell marking only indicates the e.m.f. to the nearest volt. Hence the null point at 52 cm gives a more precise value of 2.08 V for the e.m.f.

**3.13** Peak e.m.f. $= 240 \times \sqrt{2} = 340$ V.
A frequency of 50 Hz has 50 cycles per second, but the e.m.f. drops to zero twice in each cycle, therefore the e.m.f. falls to zero 100 times in one second.

**3.14** p.d. across 52 cm $= 1.04$ V.
p.d. AB (100 cm) $= 2$ V.
A large resistor R is placed in series with the potentiometer wire.

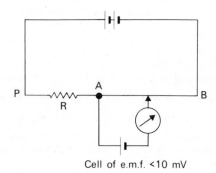

Cell of e.m.f. <10 mV

Most of the 2 V must be dropped across this resistor.
p.d. PB = 2 V, p.d. AB = 10 mV, p.d. PB = 1.99 V.
The current through PA = the current through AB.

Using $I = \dfrac{V}{R}$, $\dfrac{1.99}{R} = \dfrac{0.01}{5}$

$\Rightarrow R = 995\ \Omega$.

**3.15**   With S open, e.m.f. of E = 75 × 0.024 = 1.8 V.

With S closed p.d. across 10 Ω resistor = 62.5 × 0.024 = 1.5 V.

Current is only flowing from E through the 10 Ω resistor, the current in this

circuit is $I = \dfrac{1.5}{10} = 0.15$ A (using $V = IR$ across the 10 Ω resistor).

Using $E = I(R + r)$ for the whole of this circuit:

$$1.8 = 0.15(10 + r)$$

giving                                   $r = 2\ \Omega$.

# Chapter 4

**4.1**   (a) Using $C = \dfrac{Q}{V}$,

$Q = 50 \times 10^{-6} \times 8$
$= 400\ \mu C$.

(b) p.d. across C just before discharging = 8 V and $R = 32\ \Omega$.
Using $V = IR$, $I = 0.25$ A.
(c) The current decreases from 0.25 A to zero as the capacitor discharges.
(d) If the resistance increases the initial current would be less and the ammeter pointer would move more slowly to zero; the capacitor taking longer to discharge.

**4.2**   (a) Charge = current × time
$Q$ after 10 s = 0.2 × 10$^{-3}$ × 10
$\qquad = 2 \times 10^{-3}$ C
$Q$ after 30 s = 0.2 × 10$^{-3}$ × 30
$\qquad = 6 \times 10^{-3}$ C

Using $C = \dfrac{Q}{V}$ and the 10 s result

$$C = \dfrac{2 \times 10^{-3}}{1.6} = 1.2 \times 10^{-3}\ F$$

with the 30 s result

$$C = \dfrac{6 \times 10^{-3}}{5} = 1.2 \times 10^{-3}\ F$$

Capacitance = $1.2 \times 10^{-3}$ F
(b) Initially there is no charge on the capacitor and the maximum current will flow.
Using $V = IR$, 6 = 0.2 × 10$^{-3}$ × $R$ hence $R = 30$ kΩ.
As the capacitor charges up the value of $R$ must be *decreased* in order to maintain a 0.2 mA current.
Range of $R$ must be 0–30 kΩ.

**4.3** B₁ will light up before B₂. The current through the inductor takes time to build up due to the induced back e.m.f. If the core is removed the inductance is reduced and B₂ will light up more quickly.

**4.4** (a) $\frac{1}{6} = \frac{x}{240}$, $x = 40$. Hence the secondary p.d. = 40 V.

(b) If there is no power loss $240 \times 2 = 40 \times I$, $I = 12$ A. But there is power loss and therefore the secondary current will be *less* than 12 A.

(c) The core should be laminated with strips of non-conducting material. The answer to (a) will be the same, the turns ratio affecting the p.d. The answer to (b) will be different. The current will be nearer the 12 A but there may be other power losses and it is unlikely that the current will attain the full 12 A.

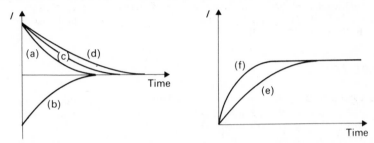

**4.5** (a) The initial current dies away as the capacitor charges up.

(b) The current is in the opposite direction as the capacitor discharges.

(c) If the overlap of the plates is increased the capacitance increases and therefore the time for all the charge to flow off the plates increases.

(d) An increase in dielectric constant increases the capacitance hence the time for the current to decay is greater.

(e) With an inductor the current takes time to build up to a steady value due to the induced back e.m.f.

(f) The inductance decreases when the core is removed, hence the back e.m.f. decreases and the build-up time will be shorter.

**4.6** As the frequency is increased, the opposition to the current $X_C$ decreases, therefore the current will increase. If both switches are closed the two capacitors are in parallel. This results in a *larger* overall capacitance. A larger capacitance has a lower opposition $X_C$ to the current and therefore higher current readings are obtained over the whole frequency range.

**4.7** (a) Z is an inductor. When the frequency increases $X_L$ increases hence the current decreases.

(b) Z is a resistor. Resistance is independent of frequency.

**4.8** Because of the initial calibration the *height* of the trace on each c.r.o. indicates the *potential difference* across that component.

(a) At high frequencies $X_L$ is much larger than $X_C$ and therefore the p.d. across L will be larger, giving the trace shown below. Remember, $V = IX$ and the

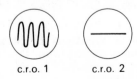

c.r.o. 1          c.r.o. 2

currents through L and C are the same. There will be no observable trace on c.r.o. 2, the p.d. across C being very small.

(b) At low frequencies $X_C$ is large and hence the p.d. across the capacitor will be much greater. Observe the trace on c.r.o. 2.

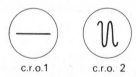

c.r.o.1          c.r.o. 2

**4.9**  (a) At low frequencies $X_C$ is greater than $X_L$ and more current will pass through L making $B_1$ brighter.

(b) At high frequencies $X_L$ is larger and the easier current path is now through C. Bulb $B_2$ will be brighter.

# Chapter 5

**5.1**  No. An n-type semiconductor crystal contains small amounts of a *donor* not an acceptor. The crystal is *neutral* as the charges on the electrons are balanced by the positive charges on the nuclei.

**5.2**  (a) The transfer characteristic of the transistor is the graph of collector current obtained against base current, as the latter is altered.

(b) The current amplification factor is equal to

$$\frac{\text{change in collector current}}{\text{change in base current}}.$$

**5.3**  So that the electrons may travel to the anode without collisions on the way. If the envelope were not evacuated a considerably larger p.d. would be required to obtain any current flow.

**5.4**  Using $V = IR$, $3 = 3 \times 10^{-3}\, R$ hence $R = 10^3\, \Omega$.

**5.5**  No heater circuits are required; no warm up time; small size; cheaper, low operating voltage, low supply currents; less easily damaged.

**5.6**  The frequency $f$ is given by $f_X : f_Y = 1 : 2$.

So $\dfrac{f_X}{f_Y} = \frac{1}{2}$ and $\dfrac{80}{f} = \frac{1}{2}$, giving $f = 40$ Hz.

**5.7**  A rejector circuit is a parallel tuned circuit. The p.d. across the inductor remains constant but the impedance of the inductor increases as the frequency increases, hence the current will decrease, until at resonance the current through the inductor equals the current through the capacitor.

**5.8**  If the capacitance is decreased the resonance frequency will increase. Hence to restore resonance, the frequency of the supply will need increasing. To show that resonance has been achieved, an ammeter may be placed in series with the LC components and the supply frequency adjusted until the reading on the ammeter is at a maximum.

**5.9**  (a) After the initial build-up of the current the p.d. across L will remain steady. If the rectifier is reversed almost no current will flow and the p.d. across L will fall to zero.

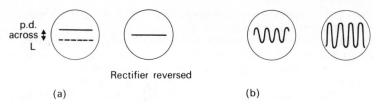

Rectifier reversed

(a)　　　　　　　　　　　　　　　　(b)

(*b*) If the frequency increases the reactance $X_L$ increases and the p.d. across L will be larger. The amplitude of the trace will increase.

**5.10**　*Either* current $I$ in a series circuit *or* impedance $Z$ in a parallel circuit.

# Chapter 6

**6.1**　Stationary longitudinal wave – organ pipe.
Travelling longitudinal wave – sound wave.
Stationary transverse wave – sonometer wire.
Travelling transverse wave – water wave.

**6.2**　No. He has measured the wavelength.

**6.3**　$\frac{1}{4}$ wavelength. The distance between consecutive maxima is $\frac{1}{2}\lambda$.

**6.4**　A change in the depth of the water. The 3 cm wavelength waves are in the shallow water. Relative change in velocity will be in the ratio 5 : 3 for A to B. There is no change in frequency.

**6.5**　(*a*) A standing wave is set up as the incident and reflected waves interfere. Hence the distance between consecutive minima will be $\frac{1}{2}$ the incident wavelength, that is 0.05 m.
(*b*) The two travelling waves interfere hence the distance between two minima is equal to the wavelength, that is 0.1 m.

**6.6**　$D$ is the distance between the slits and screen. $d$ is the distance between the two slits.
(*a*) $D$ is a relatively large quantity so may be measured with some accuracy. $x$ the distance between fringes is small but the total distance between a number of fringes may be measured with a travelling microscope and thus $x$ determined with a low error. The readings for $x$ may also be repeated over different sets of fringes. $d$ is also a small quantity and must be determined directly, this quantity will carry the largest error of the group into the final determination of $\lambda$.
(*b*) If $D$ increases, $x$, the distance between fringes, also increases.
(*c*) If the slits are increased too much no interference will be observed as the width of the slits will not be of the same order as the wavelength of the light.
(*d*) The blue fringes are closer together than the yellow fringes.
(*e*) A series of yellow and blue fringes are obtained with the blue ones nearer the central patch.

**6.7**　(*a*) Microwaves. (*b*) Phosphorescence.

**6.8**　The time taken for the reflection of the waves will remain at $10^{-5}$ s as the velocity of the waves remains the same. The 8 cm waves will be reflected with a broader spread, causing a more diffuse signal to be received. Hence shorter wavelength waves enable a more detailed outline of the object to be determined.

**6.9** Pupil P: no difference, only a direct current is required, in one direction or the other. It would matter if a transistor was included (Figure 6.27)!

Pupil Q: $C_1$ is much smaller in value than $C_2$, hence $C_2$ would be no use as a tuning capacitor for radio waves, the L,C circuit will not respond to radio frequency waves, and nothing will be heard in the earphones.

Pupil R: the radio waves will be detected but the average value of the current will have radio frequency ripples upon it. The earphones will detect the audio frequency information but with considerable background 'noise'.

# Chapter 7

**7.1** The refractive index $= \dfrac{\text{velocity of light in vacuum}}{\text{velocity of light in the medium}}$

hence refractive indices will *always* be greater than unity.

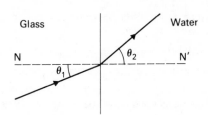

**7.2** (*a*) The angle in glass will be *smaller* than the angle in water because glass has the *higher* refractive index.

(*b*) Notice that the angles of incidence $\theta_1$ are not given directly; $\theta_1$ being the angle between the ray and the *normal*.

Using $n_1 \sin \theta_1 = n_2 \sin \theta_2$, and $n_1 = 1$ for air.

For perspex: $n = 1.5$, $\theta_1 = 90 - 30 = 60°$.

  $1 \times \sin 60 = 1.5 \sin \theta_2$, hence $\theta_2 = 35.3°$.

  Angle of refraction $= \theta_2 = 35.3°$.

For water: $1 \times \sin 50 = 1.33 \times \sin \theta_2$, hence $\theta_2 = 35.1°$.

For quartz crystal: $1 \times \sin 30 = 1.54 \sin \theta_2$, hence $\theta_2 = 18.9$.

For glycerol: $1 \times \sin 40 = 1.47 \times \sin \theta_2$, hence $\theta_2 = 25.9°$.

**7.3** The frequency remains *unchanged* as the number of waves produced per second is determined by the *source* not the material.

The velocity in the glass $v_g$ may be calculated from the relation $n = \dfrac{v_0}{v_g}$ where $v_0$ is the velocity of light in air.

$$1.5 = \frac{3 \times 10^8}{v_g},$$

hence $v_g = 2 \times 10^8 \text{ m s}^{-1}$

As would be expected, the velocity of the light in the glass is less than that in air.

The wavelength is given from $v = \lambda f$ where $v$ is the velocity of light in glass and $\lambda$ the wavelength in the glass.

Hence $2 \times 10^8 = \lambda \times 6 \times 10^{14}$, giving $\lambda = 3.3 = 10^{-7}$ m.

*Note:* compare this with the wavelength of light of this frequency in air which is $\frac{3 \times 10^8}{6 \times 10^{14}}$ equal to $5 \times 10^{-7}$ m.

This illustrates that when light enters a medium of higher refractive index the velocity *and* the wavelength decrease.

**7.4** A has the larger focal length. The refractive index of B is greater so light will be 'bent' more by this lens and be brought to a focus *nearer* the lens, hence its focal length is shorter.

**7.5** Either. If the image was magnified a converging lens was used with the object nearer to the lens than its focal length. If the image was diminished the lens used was diverging for any object position.

**7.6** The astronomical telescope is shorter. The difference in length being *four* times the focal length of the extra lens required to produce an erect final image in the terrestrial telescope.

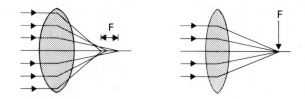

**7.7** (*a*) A wide beam of light will give a blurred focus. This lens is thicker and so will have the shorter focal length.
(*b*) The light is directed nearer to the centre of this lens so a sharper focus is obtained.

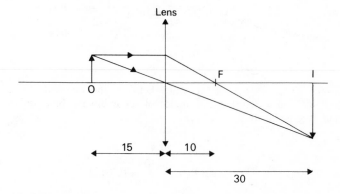

**7.8** The image is magnified, real, and inverted. The projector must produce a real magnified image. Therefore the object distance must lie between $f$ and $2f$, where $f$ is the focal length. Thus the object distance is between 10 cm and 20 cm.

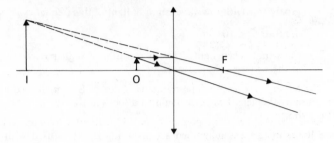

**7.9** The image is magnified, virtual, and erect and 60 cm from the lens.

Using $\dfrac{1}{f} = \dfrac{1}{u} + \dfrac{1}{v}$, $\frac{1}{20} = \frac{1}{15} + \dfrac{1}{v}$, giving $v = -60$ cm.

The magnification is $\frac{60}{15} = 4$. Hence the width of the image $= 3.5 \times 4 = 14$ cm. Only useful in a slide viewer. A slide projector throws a *real* magnified image on to a screen.

**7.10** Energy $= hf = \dfrac{hv}{\lambda}$

where $v$ is the velocity of light, $h$ is Planck's constant, and $\lambda$ is the wavelength

$$\text{Energy} = \frac{6.6 \times 10^{-34} \times 3 \times 10^{8}}{5.46 \times 10^{-7}}$$

$$= 3.6 \times 10^{-19} \text{ J}$$

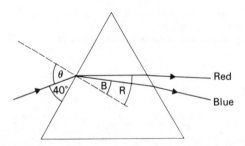

**7.11** Angle of incidence $\theta$ is the angle between the ray and the normal. Hence $\theta = 90 - 40 = 50°$. Let the angles of refraction for blue and red light be $B$ and $R$ respectively.

For red light: $\qquad\qquad 1.51 = \dfrac{\sin 50}{\sin R}$

$$\sin R = \frac{\sin 50}{1.51} = 0.5072$$

$$R = 30.5°.$$

For blue light: $\qquad\qquad B = 30.5 - 0.7 = 29.8°$

$$n_{\text{blue}} = \frac{\sin 50}{\sin 29.8} = 1.54$$

Refractive index for blue light $= 1.54$.

# Chapter 8

**8.1** Isotopes: $^{206}_{82}$Pb, $^{207}_{82}$Pb, $^{208}_{82}$Pb.
Isobars: $^{40}_{19}$K, $^{40}_{18}$A.

**8.2** $\alpha$ and $\beta$ particles. Neutrons and $\gamma$-rays are uncharged.

**8.3** Their half lives will be the same.

**8.4** $6\frac{1}{4}\%$. After 2 hours, 50% left; after 4 hours, 25% left; after 6 hours, $12\frac{1}{2}\%$ left, and after 8 hours, $6\frac{1}{4}\%$ remains.

**8.5** The background count must be subtracted. Thus data to be plotted is:

| *Time in days* | 0 | 1 | 2 | 3 | 4 | 5 |
|---|---|---|---|---|---|---|
| *Activity* | 130 | 85 | 56 | 37 | 24 | 15 |

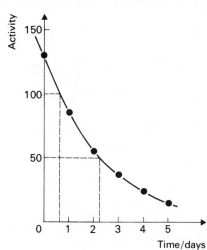

From the graph the time taken for the count rate to fall from 100 to 50 is $2.25 - 0.65 = 1.6$ days.

**8.6** In Thomson's model the positive charge was spread throughout the entire atomic volume, hence the electrostatic repulsion on a small $\alpha$ particle would never be sufficient to cause appreciable deflection. With Rutherford's model the concentrated positive charge in the central nucleus exerts a high electrostatic repulsion on the occasional $\alpha$ particle which travels near by, causing the deflections observed. The events at position D being the most significant.

**8.7** Momentum is conserved in any collision providing no external forces act on the system.
Current is not conserved.
Energy is conserved in all isolated systems providing the equivalence of mass is taken into account.
Power is not conserved.
Mass is conserved in chemical reactions where no nuclear changes take place.
The total charge in any isolated system is conserved.

**8.8** This is an example of nuclear fusion, a larger nucleus, oxygen, is built up from nitrogen. A proton is emitted.

**8.9** If the surface of the zinc plate is rusty or has surface impurities, the electrons will require greater energy to escape from the surface so that photoelectric emission will only take place with frequencies *higher* than those usually required. There is also the possibility that the impurities will absorb the radiation.

**8.10** Some photoelectrons are nearer the surface or less easily bound and so require less energy to escape than others which are more strongly bound in the metal interior.

**8.11** This depends on the momentum $p$ of the particles. As $p$ increases the associated wavelength decreases. For electrons with their light mass the wavelength is comparable to that of X-rays where the spacing in crystals, used to demonstrate diffraction, is of the same order as these wavelengths. For heavier particles, or objects such as ball bearings, as $p \uparrow$ and $\lambda \downarrow$ there will be no suitable aperture or obstacle with small enough dimensions to give *observable* diffraction effects.

# Exercise Section

**1** A traveller drives 7 km north, then 7 km due west, then 2 km south-east. What is the distance and displacement from the starting point?

**2** Four forces act on an object O as shown.

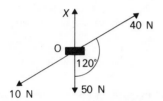

(a) By choosing a suitable value of $X$ is it possible to maintain the object in equilibrium?
(b) What is the resultant force if $X = 20$ N?

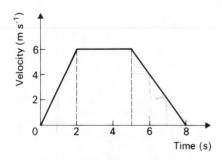

**3** This graph of velocity against time shows the motion of a boy running in a straight line, away from a point P. Determine:

(a) the acceleration in the first two seconds.

(b) the total distance travelled.
(c) the average velocity for these 8 seconds.
(d) Calculate the displacement at the end of each second and plot a displacement/time graph for these 8 s, giving numerical values on both axes.

**4** An object was thrown vertically upwards with a velocity of 35 m s$^{-1}$. What was its position after 6 s?

**5** An object is released from an aircraft travelling upwards at 25 m s$^{-1}$.

(a) Sketch speed/time and velocity/time graphs for the first 4 s.
(b) Sketch a graph of kinetic energy $E_k$ with time for these 4 s. Numerical values are required on the time axes.

**6** A boy runs 300 m to a letter box. He takes 75 s to reach the box, pauses for 3 s to post the letter, and then returns in $1\frac{1}{2}$ minutes.

(a) Draw a displacement/time graph.
(b) Sketch a velocity/time graph for the complete trip, giving numerical values on both axes. State any assumptions made.

**7** When an object moves along a horizontal surface, the following velocity/time graph is obtained.

(a) Did the time measurements commence when the object started to move?
(b) What is the acceleration in the first 10 s, between the 40th and 45th s, and in the last 10 s?

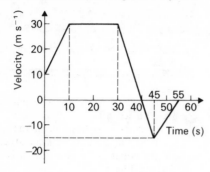

(c) Sketch a displacement/time graph. Numerical values are required only on the time axis, but it should be clear whether the graph is a straight line or a curve.

(d) Sketch an acceleration/time graph giving numerical values on both axes.

**8** An object has an acceleration of 2 m s⁻². Complete the table below showing the instantaneous velocities and displacements at the *end* of each second, and the average velocity *over* each successive second.

| time (s) | 1 | 2 | 3 | 4 | 5 | 6 |
|---|---|---|---|---|---|---|
| instantaneous velocity (m s⁻¹) | 2 | 4 | | | | |
| displacement (m) | 1 | 4 | | | | |
| average velocity (m s⁻¹) | 1 | | | | | |

From the table state: (a) the average velocity over the 4th s, (b) the velocity after 4.5 s, (c) the distance travelled after 5 s.

**9** A ship steaming due north at 24 km hr⁻¹ encounters a cross current of 7 km hr⁻¹ due west.

(a) Determine the resultant velocity of the ship.

(b) In what direction and with what velocity must the ship steam in order to effectively travel 24 km hr⁻¹ due north?

**10** A man is paddling due north in a canoe at 3 m s⁻¹ up a river when he meets a strong wind blowing at 1.25 m s⁻¹ due west. What is the relative velocity of the canoe to the bank? If the canoe was originally in the middle of the river, which is 10 m wide, how long did it take before the canoe hit the bank, assuming the strength of the wind remained constant?

**11** An object is knocked off the end of a table with a horizontal speed of 20 m s⁻¹. If the vertical height of the top of the table above the floor is 1.25 m determine:

(a) the time taken for the object to hit the floor.

(b) the resultant velocity just before impact (magnitude and direction).

**12** An object is projected at an angle of 30° to the horizontal with a velocity of 24 m s⁻¹. Neglecting air resistance, calculate:

(a) its position and velocity in the horizontal and vertical directions after one second.

(b) the greatest height reached.

(c) the total horizontal distance travelled and the time for it to return to the ground.

(d) Draw *separate* velocity/time graphs for the horizontal and vertical velocities for the entire flight of the object. Numerical values are required on the axes.

**13** A pellet leaves an air gun with a velocity of 100 m s⁻¹ at an angle of 30° to the horizontal. Calculate:

(a) the maximum height reached.

(b) the total time of flight.

(c) the horizontal distance travelled.

**14** A conker is whirled in a horizontal circle with a uniform speed of 0.5 m s⁻¹. If the circumference of the circle is 2 m:

(a) how long does it take the conker to make one revolution?

(b) what change in velocity occurs in 1 s?

(c) what would happen to the conker if the string was cut?

**15** A ball of mass 4 kg accelerates from rest to 30 m s$^{-1}$ in 5 s. Sketch graphs of momentum against velocity, and kinetic energy against velocity for these 5 s.

**16** A boy points his arrow horizontally at the central spot of a target. If the arrow leaves his bow with a velocity of 50 m s$^{-1}$ and strikes the target 20 cm below the spot, how far from the target was he standing?

**17** A trolley of mass 1.5 kg, initially at rest, is pulled along a horizontal board with a force of 5 N. If the frictional resistance is 0.5 N:

(a) what is the velocity of the trolley after 1 m?

(b) how would you reproduce this motion experimentally?

(c) explain in detail how you would determine the velocity at this 1 m position.

(d) how could you reduce considerably or eliminate the frictional resistance?

**18** A trolley of mass 2 kg is at rest on a horizontal floor. A force of 4 N acts for 3 s. If the frictional resistance is 1 N throughout, describe the position and velocity of the object after 6 s.

**19** A trolley of mass 1.2 kg is situated on a plane. Determine the component of the weight down the plane, and hence the acceleration, if the angle of inclination of the plane to the horizontal is:

(a) 45°

(b) 30°

(c) How would these answers be affected if there is a frictional resistance of 1 N?

**20** A puck slides down a rough plane. The following table indicates the distance travelled at the end of each second after the object is released.

| time | 0 | 1 | 2 | 3 | 4 |
|---|---|---|---|---|---|
| distance | 0 | 0.2 | 0.8 | 1.8 | 3.2 |

(a) Calculate the acceleration of the puck.

(b) State the average velocity in the third second.

(c) Estimate the velocity at the end of the fifth second.

(d) If the plane is inclined at an angle of 11.5° to the horizontal, what acceleration would you expect if there is no frictional force?

(e) If the mass of the puck is 500 g, calculate the frictional force.

**21** An object of mass 2 kg is projected with a velocity of 4 m s$^{-1}$ up a plane inclined at 30° to the horizontal. How far up the plane does it go if.

(a) there is no frictional resistance?

(b) the frictional resistance is 2 N and independent of the speed?

**22** What is the least force which must be supplied to a helicopter of mass $2 \times 10^3$ kg to enable it to lift off vertically with an initial acceleration of 5 m s$^{-2}$, if the air resistance is 2 N kg$^{-1}$?

**23** A piece of cord is attached to a trolley of mass 0.9 kg held at one end of a plane. The cord is then passed over a pulley situated at the other end of the plane and a 100 g mass is attached and allowed to hang vertically. The trolley is released. Determine the acceleration of the trolley and mass system if:

(a) the plane is friction compensated.

(b) there is a 0.2 N frictional resistance.

**24** A cyclist of mass 48 kg has to overcome air resistance of 20 N when travelling along a level road at 6 m s$^{-1}$. Calculate:

(a) the average force he exerts.

(b) the power he must supply.

(c) his velocity if he ascends a hill of 1 in 8 (measured along the slope), assuming his power output remains unchanged.

**25** A truck of mass $10^3$ kg with a power output of 7.5 kW ascends a hill of 1 in 20 (measured along the slope). If the acceleration is 0.2 m s$^{-2}$ when the car is moving at 9 m s$^{-1}$, determine:

(a) the resultant force on the truck.
(b) the force exerted by the engine.
(c) the frictional resistance.

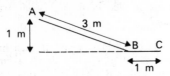

**26** A ball of mass 1.5 kg is placed at the top of a rough plane AB where the frictional force is 1 N. BC is a smooth horizontal surface. Determine:

(a) the potential energy at A.
(b) the work done against friction when travelling from A to B.
(c) the kinetic energy at B.
(d) the kinetic energy at C.
(e) the velocity at C.
(f) Explain carefully how you would measure experimentally the velocity just before C.

**27** A bullet is fired from a rifle into a block of Plasticine attached to a stationary trolley on a rough horizontal plane. The bullet passes through the Plasticine. Describe the motion of the trolley and the bullet. Discuss in detail the energy changes taking place from the moment the bullet is fired until both the bullet and trolley are at rest.

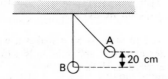

**28** A pendulum bob is pulled to one side such that it is 20 cm vertically above its rest position. The mass of the bob is 30 g.

(a) Determine the change in potential energy taking place when the bob falls from A to B.
(b) What is the velocity of the bob at B?

(c) How could this velocity at B be measured experimentally?
(d) State the acceleration of the bob at B.
(e) If the bob takes 0.1 s to fall from A to B what is the period of the pendulum and the frequency of the oscillations?

**29** An 80 kg man stands on scales placed on the floor of a lift. Describe the *two* possible motions of the lift in each case, if the scales read: (a) 800 N, (b) 720 N, (c) 960 N.

**30** A 30 g box of side 5 cm is given a sharp tap, causing it to slide along a smooth horizontal table. It interrupts a light beam directed on to a photocell. An electric clock, connected to the photocell, records a time of 0.025 s. The box then falls off the edge of the table. If the height of the table is 0.8 m, determine:

(a) the momentum with which it leaves the table.
(b) the time taken to reach the ground.
(c) the precise position where the object lands.
(d) the horizontal and vertical components of the velocity just before impact with the ground.
(e) the kinetic energy just before impact.

**31** A trolley of mass 1 kg, travelling on a smooth horizontal plane with a speed of 4 m s$^{-1}$, collides with another stationary trolley of mass 2 kg and rebounds back along its initial path with a speed of 1.4 m s$^{-1}$.

(a) Determine the velocity acquired by the 2 kg trolley.
(b) Describe how this velocity could be measured experimentally using a ticker tape. Comment on any disadvantages.

**32** An object of mass 6 kg explodes into three pieces. Two pieces, each of mass 1.5 kg, fly off with speeds of 4 m s$^{-1}$ at right angles to each other. Determine the velocity of the other piece and calculate the total kinetic energy after the explosion.

**33** A red billiard ball of mass 2 kg travelling at 2.5 m s⁻¹ strikes a green ball of the same mass and moves off with a reduced velocity of 1.5 m s⁻¹. If the balls move off at right angles to each other after the collision:

(a) determine the velocity acquired by the green ball.
(b) determine the kinetic energy before and after the collision. Is the collision elastic?
(c) In another collision with a stationary yellow ball, the velocity of the red ball is again reduced from 2.5 m s⁻¹ to 1.5 m s⁻¹ but the angle between the directions of motion of the two balls after the collision is *not* 90°. Suggest *two* possible reasons for this observation.

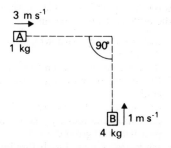

**34** The two objects A and B, as illustrated, collide and join together. Determine the resulting velocity after collision (magnitude and direction).

**35** An object of mass 100 g is dropped from a height of 2 m and rebounds to a height of 1.8 m. Determine:

(a) the kinetic energy before and after impact with the ground.
(b) the change of momentum at the ground.
(c) the impulse on the ground.
(d) the force of impact of the ball on the ground if the impact lasts 3 m s.

**36** In an experiment to determine the force of impact when kicking a ball, the time of impact was measured on an electric clock and found to be 22 ms. The

pupil then recorded other results in her book as follows:

mass of ball = 3.3 kg,
diameter of the ball = 20 cm.

After a calculation she stated that the force of impact was $1.5 \times 10^3$ N. Explain in general terms how she calculated this force. What measurement did she fail to record in her book and what was its value?

**37** Two marbles A and B each have a mass of 40 g. A rolls down a smooth chute, strikes B which is stationary at the bottom, and drops vertically downwards. B hits the ground at P.
Determine:

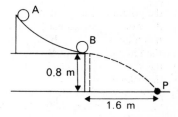

(a) the velocity of B as it leaves the bottom of the chute.
(b) the momentum of B after the collision.
(c) the kinetic energy of A just before it lands on the ground.
(d) the kinetic energy of B just before it lands at P.
(e) the momentum of B just before it lands at P.
(f) How is the position P determined experimentally?

**38** A ball of mass 50 g strikes a wall at an angle of 45° and rebounds with the same speed as shown.
Find:

(a)  the change of momentum of the ball.
(b)  the impulse of the ball on the wall.
(c)  the impulse of the wall on the ball.
(d)  the force of impact of the ball on the wall if the impact lasts 0.3 ms.

**39**  The diagram illustrates a multiple flash photograph of a moving ball. The flash rate is 15 per second.

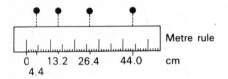

Metre rule

0    13.2   26.4    44.0    cm
  4.4

(a)  Calculate the acceleration of the ball.
(b)  Why was the metre rule included?
(c)  What do you think was happening to the ball?
(d)  Explain what difference, if any, you would expect in the result to part (a) if a ticker timer was used to determine the acceleration.

**40**  One ball A was dropped freely at the same instant that another ball B was thrown horizontally. The diagram of the multiple flash photograph indicates the subsequent motion of the two balls. The

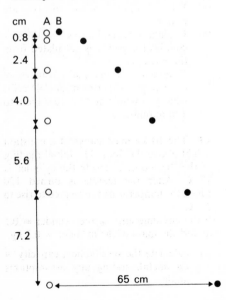

cm    A B
0.8
2.4
4.0
5.6
7.2
65 cm

distances marked are the actual distances traversed.

(a)  Calculate the flash rate.
(b)  Find the velocity with which B was thrown horizontally.
(c)  Give one advantage of multiple flash methods over ticker timer methods.
(d)  What else might you expect to see included in the photograph?

**41**  A puck A slides along a smooth surface and collides with a stationary puck B. The masses of both A and B are 2 kg. A scale diagram of the multiple flash photograph shows the motion of the pucks.

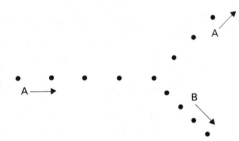

(a)  If the flash rate is 50 Hz, determine the initial momentum of A.
(b)  Show clearly that momentum is conserved.
(c)  By considering the kinetic energy, determine if the collision is elastic.
(d)  A similar experiment is performed with puck B replaced by puck C of mass 1 kg. What difference might you expect in the angle between the directions of motion of the pucks after the collision?

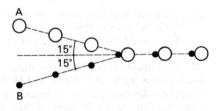

**42**  The pucks A and B are of unequal size and are made from different materials. The pucks move in from the left and join together. The diagram is a scale reduction of a multiple flash photograph.

(a) What is the ratio of the mass of A to that of B. Explain your answer carefully.

*Relevant values of specific heat capacities, specific latent heats, and densities may be found from science data books.*

**43** A waterfall 300 m high has water flowing over the top at a rate of 100 kg per second. Calculate the rise in temperature of the water at the bottom. State any assumptions that have been made. How much power is available?

**44** A lead bullet of mass 20 g travelling at 200 m s$^{-1}$ comes to rest in a block of naphthalene of mass 50 g. If the initial temperatures of the bullet and naphthalene are both 20 °C, find:

(a) the kinetic energy of the bullet just before entering the naphthalene.
(b) the final temperature of the naphthalene and bullet. State any assumptions made.

**45** A 30 g block of ice at 0 °C was placed in a polystyrene cup containing water at 25 °C. The final temperature was found to be 5 °C. How much water was in the cup? State any assumptions made.

**46** Water flows at a steady rate of 0.04 kg s$^{-1}$ through a glass tube containing a 650 W heating element. If the initial temperature of the water entering the tube is 18.2 °C and the temperature of the water leaving the tube is 21.8 °C:

(a) calculate the heat loss per second from the sides of the tube.
(b) How could the heat loss be reduced?

**47** The graph shows the variation of temperature with time when a 0.45 kg block of solid metal at 80° is heated at a constant rate of 75 W until it has all melted.

(a) Calculate the specific heat capacity of the metal.

(b) Calculate the specific latent heat of fusion.

(c) What metal do you think has been used?

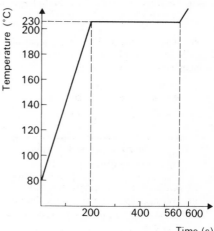

**48** In an experiment to determine the specific heat capacity of a solid, a block of the solid is suspended in a beaker of boiling water for a few minutes, then transferred into another beaker containing a measured amount of water (m) at 20 °C. The final temperature of the water (T) is recorded.

(a) What other measurements are required?
(b) Explain in general terms how the specific heat capacity is calculated from these results.
(c) Comment on the main sources of error in this experiment and describe what you would do to reduce them to a minimum.

**49** The 10 kg mass hangs at a constant height above the floor. The initial reading of the thermometer inside the cylinder is 17 C. After the handle is turned 120 times, the temperature is observed to rise to 25 °C.
If the circumference of the cylinder = 0.1 m and the mass of the cylinder = 0.3 kg,

(a) calculate the specific heat capacity of the metal, stating any assumptions made.

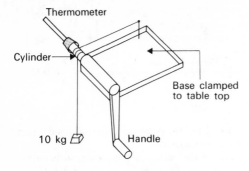

Thermometer

Cylinder

Base clamped
to table top

10 kg

Handle

(b)   Another pupil repeats the experiment
with a 5 kg mass but produces the
same temperature rise. How many
times did he turn the handle? Do you
think he took longer to complete the
experiment?

(c)   Discuss the main sources of error and
how you would minimize them.

**50**   A small electrical heater, rated at 10
W, was placed in a block of ice for 7
minutes, and it was found that 11 g of ice
melted.

(a)   Determine the apparent efficiency of
the heater.

(b)   Comment on any assumptions that
you have made.

**51**   According to the kinetic theory of
gases, pressure and volume are related
by the expression:

$$pV = \tfrac{1}{3} Nm\overline{c^2}$$

(a)   Explain the significance of the fraction $\tfrac{1}{3}$ and the term $\overline{c^2}$.

(b)   Use the above expression to derive a
formula for the root mean square
velocity of a gas in terms of the pressure and density.

(c)   From this formula determine the root
mean square velocity of argon molecules at s.t.p.

(d)   How would this r.m.s. velocity be affected if:

(i)   the temperature was increased
without a change in pressure?

(ii)   the pressure was increased without a change in temperature?

**52**   A relationship between the pressure
($p$) and volume ($V$) of an ideal gas is given
by the kinetic theory:

$$pV = \tfrac{1}{3} Nm\overline{c^2}.$$

(a)   Explain how the temperature is
introduced into this equation.

(b)   Show that this equation is consistent
with the gas law, $\dfrac{pV}{T}$ is a constant for
a fixed mass of gas; (or $pV \propto T$ if the
mass is constant).

(c)   A certain mass of gas is contained in
a cylinder and gently heated for a few
minutes; some gas is allowed then to
escape until the pressure returns to its
initial value. Consider each quantity
$p$, $N$, $m$, $\overline{c^2}$ separately and state if its
value has changed: (i) during, (ii) at
the end, of this experiment.

**53**

(a)   In the kinetic theory of gases, use is
made of the relationship

$$T \propto \tfrac{1}{2}m\overline{c^2}.$$

What physical quantity is associated
with the term $\tfrac{1}{2}m\overline{c^2}$?

(b)   Show that the ratio of the root mean
square velocities of carbon dioxide
($CO_2$) to hydrogen ($H_2$) molecules is
$\sqrt{11}$, if both gases are at 20 °C.

(c)   Why does this help to explain the
lack of hydrogen in the Earth's
atmosphere?

(d)   If the root mean square velocity of
hydrogen ($H_2$) is 1900 m s$^{-1}$ at 20 °C,
at what temperature does Helium
(He) have the same root mean square
velocity?

Relative atomic masses: H = 1, He = 4,
C = 12, O = 16.

**54**   A certain volume of helium at s.t.p.
contains $10^{24}$ molecules. How many oxygen molecules would this same volume
contain at s.t.p.? Which law does your
answer illustrate?

**55**   A statement in a book reads, 'The
molar volume of a gas at s.t.p. is

22.4 × 10⁻³ m³.' Explain clearly what is meant by this statement.

Another statement reads, 'Avogadro's constant = 6 × 10²³ mol⁻¹.' Explain in detail the physical significance of the number 6 × 10²³ and the unit – the mole.

**56** From the kinetic theory of gases, the relationship $pV = \frac{2}{3}N(\frac{1}{2}mc^2)$ may be derived.

(a) Show how this equation predicts Charles' law relating the volume and temperature of a gas.
(b) Describe an experiment which might verify this law experimentally.
(c) What is meant by an ideal gas?
(d) Under what conditions would you expect a gas *not* to obey the ideal gas law, namely $\dfrac{pV}{T}$ is a constant for a fixed mass of gas?

**57** Zinc has a density of 7.14 × 10³ kg m⁻³ and a relative atomic mass of 65.4. Find:

(a) the mass of one atom of zinc in kg.
(b) the volume of one atom and hence estimate the distance between the centres of the zinc atoms in the solid state.
(c) the approximate separation of the atoms in the gaseous state.

**58** Radium-224 decays into the gas radon. If the half life of radium is 3.5 days how many atoms of radon are produced from a 1 mg sample of radium in 10.5 days?

**59** A 3-litre vessel of oxygen at 10⁵ Pa is joined by a connecting tap to a 4 litre vessel of nitrogen at 2 × 10⁵ Pa.

(a) Determine the pressure of the mixture.
(b) If the initial temperature of both gases was 17 °C, what would be the pressure of the mixture if heated to 91 °C?

**60** In the experiment shown, the atmospheric pressure is 75.6 cm of mercury.

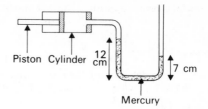

Piston  Cylinder  12 cm  7 cm

Mercury

(a) Find the pressure of the gas inside the cylinder.
(b) If the piston is pushed inwards such that the volume decreases by 10%, estimate values for the heights X and Y to the nearest cm.
(c) What would you expect to happen to the mercury levels X and Y if the cylinder was gently heated?

**61** A tray of water is lightly dusted with lycopodium powder. A small drop of oil of diameter 1.2 mm is placed gently in the centre of the water surface where it spreads out to cover a circular area of diameter 60 cm.

(a) Estimate the length of the oil molecule, stating any assumptions made.
(b) What precautions should be taken with the water surface?
(c) Why is lycopodium powder sprinkled on the water surface?

**62** Explain in general terms how the unit, the ampere, is defined. If a current of one ampere flows down a wire how many electrons pass a point P in 2 s?

**63** The resistances of three 1 m lengths of wire were found to be 1 Ω, 4 Ω, and 0.25 Ω. What was the ratio of their diameters, assuming they were made of the same material?

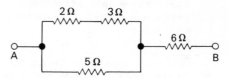

2 Ω   3 Ω

6 Ω

A   5 Ω   B

**64** Using the circuit shown, determine:

(a) the total resistance AB.

(b) the currents through the 6 Ω and 5 Ω resistors, if the current through the 2 Ω resistor is 2 A.

(c) the p.d. AB.

**65** When determining the resistance of a bulb the following results were obtained:

| potential difference (V) | 1 | 1.5 | 2 | 2.5 | 3 |
|---|---|---|---|---|---|
| current (A) | | 0.18 | 0.25 | 0.29 | 0.31 | 0.36 |

(a) Calculate the resistance of the bulb for each set of results.

(b) Comment on any departure from Ohm's law.

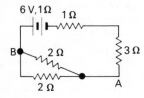

In the figure, the 6 V battery has an internal resistance of 1 Ω.
Calculate:

(a) the current through each of the 2 Ω resistors.

(b) the p.d. across each 2 Ω resistor.

(c) the potential of B if A is earthed.

(d) how much energy is dissipated in the 3 Ω resistor, in 1 s.

**67** In the circuit shown, each battery has an internal resistance of 1 Ω.

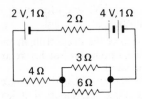

Calculate:

(a) the current through the 2 Ω resistor.

(b) the p.d. across the 4 Ω and 6 Ω resistors.

(c) the p.d. across the 4 Ω resistor if the 2 V battery is reversed.

**68** Using the circuit, determine:

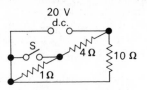

(a) the p.d. across the 10 Ω resistor when (i) S is open, (ii) S is closed.

(b) the p.d. across the 4 Ω resistor when (i) S is open, (ii) S is closed.

(c) the current through each resistor when (i) S is open, (ii) S is closed.

**69** A moving coil galvanometer has a resistance of 50 Ω and a f.s.d. of 1 mA. How could you adapt this galvanometer as:

(a) an ammeter with a f.s.d. of 0.5 A.

(b) as a 0–5 V voltmeter.

(c) If the galvanometer has a scale of 50 divisions find the sensitivity per division of the ammeter in (a) and the voltmeter in (b).

**70** A sensitive galvanometer is marked 40 Ω, 5 mA.

(a) How could you adapt this galvanometer as a voltmeter to measure p.d. up to 5 V?

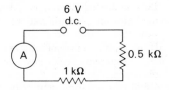

(b) From the circuit estimate the p.d. across the 1 kΩ resistor, assuming the resistance of the ammeter is about 1 Ω.

(c) What would the voltmeter in (a) read if placed across the 1 kΩ resistor?

(d) Comment on the difference in the answers to (b) and (c).

(e) Why did the reading on the ammeter rise when the voltmeter was included in the circuit?

(*f*) Would the voltmeter give a more 'accurate' measurement of the p.d. across the 0.5 kΩ resistor?

(*g*) What would happen to the reading on the *ammeter* if a 5 Ω resistor were connected across it?

**71** A generating station produces electricity at the rate of 1000 kW and at 250 V a.c. It is delivered to the nearest town through transmission lines whose total resistance is $\frac{1}{20}$ Ω. Find the power loss in the lines when:

(*a*) the electricity is supplied directly to the lines.

(*b*) a 1 : 50 step up transformer is used before the transmission lines. State any assumptions that have been made.

**72** The secondary of a 40 : 1 step down transformer is connected to three bulbs rated at 0.75 W, 2.5 V.

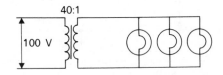

(*a*) By considering the turns ratio, deduce the p.d. across the secondary circuit.

(*b*) Determine the secondary current if the bulbs are operating at their rated value.

(*c*) If the primary current is 0.025 A, find the apparent efficiency of the transformer.

(*d*) Give *two* reasons why the transformer is not 100% efficient.

(*e*) A pupil states that the value of the primary current is affected by the value of the secondary current. By determining the value of the primary current when one bulb is removed from the secondary circuit, find if this is correct. Assume that the remaining bulbs operate at their rated value and that the efficiency remains unchanged.

**73** In a demonstration Millikan experiment, a small polystyrene ball of mass $10^{-5}$ kg remains stationary between two parallel plates 0.1 m apart. The electric field strength between the plates is $20 \times 10^3$ N C$^{-1}$.
Find:

(*a*) the potential difference between the plates.

(*b*) the charge on the ball in coulombs. State any assumptions involved.

(*c*) the number of electronic charges on the ball.

**74** In a Millikan type experiment, the p.d. (*V*) between the plates a distance (*d*) apart is adjusted until a small drop of oil remains stationary.

(*a*) How could the charge on the drop be altered?

(*b*) Neglecting the upthrust of the air, state the two forces acting upon the drop.

(*c*) A p.d. of 2.2 kV is required to maintain the drop at rest. If the distance between the plates is 6.4 mm and the mass of the drop is $3.3 \times 10^{-14}$ kg, estimate the number of electrons on the drop.

**75** In a simple cathode ray tube a heated cathode emits electrons which are attracted to a cylindrical anode. After passing through the anode, the electrons impinge on a fluorescent screen 20 cm beyond the anode. The p.d. between cathode and anode is 4 kV, and the anode/cathode separation is 10 cm. Find:

(*a*) the force on an electron, (i) on leaving the cathode, (ii) just before arrival at the anode.

(*b*) the energy acquired by an electron on reaching the anode, if it leaves the cathode with zero velocity.

(*c*) the velocity of the electron at the anode.

(*d*) the velocity of the electron just before striking the screen.

(*e*) the power output if $10^{16}$ electrons strike the screen in one second.

**76** Draw a circuit diagram of a *metre bridge* that would enable the resistance of a resistor in the range 4.7 $\Omega$ to 4.8 $\Omega$ to be measured. Standard resistors of values 4 $\Omega$, 5 $\Omega$, and 6 $\Omega$ are available.

(a) Explain the experimental procedure for determining the balance point and indicate how the unknown resistance is calculated.

(b) Which standard resistor is used and why?

(c) Comment on the accuracy, sensitivity and range of the galvanometer used.

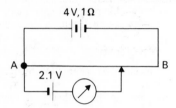

4 V, 1 $\Omega$

**77** A student connects up a 1 m potentiometer wire AB as shown.

(a) The supply battery has an e.m.f. of 4 V and internal resistance of 1 $\Omega$. Determine the potential gradient in V cm$^{-1}$ down AB if the resistance of AB is 3 $\Omega$.

(b) The student finds it impossible to obtain a balance point. Why?

(c) After correcting the circuit, where is the balance point obtained?

(d) Describe how the galvanometer is protected in an 'out of balance' condition.

**78** The 80 cm potentiometer wire AB illustrated, has a driver cell of nominal value 4 V. When K is joined to X there is zero reading on the galvanometer at AC = 34 cm.
The e.m.f. of the standard cell is 1.02 V.

(a) What is the function of $R_1$?

(b) Explain the use of $R_2$.

(c) Calculate the p.d. between the ends of the wire AB.

(d) When the switch K is connected to Y, the galvanometer shows zero deflec-

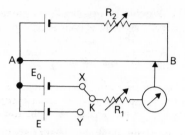

tion at AC = 50 cm. Determine the e.m.f. of the cell E.

(e) Explain the advantage of using a potentiometer to measure e.m.f.

**79** The 1 m potentiometer wire AB shown has a potential gradient of 2.0 V m$^{-1}$. When the switch S is open, a balance point is obtained 0.75 m from A. When S is closed, a balance point is obtained 0.60 m from A.

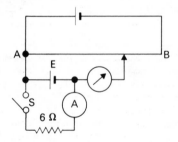

Determine:

(a) the e.m.f. of the cell E.

(b) the reading on the ammeter when S is closed.

(c) the internal resistance of the cell E.

**80** A charged capacitor is connected to an electroscope, as shown in the diagram.

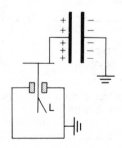

Describe the effect on leaf L when another uncharged capacitor is connected:

(*a*) in series,

(*b*) in parallel with the capacitor C.

**81** A charged parallel plate capacitor is connected across a gold leaf electroscope. Comment on the divergence of the leaf if:

(*a*) the plates are moved further apart.

(*b*) a block of perspex is placed between the plates.

(*c*) the charge on the plates is increased.

**82** In the circuit shown, the switch K vibrates between X and Y at a rate of 50 Hz when the reading on the milliammeter is 75 mA.

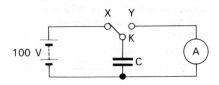

(*a*) Calculate the charge passing through the milliammeter each time K touches Y.

(*b*) Find the capacitance of C.

(*c*) Determine the reading on the ammeter if: (i) another identical capacitor is connected in parallel with C, (ii) the switching frequency is doubled.

**83** The inductor L in the circuit shown has a large number of turns.

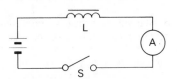

Sketch graphs on the same axes to show how the current varies with time when S is closed, and:

(*a*) the inductor has a core in position,

(*b*) the core is removed.

**84** Explain, with an example, why Lenz's Law is a result of the law of conservation of energy.

In a motor, a coil carrying a current rotates in a magnetic field. Explain, using Lenz's Law, why a back e.m.f. $E_B$ is induced in the coil, and hence discuss the equation $V - E_B = IR$, where $V$ is the p.d. applied to the coil of resistance $R$, and $I$ is the working value of the current. Comment on the magnitude of the *initial* current when the motor is first switched on.

**85** In the following circuit, at a certain frequency of the a.c. supply, the high resistance a.c. voltmeter reads 1.5 V.

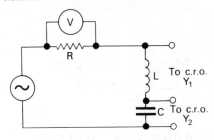

(*a*) Sketch, with an appropriate numerical value, the trace observed on a c.r.o. placed across the resistor R.

(*b*) Comment on the values of the current flowing through each component.

(*c*) The Y terminals of a double beam oscilloscope are connected across the inductor and capacitor as illustrated. Sketch the traces observed if the frequency of the supply is: (i) 5 Hz, (ii) 10 Hz.

(*d*) What physical quantity does the c.r.o. indicate in part (*c*).

(*e*) State the important advantage of a c.r.o. over an a.c. voltmeter.

**86** In the circuit shown, the e.m.f. of the supply is kept constant. The frequency of the source is steadily increased.

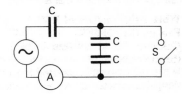

Sketch graphs, on the same axes of the current recorded on the ammeter against frequency when: (a) S is open, (b) S is closed.

**87** In the circuit shown, the e.m.f. of the supply is kept constant. The frequency of the source is steadily increased.

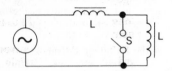

Sketch graphs, on the same axes, of the current recorded on the ammeter against frequency when: (a) S is open, (b) S is closed.

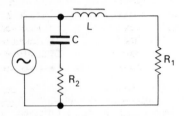

**88** In the circuit shown, $R_1$ and $R_2$ are both 1 kΩ resistors. Which component, $R_1, R_2, C,$ or L, dissipates the most energy when: (a) the frequency is high?, (b) the frequency is low?

**89** In the circuit shown, C is a variable capacitor. The e.m.f. and frequency of the supply are maintained constant.

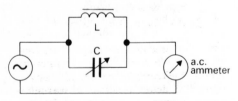

Explain what is observed on the ammeter as the capacitance of the capacitor is steadily increased. Comment if there is any change in the ammeter reading, for a given value of C, if the core is removed from the inductor.

**90** A constant a.c. potential difference is maintained across an inductor and capacitor in series.

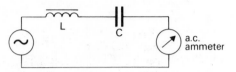

(a) What is observed on the ammeter when the frequency of the source is steadily increased.

(b) The X plate terminals of a c.r.o. are connected across the capacitor and the Y plate terminals are connected across the inductor. At a particular frequency, a circle is observed on the c.r.o. What is this frequency, and explain the observation?

**91** Given a moving coil galvanometer and four diodes, draw a circuit diagram to show how you could make an a.c. galvanometer. Would you prefer p-n junction diodes or thermionic diodes?

**92** The p.d. across the primary has an r.m.s. value of 10 V a.c. The turns ratio of the transformer is 1 : 3.

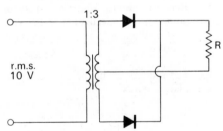

(a) Assuming no transformer losses, sketch the trace, giving a numerical value, observed on a c.r.o. placed across R.

(b) Explain the trace observed when a 20 V d.c. source is used in place of the 10 V a.c. supply.

**93** The output from a full wave rectifier is connected to a capacitor and an inductor as illustrated.

Full wave rectifier

L

R

(a) the aerial.
(b) the variable capacitor.
(c) the inductor.
(d) the diode.
(e) the transistor.

(a) Sketch the trace observed on a c.r.o. placed across R.
(b) Consider the capacitor and inductor separately and explain the effect these components have on the varying unidirectional input.
(c) Would these components be more or less effective at higher frequencies? Why?

**94** Describe experiments to illustrate:

(a) that a mechanical system has a natural frequency which depends on the physical properties of the system.
(b) damping in a vibrating mechanical system.
(c) standing waves radiating travelling sound waves.
(d) resonance in a mechanical system.
(e) that the frequency of electrical oscillations depends on the values of capacitance and inductance in the circuit.

**95** Refer to Figure 5.37, the transistor oscillator.

(a) If $R_1 = 9$ kΩ, suggest a suitable value for $R_2$ if a base bias of 2 V is required. The 6 V d.c. supply battery is used.
(b) The following components are used:

$$L_1 = 125 \text{ turns,}$$
$$L_2 = 1200 \text{ turns,}$$
$$C = 32 \ \mu F.$$

Will the frequency of the electrical oscillations be too high or too low to produce an audible note in earphones placed at D?
(c) What will be the effect on the frequency if $L_2$ is increased to 2400 turns?

**96** Draw a circuit diagram of a simple radio receiver with a single transistor. Briefly explain the function of:

**97** In a ripple tank of length 0.8 m, a bar produces a wave every 0.2 s. The distance between consecutive crests is 2 cm.

(a) How long will one crest take to travel the length of the tank?
(b) After a while, standing waves are observed in the tank. Explain how these are formed and state the distance between two maxima (antinodes).

**98** Plane waves of wavelength 2.5 cm are generated in a ripple tank. The waves are incident normally on a metal barrier containing two slits, each of width 2 cm. Sketch and explain the pattern observed beyond the slits. Outline an experiment using the *same* barrier which demonstrates the wave nature of electromagnetic radiation.

**99** Describe a simple laboratory experiment to determine the velocity of sound in air. If the velocity of sound is $330 \text{ m s}^{-1}$ in air, comment on the frequency of the sound waves employed in the experiment.

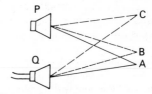

PA = PB = PC = 25 cm
QA = 25 cm   QB = 30 cm

**100** Two loudspeakers P and Q are connected to the same signal generator as shown. A microphone, connected to a c.r.o. is used to detect positions of maximum and minimum. A maximum is detected at A, and minima at B and then C.
If the velocity of sound in air is 330 m $s^{-1}$, determine:

(a) the wavelength of the sound waves.
(b) the frequency employed.
(c) the distance QC.

**101** The velocity of sound is increased fourfold on travelling from water into granite. Estimate the wavelength of sound in the water if the wavelength of the sound in the rock is 0.5 m. Draw a sketch to indicate how the direction of the wave alters if it emerges obliquely at the rock surface.

**102** Two narrow lines are scratched on a blackened microscope slide. Describe and explain in terms of the wave nature of light what is observed when a distant tungsten lamp is viewed through these lines if:

(a) a red filter is placed in front of the tungsten lamp.
(b) a blue filter is placed in front of the tungsten lamp.
(c) no filter is used.
(d) What happens to the observed fringes if the lamp with the blue filter in front of it is moved further away?

**103** A diffraction grating is required which will produce a high degree of dispersion.

(a) What property of the grating is important to meet this requirement?
(b) When a white light source is viewed through this grating a central white band is obtained with a spectrum on either side. Discuss in terms of the wave nature of light whether the blue or the red end of the spectrum is closest to the white band. Explain the presence of the white band.

**104** In a refractometer light is scattered from a sugar solution into a glass prism. If the critical angle in the glass is 67.1°, and the refractive index of the glass is 1.52, calculate the refractive index of the sugar solution.

**105** The diagram shows a ray of light incident on a perspex block immersed in water. Determine the angle of refraction in the perspex.

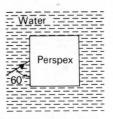

**106** An object is positioned 25 cm from a converging lens. Find, by ray diagrams or otherwise, the nature of the image and the magnification if the focal length of the lens is: (a) 15 cm, (b) 22 cm.

**107** A slide projector has a lens of +10 D. The distance of the slide from the lens is 10.5 cm.

(a) Determine the distance the projector lens must be placed from the screen in order to obtain a clear picture.
(b) If the slide is 35 mm wide, what is the width of the picture?
(c) The screen is 1 m wide. What must be done to make the picture fill the screen?
(d) This enlarged picture is not in focus. How may it be refocused?

**108**
(a) Draw ray diagrams to illustrate the nature of the *two* different magnified images which may be produced by a converging lens.
(b) A telescope has two converging lenses. Discuss the differences between: (i) the lenses, and (ii) the images each lens produces.

**109** Distinguish between deviation and dispersion. Illustrate your answer.

**110** A prism spectrometer is set up to view the emission spectrum from a helium vapour lamp.

(a) Explain *why* a series of coloured lines are observed.
(b) Is there any change when a red filter is placed between the collimator and the prism?
(c) The yellow line in this helium spec-

trum has a wavelength of 588 nm. Calculate the frequency of this radiation and the energy of the photons.

(d) Explain carefully the difference between the emission spectrum and the absorption spectrum of sodium vapour.

**111**

(a) Explain what is meant by the half-life of a radioactive isotope.

(b) An impure radioactive sample is found to emit $\alpha$ and $\beta$ particles. Describe in detail how you would measure the half-life of the $\beta$ emission. Draw a clear diagram showing the experimental arrangement.

(c) In an experiment to determine the half-life of the isotope iodine-131 the following results were recorded:

background count = 21 counts/minute

| time (days) | 0 | 3 | 6 | 9 | 12 | 15 |
|---|---|---|---|---|---|---|
| counts/minute | 107 | 88 | 73 | 61 | 53 | 46 |

Determine by graphical means the half-life of this isotope.

(d) The radioactive decay of iodine-131 may be written;

$$^{131}_{53}\text{I} \xrightarrow{\beta} {}^{A}_{Z}\text{X}$$

What are X, A, and Z?

**112** Certain physical quantities are said to be conserved.

(a) State the conservation laws associated with the following four quantities: (i) mass, (ii) energy, (iii) momentum, (iv) charge.

(b) Are these four quantities vectors or scalars?

(c) Give examples to illustrate each of the four conservation laws.

**113** In the Rutherford scattering experiment performed by Geiger and Marsden, about 1 in 8000 particles were deflected backwards. Explain why these events led to a new model of the atom.

**114** A clean zinc plate is fitted to the top of a gold leaf electroscope and illuminated by ultra-violet radiation for 5 seconds.

(a) Explain carefully why the leaf is observed to rise.

(b) What difference would you expect if:

(i) the intensity of the ultra violet is increased?

(ii) the electroscope is given a negative charge?

(iii) the electroscope is given a positive charge?

(iv) the ultra-violet source is replaced by a green/blue light?

Further problems may be found in *H Grade Questions in Physics* (see bibliography).

*N.B.* The following units have *not* been incorporated into the SI system, but they may be encountered in other texts:

*electron volt* (eV)   The electron volt is the energy acquired by one electron accelerating betwe3n a potential difference of one volt. 1 eV = $1.602 \times 10^{-19}$ J.

*calorie*   The calorie, also a unit of *energy*, is the *heat* required to raise the temperature of 1 g of water by 1 °C. 1 calorie = 4.19 J (approx.).

*angstrom* (Å)   This was a convenient unit of *length* for measuring atomic dimensions. 1 Å = $10^{-1}$ nm = $10^{-10}$ m.

Also it may be mentioned here that the millimetre of mercury is *not* an SI unit. 1 mmHg = 133 Pa.

# Answers to the Exercise Section

1 Distance $= 16$ km; displacement $= 7.9$ km due NW.

2 (a) No (b) 30 N, bisecting 120° angle.

3 (a) 3 m s$^{-2}$ (b) 33 m (c) $4\frac{1}{8}$ m s$^{-1}$

(d)

| $t$ | 1 | 2 | 3 | 4 | 5 | 6 | 7 | 8 |
|---|---|---|---|---|---|---|---|---|
| $s$ | 1.5 | 6 | 12 | 18 | 24 | 29 | 32 | 33 |

4 30 m, falling downwards.

6 (b) 0–75 s, $v = 4$ m s$^{-1}$; 75–78 s, $v = 0$; 78–168 s, $v = -3.3$ m s$^{-1}$ Assumptions: velocity constant in each range, accelerations neglected.

7 (a) No (b) $+2$ m s$^{-2}$, $-3$ m s$^{-2}$, $+1.5$ m s$^{-2}$.
(d) 0–10 s, $a = 2$ m s$^{-2}$; 10–30 s, $a = 0$; 30–45 s, $a = -3$ m s$^{-2}$; 45–55 s, $a = 1.5$ m s$^{-2}$.

8 (a) 7 m s$^{-1}$ (b) 9 m s$^{-1}$ (c) 25 m.

9 (a) 25 km hr$^{-1}$, 16.3° W of N (b) 25 km hr$^{-1}$, 16.3° E of N.

10 3.25 m s$^{-1}$, 22.6° W of N; time 8 s.

11 (a) 0.5 s (b) 20.6 m s$^{-1}$, 14° to horizontal.

12 (a) Position: 20.8 m horizontal, 7 m vertical. Velocities: 20.8 m s$^{-1}$ horizontal, 2 m s$^{-1}$ vertical. (b) 7.2 m (c) 49.9 m, 2.4 s.

13 (a) 125 m (b) 10 s (c) 866 m.

14 (a) 4 s (b) 0.707 m s$^{-1}$ towards the centre.

16 10 m.

17 (a) 2.45 m s$^{-1}$.

18 18 m from the start travelling at 3 m s$^{-1}$.

19 (a) 8.48 N, 7.07 m s$^{-2}$ (b) 6 N, 5 m s$^{-2}$.
(c) component of weight unchanged, accelerations reduced to (a) 6.2 m s$^{-2}$, (b) 4.2 m s$^{-2}$.

20 (a) 0.4 m s$^{-2}$ (b) 1.0 m s$^{-1}$ (c) 2.0 m s$^{-1}$ (d) 2 m s$^{-2}$ (e) 0.8 N.

21 (a) 1.6 m (b) 1.3 m.

22 $34 \times 10^3$ N.

23 (a) 1 m s$^{-2}$ (b) 0.8 m s$^{-2}$.

24 (a) 20 N (b) 120 W (c) 1.5 m s$^{-1}$.

25 (a) 200 N (b) 833 N (c) 133 N.

26 (a) 15 J (b) 3 J (c) 12 J (d) 12 J (e) 4 m s$^{-1}$.

28 (a) 0.06 J (b) 2 m s$^{-1}$ (d) 0 (e) 0.4 s, 2.5 Hz.

29 (a) Steady speed up or down (b) Acceleration of 1 m s$^{-2}$ downwards or deceleration of 1 m s$^{-2}$ upwards (c) acceleration of 2 m s$^{-2}$ upwards or deceleration of 2 m s$^{-2}$ downwards.

30 (a) 0.06 kg m s$^{-1}$ (b) 0.4 s (c) 0.8 m out from base of table (d) horizontally 2 m s$^{-1}$, vertically 4 m s$^{-1}$ (e) 0.3 J.

31 2.7 m s$^{-1}$.

32 2.83 m s$^{-1}$ at an angle of 135° to each of the other pieces; 36 J.

33 (a) 2 m s$^{-1}$ (b) 6.25 J, 6.25 J, yes (c) yellow ball is not 2 kg or the collision is inelastic.

34 (a) 1 m s$^{-1}$, 36.9° to the original direction of B.

35 (a) 2 J, 1.8 J (b) 1.23 kg m s$^{-1}$ (c) 1.23 N s (d) 411 N.

36 The time for the ball to interrupt the light beam $= 0.02$ s.

37 (a) 4 m s$^{-1}$ (b) 0.16 kg m s$^{-1}$ (c) 0.32 J (d) 0.64 J (e) 0.23 kg m s$^{-1}$.

38  (a) 0.21 kg m s$^{-1}$ (b) 0.21 N s →

   (c) 0.21 N s ← (d) 7 × 10$^2$ N.

39  (a) 9.9 m s$^{-2}$ (d) less than 9.9 m s$^{-2}$.

40  (a) 25 flashes per second (b) 3.25 m s$^{-1}$.

41  (a) 0.9 kg m s$^{-1}$ (c) Yes, $E_k = 0.81$ J before and after the collision (d) less than 90°.

42  Equal mass.

43  0.7 °C, 300 kW.

44  25.7 °C.

45  127 g.

46  47 J.

47  (a) 222 J kg$^{-1}$ K$^{-1}$ (b) 60 × 10$^3$ J kg$^{-1}$.

49  500 J kg$^{-1}$ K$^{-1}$.

50  87.5%.

51  (c) 410 m s$^{-1}$.

53  586 K (313 °C).

54  10$^{24}$, Avogadro's law.

57  (a) 10.9 × 10$^{-26}$ kg (b) 1.53 × 10$^{-29}$ m$^3$, separation 0.25 nm (c) approx. 2.5 nm.

58  2.3 × 10$^{18}$ atoms.

59  (a) 1.57 × 10$^5$ Pa (b) 1.97 × 10$^5$ Pa.

60  (a) 70.6 cmHg (b) Y = 8 cm, X = 11 cm (c) Y decreases.

61  3.2 nm, monomolecular layer.

62  1.25 × 10$^{19}$ electrons.

63  1 : 0.5 : 2.

64  (a) 8.5 Ω (b) 4 A, 2 A (c) 34 V.

65  (a) 5.6 Ω, 6 Ω, 6.9 Ω, 8.1 Ω, 8.3 Ω.

66  (a) 0.5 A (b) 1 V (c) +1 V (d) 3 W.

67  (a) 0.6 A (b) 2.4 V, 1.2 V (c) 0.8 V.

68  (a) (i) 20 V, (ii) 20 V (b) (i) 16 V, (ii) 20 V (c) currents through 1 Ω, 4 Ω and 10 Ω are (i) 4 A, 4 A, 2 A, (ii) 0. 5 A, 2 A, respectively.

69  (a) Shunt 0.1 Ω (b) multiplier 4950 Ω (c) sensitivity per division of (a) 0.01 A, of (b) 0.1 V.

70  (a) 960 Ω (b) 4 V (c) 3 V (g) decreases.

71  (a) 800 kW (b) 320 W, transformer 100% efficient.

72  (a) 2.5 V (b) 0.9 A (c) 90% (d) primary current = 0.0167 A.

73  (a) 2 kV (b) 5 × 10$^{-9}$ C, upthrust of air neglected (c) 3.1 × 10$^{10}$.

74  6.

75  (a) 6.4 × 10$^{-15}$ N for both (i) and (ii) (b) 6.4 × 10$^{-16}$ J (c) 3.75 × 10$^7$ m s$^{-1}$ (d) 3.75 × 10$^7$ m s$^{-1}$ (e) 6.4 W.

76  (c) 5 Ω.

77  (a) 0.03 V cm$^{-1}$ (c) 70 cm from A.

78  (c) 2.4 V (d) 1.5 V.

79  (a) 1.5 V (b) 0.2 A (c) 1.5 Ω.

80  (a) leaf rises (b) leaf falls.

82  (a) 1.5 mC (b) 15 $\mu$F (c) both double.

85  (a) peak value 2.12 V (b) same (c) (i) Y$_1$ trace has the smaller amplitude, (ii) Y$_1$ trace has the larger amplitude (d) p.d. (e) high impedance.

86  Both graphs are straight lines, (b) has the larger gradient.

87  The graphs are curves, $I$ decreases as $f$ increases, (a) lies below (b).

88  (a) R$_2$ (b) R$_1$.

92  (a) full wave rectified trace, peak value 21.2 V (b) zero p.d.

95  (a) 3 kΩ (b) too low (c) $f$ decreases.

97  (a) 8 s (b) 1 cm.

99  If 1 cm < $\lambda$ < 10 cm then frequency lies in the range 3.3–33 kHz.

100 (a) 10 cm (b) 3300 Hz (c) 40 cm.

101 0.125 m.

104 1.4.

105 26.3°.

106 (a) image is real inverted, 37.5 cm from lens, magnification = 1.5 (b) image is real inverted, 183 cm from the lens, magnification = 7.3.

107 (a) 2.1 m (b) 0.7 m.

110 (c) 5.1 × 10$^{14}$ Hz, 3.4 × 10$^{-19}$ J.

111 (c) 8.1 days (d) $^{131}_{54}$Xe.

# Bibliography

Books designed specifically for S.C.E. Higher Grade Physics include:

*Scottish Certificate of Education, Past Papers in Physics (Higher Grade)* (Glasgow: Gibson, published annually).
*H Grade Questions in Physics*, Lanarkshire Physics Group (London: Heinemann Educational, 1972).
*H Grade Physics*, S. G. Burns (London: English Universities Press, 1974).
*Nat Phil 5*, J. Jardine (London: Heinemann Educational, 1973).

Texts which will be useful for providing descriptions of experiments and further background material include:

*Nuffield Guide to Experiments*, Nuffield Foundation (Harlow: Longman/ Penguin, 1966).
*PSSC Physics* (Farnborough: D.C. Heath and Co., 1965).
*Physics for the Enquiring Mind*, E. M. Rogers (Princeton, New Jersey: Princeton University Press, 1960).
*Advanced Level Physics*, 4th Edition, M. Nelkon and P. Parker (London: Heinemann Educational, 1977).
*Patterns in Physics*, W. Bolton (Maidenhead: McGraw-Hill, 1974).
*Electricity and Atomic Physics*, R. Brown (London: Macmillan, 1973).

# Index